THE BOTANISTS AND MOUNTAIN
GUIDES OF SNOWDONIA

The Botanists and Mountain Guides of Snowdonia

Dewi Jones

I Ioan Ynyr a Mared Haf

ISBN: 1-84524-064-2
978-1-84524-064-6

Cover design: Sian Parri

First published in 1996 by
Gwasg Carreg Gwalch, 12 Iard yr Orsaf, Llanrwst,
Wales LL26 0EH.
℡ 01492 642031   📠 01492 641502
📧 books@carreg-gwalch.co.uk   Web site: www.carreg-gwalch.co.uk

New edition: 2007
Llygad Gwalch, Ysgubor Plas, Llwyndyrys,
Pwllheli, Gwynedd LL53 6NG
℡ 01758 750432   📠 01758 750438
📧 gai@llygadgwalch.com   Web site: www.carreg-gwalch.co.uk

Contents

Acknowledgements (first edition)

I am grateful for the assistance received from the staff of Gwynedd Archives and County Library, Caernarfon; Thomas Roberts and the staff of the Archives and Library of the University of Wales, Bangor; National Library of Wales, Aberystwyth, and the Department of Botany, National Museum of Wales, Cardiff, and Serena K. Marner (Herbarium Manager, Fielding-Druce Herbarium) of the Department of Plant Sciences, University of Oxford. I would like to acknowledge the help of Mr Peter Rogerson, Warrington Central Library, concerning the letters of John Roberts and William Wilson. I am indebted to Dr Iwan Edgar for his consultation and for permitting me the use of his Ph. D thesis on William Salesbury's Herbal, and to Dr Brynley F. Roberts and Gwynn Ellis for reading the original manuscript text and providing me with much valued opinions and encouragement. I would also like to thank those, who, during the course of conducting their own researches, brought to my attention certain facts relating to my chosen subject, namely, Wil Aaron, Dafydd Guto Ifan, the late Professor Bedwyr Lewis Jones, Edgar W. Parry, Medwen Roberts, D. Whiteside Thomas, and Reverend Dafydd Wyn Wiliam. I appreciate the kindness of Mr Owen George Hughes of Llanberis who granted me the use of his great-grandfather's pocket book for consultation and for permitting me to quote freely from its contents. My thanks are also due to Dr Fred Rumsey and Griff Williams for providing some of the photographs which appear in the first edition. I have for a considerable number of years, had the privilege of having among my correspondents and field companions Arthur Chater, William Condry, Robert Lewis and R. H. Roberts, whose advice, support and knowledge have been a constant inspiration. One debt which I can record but regrettably can never repay is to the late Evan Roberts of Capel Curig, who was the foremost authority on the alpine plants of Snowdonia . . . *disgybl oeddwn, ti a'm dysgawdd* . . .

Dewi Jones, Pen-y-groes.
February 1996.

6

Acknowledgements (second edition)

In addition to the previously named establishments and individuals I wish to extend my gratitude to the following who assisted, advised and provided valuable information during the preparation of this edition. Anne Barrett, Imperial College; Lynda Brooks and Gina Douglas, The Linnean Society of London; Barbara Davies, National Library of Wales; Gareth Davies, Prenteg; John Edmondson, Liverpool Museum; Meredydd Evans, Cwmystwyth; Frank Horsman, Leeds; R. Elwyn Hughes, Cardiff; Bleddyn O. Huws, University of Wales, Aberystwyth; Dafydd Glyn Jones, Bangor; Robert Morris, University of Wales, Bangor; Philip Oswald, Cambridge; Ian Salmon, University of Wales, Aberystwyth; Anne Secord, Cambridge; Stephen Sinon, Archives of the New York Botanical Garden and Bernard Thomason, Aston, Nantwich. I am grateful to the late Showell Styles whose comments on the first edition were helpful during the preparation of this edition.

Dewi Jones, Pen-y-groes.
February 2006.

Foreword (first edition)

For over thirty years I have had an interest in the history of the botanical exploration of Wales. As a technician, and later student, in the Department of Botany, University College of Wales, Aberystwyth, in the early 1960s, I was fortunate enough to come into contact with the late Price W. Carter. Percy, as he was affectionately known, was the pre-eminent scholar on this subject, and published innumerable papers and articles, including the History of Botanical Exploration in most of the Welsh and many English counties. He presented me with a copy of his *Botanical Exploration in Cardiganshire*, and I was hooked! I found the whole topic quite enthralling, and, as a very green and naïve teenager, decided that this was a subject that I would like to pursue. Fate took a hand, when, after graduating, I was fortunate enough to be appointed Assistant Keeper of Botany at the National Museum of Wales. While browsing through its extensive library, I came across a little book containing a manuscript in the hand of the Reverend Hugh Davies. This consisted of a copy of *Doctor Richardson's directions for Welch Plants to Dr John Jac. Dillenius* dated May 7th, 1726 and running to 12 pages, and a transcript of Samuel Brewer's diary of his journey to North Wales with Dillenius in 1726 and his subsequent stay in Snowdonia. This prompted me to start thinking about preparing a book which would cover the history of botanical exploration of Wales and eventually a booklet, *Plant Hunting in Wales*, was published by the National Museum of Wales in 1973. Some years after the death of Mr Carter (in 1971), I was given his unpublished writings on the history of botanical exploration in Monmouthshire and Pembrokeshire and agreed to prepare these for publication. *Some account of the history of botanical exploration in Pembrokeshire* appeared in 1986 and the Monmouthshire paper is now ready for publication.

In this account of the botanists and guides of Snowdonia, Dewi Jones has produced a book that I have no doubt Percy Carter would have approved of. This is no mere passing glance at the personalities involved but an in-depth study which presents scholarly research in a style that makes the book difficult to put down. Whilst reading it I was constantly amazed at the amount of detail that is crammed in, but always so clearly presented that it never becomes overpowering, nor does it detract from the easy flow of the text.

We are led from the serene existence of William Salesbury in the middle of the 16th century, through the wretchedness of poverty and squalor in which many of the country folk existed in the 17th to 19th centuries, to the professional tourist's guides of the late 19th century. The story never flags, and out of this poverty, acts of courage by those who acted as guides stand out as beacons of light in a dark period. The contrast between the life style of the English gentry who wished to see the sights and plants of Snowdonia and the local peasantry who guided them, although never dwelt upon, is an underlying theme and the book thus gives us an insight into the conditions that existed during that period.

Dewi Jones is to be congratulated on writing a highly readable account of a fascinating subject. An achievement even more remarkable when one realises that he is a self-taught scholar and botanist who has never belonged to a botanical society! He describes his acquaintance with the late Evan Roberts of Capel Curig as a turning point in his hobby for it was Mr Roberts who introduced him to County Floras and the historical aspect of plant hunting. We have much to thank Evan Roberts for. Dewi Jones has proved himself a meticulous researcher, an able and lucid author, and an accomplished field botanist. He is in his element among the wild cwms of Snowdonia climbing some difficult crag to see how the *Woodsia alpina* or some other plant is doing and does his 'rounds' of them annually.

It is surely no exaggeration to say that Dewi Jones has assumed the mantle of those botanists of old that he writes about so passionately and is without doubt today's leading authority on Snowdon's plants.

R. *Gwynn Ellis, June 1995.*

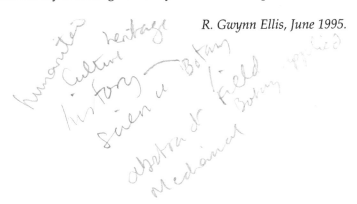

9

Foreword (second edition)

In the ten years since the publication of the first edition of this book, its author, Dewi Jones, has by no means 'rested on his laurels'. He has painstakingly continued his researches into the history of botanical collecting and botanical guides in north Wales and has skilfully and seamlessly inserted the results into this second edition. Most of the additions occur in the chapters on *John Roberts Penclip, The Great Victorian Fern Craze* and *The Golden Age of the Mountain Guide*, whilst two new chapters on John Lloyd Williams and William Williams greatly expand the accounts of those gentlemen given previously.

Such is the esteem in which he is held by his peers that Dewi Jones was awarded an honorary MA (Master of Arts) by the University of Wales at a Congregation held at Bangor during July 2005. The citation reads: 'in recognition of his contribution to the history of botany and literary studies in Wales'. I am sure that all who take a delight in the story of plant hunting in Snowdonia will agree that this was a well-deserved and timely accolade.

Gwynn Ellis, Cardiff, May 2006.

William Salesbury's Herbal

The first unpublished localized records of Welsh plants appear in a 16th century manuscript which was written by William Salesbury. William Salesbury (c.1520-1591) was perhaps the best example of the renaissance polymath in Wales. Only a few details are known about his life, his major achievement being the translation of *The New Testament* from the original Greek into Welsh. He was born at Llansannan, Denbighshire, the second son of Ffwg ap Robert ap Salbri Hen, and Annes, daughter of Wiliam ap Gruffudd ap Robin of Cochwillan. We have his place of birth on his own authority from a passage written in the Herbal on page 6a which describes the habitat and locality of the marsh-mallow *(Althaea officinalis)* '*Mewn tir gwlyb phraeth tyf y rhyw hwnn o'r hockys a mi ai gwelais yn y ddol y dan Blas Meredydd ap Grono yn llan Sannan sef y plwy y ganwyt vi*'. (This species grows on wet land and I have seen it growing in a meadow below the mansion of Meredydd ap Grono in Llansannan, which is the parish where I was born).

He was a member of one of the junior branches of the powerful Salesbury family which was established at Llewenni in the vale of Clwyd before 1334, but spent the greater part of his life at Plas Isa, Llanrwst, and this qualifies him to be included among the botanists connected with Snowdonia.

During his period of education at Oxford, being resident at Broadgate Hall he added to his knowledge of Latin a proficiency in Greek and Hebrew, and it was here also that he decided to leave the Roman Catholic Church and become an ardent Protestant.

He later married Catrin Llwyd, sister of Dr Elis Prys of Plas Iolyn, Ysbyty Ifan, who was known as '*y Doctor Coch*' (the Red Doctor); moreover, William Salesbury's brother Robert married Lowri, who was also a sister of Elis Prys. Robert Salesbury died in 1540 at which time a quarrel arose between William Salesbury and Gwen and Elin, his late brother's daughters, concerning the inheritance of the family's lands and property. In order to resolve the dispute, the matter was put before a panel of arbitrators, among whom was Dr Elis Prys, the guardian and uncle of the two girls. The dispute was temporarily settled when the arbitrators published their judgement regarding the matter on 4 November 1546. The document records that William Salesbury 'put away' his wife Catrin Llwyd and that Elis Prys had implored him to take her back 'and her to kepe and use as his wiff'. It is not possible to explain what motives Salesbury had for behaving towards his wife in this manner as no more evidence has come to light concerning the matter. An incident, perhaps relating to these circumstances, happened (probably in January 1547) while Salesbury was on his way to London. He was riding between Wrexham and Holt when he was attacked by Elis Prys and a number of companions, forced to dismount and robbed of a box containing documents and a wallet of money. Salesbury later sent a complaint regarding this to the Court of Star Chamber in London, but no documented evidence survives that shows how Elis Prys and his companions answered the charge (Mathias, 1970: 34).

Between the years 1547 and 1552 William Salesbury wrote seven books and one manuscript; *A Dictionary in Englyshe and Welshe* (1547) was aimed at helping the Welsh people learn the English language, thus complying with and promoting the policies of Henry VIII. This however must not be misconstrued. His life's work bears testimony to an unwavering desire to see the Welsh language flourish. His two main motives were to make the Holy Scriptures available to the Welsh people in their native language, and also to develop and encourage learning and knowledge among them. These ambitions suffered a setback for a period during the reign of Queen Mary (1553-1558) when the Roman Catholic faith was revived, and Latin was once more established as the language of worship.

Further changes followed the premature death of Mary and a law was passed during the early part of the reign of her successor Elizabeth I which required the translation of the *Bible* and *The Book of Common Prayer* into Welsh. Salesbury was invited to assist Richard Davies, the Bishop of St David's with the work and *The New Testament* and *The Book of Common Prayer* were completed and published by 1567.

William Salesbury wrote his Herbal largely between 1568 and 1578, and it was not complete (even in its initial unfinished form) until after that time. The principal sources consulted by him for this were the works of Leonard Fuchs *De Historia Stirpium* (1542) and William Turner's *A New Herbal &c* (1st part London 1551; 2nd part Cologne 1562; complete works in 3 parts London 1568). These authors are acknowledged frequently by Salesbury; Fuchs he considered to be the foremost botanist of the age while Turner was immortalized as being 'the Father of Botany'. The two ancient classical writers most frequently mentioned in the work are Dioscorides and Galen; the former was a 1st century Greek physician, author of a major work which was considered as being the standard medical manual of the age. The book combined a description of the plants with details of their medicinal worth, and provided the main source for the books of Fuchs and Turner. Galen lived in the second century of the Christian era and was for a time one of the prime physicians attending the imperial family at Rome. He is referred to by Salesbury as '*yr hen bennadur Galenus*' which according to Stanton Roberts (p.xxvi) 'is not literally correct, but "pennadur" (sovereign) may have been used to imply he was a king among physicians, and his reputation among medical men for fourteen centuries after his death would justify such a compliment' (Roberts, E.S., 1916: xxvi).

As one studies the manuscript (NLW MS 4581) it becomes apparent that Salesbury kept a record of the plants he observed in the different localities that he visited. The marsh mallow (*Althaea officinalis*) already mentioned gives us the name of his place of birth, and another plant to ascribed a locality is the common restharrow (*Ononis repens*).

'*Y Dagaratr. 15./ Anonis et Ononis yn Llatin* . . . *E gephir gwelet y llyseun hwnn yn tyfy yn ampl gar llaw llwybyr a dywys ar hyt y meysydd ir plas yn Lleweni. /*' [27a] (This plant grows amply close to the path which leads across the fields to the mansion at Llewenni.) [Denbighshire].

On page 167b the maidenhair spleenwort (*Asplenium trichomanes*) is noted as growing '*Ar y bont vaen ar Lugwy y gwelais i lawer yn tyfy*' (On the stone bridge over the Llugwy [now called Pont y Pair, in Betws-y-coed] I saw many growing).

Among the fine fronds of hart's-tongue (*Phyllitis scolopendrium*) that he found at Llanefydd were specimens which measured up to eighteen inches and which he claims were as broad as the breadth of one's hand. He also describes several forked varieties of this fern, and others divided into three or four parts.

'*Tafod yr Hydd. 51. / Y rhei teccaf ac amplaf ac a welais i etto sy yn tyfy o bop tu y bwll y vwyall mewn glyn coedioc or eiddo Tudur ap Robert or tu dwyrain a Robert Wynn ap Ieuan ap dd or tu gorllewin. / Mi a gefais yno rei o'r dail hyd o hanner llath o vewn lled rhaw rhei a ei Blaenau yn phorchog a rhei a ei blaenau yn phorchog a rhei yn dri phwrch sef yn gohany yn bedwar blaen val osclae corn ben garw. / Yn emyl Talacrae y tyf rhei tec iawn*'. ([69b] The finest I ever saw grew either side of 'bwll y vwyall' in a wooded glen on land, the eastern side of which belongs to Tudur ap Robert and the western side, Robert Wyn ap Ieuan ap Dafydd. There I gathered fronds up to half a yard within the breadth of a hand some with forked ends and some thrice forked and others forked into four ends similar to a stag's horn. Some very fine ones grow near Talacre).

These are the observations of a botanist whose interests were reflected three hundred years later by the 'variety hunters' of the Victorian age. William Salesbury , unlike the herbalists of his time who studied plants purely for medical reasons, did so in order to learn more about them.

In his note on garlic (*Allium sativum*) Salesbury discloses that he spent

13

some part of his childhood in Lancashire; it is thought by some that he may have attended a school there to learn English.

'Ac yd y daw im cof a mi yn vachgen yn swydd [157b] *Lancastr myfy a welais yr ail rhyw yn tyfy yn y garddae . . . a garllec Mair y galwent.* / ([157a-157b] (As far as I can recall when I was a boy in Lancashire I saw the second species growing in gardens . . . they called it Our Lady's garlic).

The claim made by Fuchs that the mistletoe *(Viscum album)* is to be found growing on oak is repudiated by Salesbury on page 73a.

'Byth ni thyf yr vchelfa ar y ddayar anid ymbric yspaddat, efyll nei ellyc prenn as ys y dywaid Phwcsius yn enwedic ar y Dderwen yr hyn ni welais I etto, nac yn tyfy ar vn pren y tu yma i Lan Gollen. / *Y cynayaf y clescir ef ai rawn arno eithyr mi welais vis Mowrth yn emyl y bont ar Geirioc vn llwyn or vchelfa ar cibae gwynion hynny arnaw, /'* [73b] *a phob vn o yno hyd yn Llwdlo eb gibyn arnaw.* / (The mistletoe never grows on the ground but in hawthorn, apple and pear tree branches and although Fuchs states that it grows on oak I have never seen it as yet, nor have I seen it growing on any tree this side of Llangollen . . . The earliest I have observed it with berries was in March near Pont ar Geiriog (near Chirk) having one bush with white berries, but from thence to Ludlow I found none with berries).

Of the Chamomile *(Anthemis)* he writes that it is found growing frequently outside the boundaries of gardens:

'. . . O bleit mi welais ar Grîn Lleweni lanerchae llydain o hono [11a] *eb ddim cymysc llysae ere ill nac vn glaswelltyn ynto.* / *Mi welais hefyd lwyni o hono yn tyfy ar y gwyllt parth gogledd y plas Tudur ap Robert yn Llan Yvyth.* / ([10a-10b] I have observed this on the green at Llewenni growing in broad patches with no other plant or grass growing amongst it. I have also seen bushes of it growing on the rough ground which lies to the north of the mansion of Tudur ap Robert Wyn in Llanefydd).

There are some annotations on the margins of this page made by a more recent hand which state: *'felly mae ar y marian yn Nolgellau'* and *'ac ar heol y fedw yn llansantffraid glyn dawrdwy'* (it grows similarly on the 'marian' at Dolgellau) and (on Heol y Fedw at Llansantffraid Glyn Dyfrdwy).

Common gromwell *(Lithospermum officinale)* was observed by Salesbury growing on the slope between the town walls of Denbigh and the houses of Hugh Dryhurst and Robert Huxley. He also records the plant from either side of a stream at Whitford in Flintshire.

'Had y Gromandi . . . Lithospermon. Gnawd ir llysae hyn dyfy mewn mannae geirwon vchel. Ac wrth hynny chwi a gewch ei gwelet wy yn tyfy ar y lledfron rhwng gwal tref Dinbech ar tai nid amgen na'r tu disathr y Duy Huw Dryhwrst a thuy Robert Hwxley. Ac etto mi welais lwyn tec or llysae hyn ar y gwastat o

bobtu i ryd Wtphord ar Ddyfrdwy. Ac wy a dyfant o hehir wy mewn garddae.' (105a).

The family home of Llewenni is mentioned again in the paragraph dealing with the burnet-saxifrage *(Pimpinella saxifraga)*. Salesbury records it growing in clumps in a field that had to be crossed when one walked from the town of Denbigh to the mansion at Llewenni.

'Tormaen. / 92. / . . . Oenanthe yn Groec a Llatin a Philipendula yn y Llatin. Y mae y llyseun hwn yn tyfy mewn tumpathe gan y cae phordd yr eloch ar draet o Dinbech ir plas yn Lleweni. / (118a).

'Surianbren' *(Prunus avium)*, is stated as growing on the left hand side of the road leading from Llanbedr Dyffryn Clwyd towards the mountain.

'Edrychwch goruwch eich penn ar y llaw asswy pan eloch ar hyd y geuphordd sy yn tywys o Lanbedr yn Dyffryn Clwyd y tu ar mynydd a chwi a gewch weled prenne sirian cochion yn tyfy ehunain o braphter anyscedol.' (91b)

An account of the tragic death of a young boy from Hawarden follows the descriptive note of the deadly nightshade *(Atropa belladonna)* which he calls by the Welsh name (borrowed from the Latin) 'Y Morela'. (118 151a-151b). Salesbury states that he was informed of this by John Edward of Chirk who spoke of two boys from Hawarden who passed into a coma after eating the fruit of this plant. One of the boys came from a poor family who at the time had suffered several deaths resulting from the plague and, on believing that the boy had suffered a similar fate promptly interred him. The other boy in the meantime regained consciousness and revealed to his family that he and his friend had been eating the fruit of the deadly nightshade prior to the time they became ill. Another person, Elisa ap Wiliam of Penllyn, is named as having told Salesbury that the incident happened at Caergwrle.

Salesbury also notes the bulrush *(Typha)* growing in the moat of Whittington Castle, near Oswestry. *'Yr Hesc Melfedoc 138 / Mewn corsydd a llynnae y tyf. Mi a welais o hono yn y llyn sydd yn cylchyny castell y Drewen yn gyfagos i dref Groes Oswallt. /* (173b).

He transplanted a plant of wild radish *(Raphanus raphanistrum* subsp. *raphanistrum)* from a meadow on the western side of the Abbey at Maenan to his garden at Plas Isa and adds that the plant was frequently seen growing 'wild', naming one such locality near Geufron, Llandwrog south of Caernarfon. Salesbury also states having seen this plant growing in the gardens of Phowk ap Rhys in Denbigh, and Rhys ap Dafydd ap Ieuan in Llanefydd.

'Y Reddic, 112. / . . . gweirglodd y menych gynt ytu gorllewin y Vonachloc Aberconwy sef yr hwn a vuriwyd I lawr yn emyl Aberllechoc ac o yno y perais ei ysmuto im gardd./ Digon ampl y metrir arnun yn tyfy yn wyllt eithyr mi ai

15

gwelais wy yn tyfu eb ei planny mewn llwyn dyrys lle gelwir y Geufron yn plwyf Llan Twroc yn Arvon. / Mi ai gwelais wy hefyd yn tyfy yn gardd Phowk ap Rhys of yn Dinbych ac yn gardd Rhys ap dd ap Ieuan yn Lanyvydd (140b).

Botany as we know it in Salesbury's time was obviously in its infancy. Nevertheless it is worth noting that Salesbury could be designated as the first true Welsh botanist and that his Herbal could arguably be considered as the first Welsh modern scientific book. He is remarkable in that he precedes all others in having an interest in plants for their own sake and is at times ready to question the validity of claims made by even the foremost herbal writers of the day.

Just as interesting as the story of Salesbury's life and botanical researches is the way in which the text of his Herbal has reached us. The original manuscript is lost, but three copies of the work are known to have survived. One of these transcripts came into the possession of the Reverend John Peter of Bala (Ioan Pedr 1833-1877) in 1868, as an inscription on the title page implies, and it was he who gave it the title of *Llysieulyfr Meddyginiaethol gan William Salesbury* (Medicinal Herbal by William Salesbury). An earlier note in the manuscript shows that it was copied in 1763. Following the death of the Reverend John Peter the manuscript was bought by Principal Thomas Charles Edwards who later gave it to the Welsh Library of the University College of Wales, Aberystwyth from where it was passed on to the National Library of Wales in 1905. It was this version of the manuscript (NLW MS 686) that Evan Stanton Roberts edited and published as *Llysieulyfr Meddyginiaethol a briodolir i William Salesbury* (1916).

Another transcript of Salesbury's original manuscript was discovered by Sir John Williams (1840-1926, principal founder of the National Library of Wales) at the Old Hall, Cowbridge and this was presented to the National Library of Wales in 1922 by its owners Miss Edmondes and Mrs Laurence Williams, Bonvilston Cottage, Bonvilston. This manuscript (NLW MS 4581), edited by Iwan Rhys Edgar (Edgar, 1997), is in the hand of Roger Morris (fl. 1590) of Coed y Talwrn, Llanfair Dyffryn Clwyd and the following inscription appears on page 187a. (Page 206 on NLW MS 686).

'*Hyd yma o lyfr o law W. Salsburie / a gawsid ei venthic gan Syr Thomas ap Wiliam / 1597 / Deo gratias.*' (Up to this part in the hand of W. Salsburie borrowed from Sir Tomas ap Wiliam 1597. Thanks be to God).

According to the above testimony the manuscript up to page 187a was a transcript copied by Roger Morris from the original work of William Salesbury, then in the possession of Sir Tomos ap Wiliam. This was Thomas Wiliems (1545 or 46-1622?) of Trefriw, the learned lexicographer,

16

physician, scribe and priest, who by his own testimony was born at *'Ardhe'r Menych dan droet mynydh yr yri.'* This place, Ardda'r Mynaich, stands a short distance to the north of Trefriw. Unlike his contemporary William Salesbury who was a Protestant, Thomas Wiliems was a Catholic; he is remembered chiefly for compiling a Latin-Welsh dictionary which was never published but was used extensively by Dr John Davies of Mallwyd (c. 1567-1644) as the basis for his *Antiquae Linguae Britannicae Dictionarum Duplex* (1632), in which is a *Botanologium* much used by later botanists.

The manuscripts of Roger Morris were dispersed soon after his death (circa 1603) and some of them came into the possession of Thomas Evans of Hendreforfudd, Edeyrnion, near Corwen; among these was, it is believed, the original manuscript Herbal of William Salesbury. From this period on, the fate of the original work remains unknown, but there is evidence to suggest that either the original or the transcript (NLW MS 4581) came to be acquired by Robert Davyes of Gwysanau, Flintshire sometimes before 1633. This is based upon the fact that the list of Welsh plant names published in Thomas Johnson's revised edition of Gerard's *Herbal* (1633) was submitted by 'Robert Davyes of Guissaney'. This list is said to contain plant names which could only have come from William Salesbury's Herbal. Nothing further is known of transcript NLW Ms 4581 until the mid 18th century by which time three of its previous owners had written their names on it. They are Edward Evans (page 1a) Evan Thomas (page 95b) who adds a note stating he acquired it from Ellis Edwards in 1763, and Thomas Evans (page 119b). The Evan Thomas whose name appears on page 95b was Evan Thomas (d. 1781) of Cwm Chwilfod, Sarnau near Bala, a notable transcriber and owner of manuscripts. He transcribed another copy (i.e. NLW MS 686) from the earlier one in the hand of Roger Morris (NLW MS 4581) and this was the copy used by E. Stanton Roberts when, as mentioned earlier, edited and published the work under the title *Llysieulyfr Meddyginiaethol &c.* (1916).

Another copy of the original work, albeit an incomplete one, is kept at the Cardiff Central Library (MS 2.973). The name of Thomas Wiliems of Trefriw appears frequently on various pages of this manuscript; it was he who loaned Roger Morris the original work. It is therefore possible that Cardiff MS 2.973 is the remnant of yet another copy of Salesbury's work.

Roger Morris' transcript (NLW MS 4581) has survived almost intact and consists of 400 pages numbered up to 200b, of which 198a and 199b are missing. An index for the plant names has been appended to the main text; these pages have not been numbered.

Thomas Glynne, Glynllifon and his friends

On the morning of 3 August, 1639 a party of botanists rode out of Glynllifon near Caernarfon and headed in the direction of Snowdon. The leader was Thomas Johnson, an apothecary from London, a man who had already published a number of pamphlets giving details of his botanical discoveries from other parts of the country, but this journey differed from the previous plant hunting expeditions which he had undertaken in that neither of his companions seem to have been an apothecary. Johnson (c. 1597-1644) was a native of Selby, Yorkshire, and served his apprenticeship as an apothecary from 1620 until 1628 under William Bell at Westminster in the parish of St Margarets; by 1639 he had a business on Snow Hill, in the City of London. He published an account of his journey through north Wales in a book entitled *Mercurii Botanici Pars Altera* in 1641. A portion of the original Latin work was translated into English by W. Jenkyn Thomas and published in Bangor in 1908 in a booklet entitled *The Itinerary of a Botanist*. The foreword to the translated work was written by Lewis Davies Jones (Llew Tegid) a prominent literary figure.

Thomas Glynne of Glynllifon, squire and county M.P., himself a botanist, had been corresponding with Johnson during the early 1630s, and had been sending him a number of plant specimens and details of localities which were published by Johnson in his revised edition of Gerard's *Herbal* in 1633. These are the first localised records published of native Welsh plants that had been collected and recorded by a Welshman. Johnson states that the 'red floured Mountaine Avens *[Geum rivale]* was found growing in Wales by my much honoured friend Mr Thomas Glynn who sent me some plants thereof to our Harbarists, in whose gardens it thriveth exceedingly'. Thomas Glynne was the first in Britain to record the discovery of the cottonweed *(Otanthus maritimus)*. 'I also had it sent me from my worshipful friend Mr Thomas Glynn, who gathered it upon the sea coast of Wales.'(Johnson, 1633: 644). It would appear from the writings of Johnson that the cottonweed used to grow in those days on the coast near Dinas Dinlle, which is only a mile and a half from Glynllifon. The translation states '. . . we went to the sea shore, which is not further than a mile from the house, and there we dug up the *Soldanella* [sea bindweed *(Calystegia soldanella)*] and the *Gnaphalium marinum* [cottonweed *(Otanthus maritimus)*]. The Roman soldiers had a station here, on the very edge of the sea, the remains of which are still to be clearly seen.' (Thomas, 1908: 7). The 'remains' to which Johnson refers were probably those of the hill fort at Dinas Dinlle.

Johnson came to north Wales via Chester, Flint and Holywell, staying one night at Rhuddlan before going on to Aberconwy where they were met by one of Thomas Glynne's servants, who led them to Bodysgallen Hall, the home of Robert Wynne, where Thomas Glynne was waiting for them. The following day they continued their journey crossing the Penmaenmawr headland and passing through Bangor and Caernarfon before arriving at Glynllifon on 1 August after a journey that had taken twelve days to complete.

One of Johnson's companions during this visit was Edward Morgan, described by Johnson as a student of botany who had been brought along as interpreter. Little is known of Morgan's early years, but it is believed that he was born in Wales about 1619, and later moved to London as a young man to study plants. Later in life Morgan was certainly held in high esteem by the leading botanists of the day, and Brynley F. Roberts in his published lecture entitled *Edward Lhuyd the making of a Scientist* mentions the close relationship that existed between Morgan and Edward Lhuyd and asks: 'Was he, [Lhuyd] one wonders, one of Morgan's pupils?' (Roberts, B.F., 1980: 16). Morgan was later to become superintendent at the Westminster Physic Garden which appears to have been established by Dr William Howe about 1655, and he refers to himself as 'Herbalist to the Physick Garden in Westminster.' John Evelyn the diarist visited Morgan in 1658 and wrote: 'I went to see the Medical Garden at Westminster, well stored with plants under Morgan, a very skilful botanist' (Jeffers, 1951-52: 104). Morgan was also well known to John Ray the naturalist, who presented him with a copy of his *Cambridge Catalogue* following a visit he made to the Garden to collect seeds for the gardens of Trinity College, Cambridge. William Howe published his *Phytologia Britannica* in 1650 and in his personal copy the author has annotated a list of plants, together with their localities, which had been discovered by Morgan. (Jeffers, 1951-52: 103). This list proves that he was a knowledgeable botanist and a diligent plant collector. Howe also had a copy of one of Thomas Johnson's other works *Descriptio Itineris Plantarum investigationis ergo suscepti in Agrum Cantianum* and in this he had noted the following: 'consult Morgan about Orchis' (Jeffers, 1951-52: 103). In William Coles' book *The Art of Simpling* (1656) William Howe is described as 'one of the Masters of the Westminster Physic Garden', and Edward Morgan as 'gardiner' (Jeffers, 1951-52: 104). A simple in old medicine was a single unadulterated remedy for one particular illness, and so a simple herb was one which, on its own, was supposed to cure ague or fever or simples. The local wise woman or apothecary talked of going simpling when they went out gathering these herbs.

19

The beginning of August is not an ideal time to look for alpine plants in Snowdonia; the visit should have been made two months earlier. Despite the lateness of the season they managed, in a single day, to collect a considerable number of choice plants for which Snowdon is famous. It has long been debated whether or not Johnson did in fact ascend Snowdon. In his book he notes the *'stygiæ etiam hinc & inde paludes, quarum maxima Dæmonis domicilium ab incolis vocatur'* (Johnson, 1641: 8) and this was believed by some to refer to the Devil's Kitchen (Twll Du) in Cwm Idwal. *'Dæmonis domicilium'* means 'the abode of Devils', but the passage also refers to 'stygian marshes', i.e. marshes similar to those of the River Styx, the river of the Ancient Greek underworld, rather than to cliffs.

In view of the local help he received, it seems likely that Johnson did in fact visit Snowdon, and the list of plants which he records for the day also suggests this. The first plant listed is the northern rock-cress *(Arabis petraea)* and Clogwyn Du'r Arddu on Snowdon has always been a stronghold for this plant. Nowadays it is the first plant noticed when one crosses the screes towards the base of the cliff. It has also been seen in the Cwmglas Mawr area, and recorded from Moelwyn Mawr.

Also recorded by Johnson are mountain sorrel *(Oxyria digyna)*, roseroot *(Sedum rosea)*, moss campion *(Silene acaulis)*, three saxifrages, alpine saw-wort *(Saussurea alpina)*, and dwarf willow *(Salix herbacea)*, as well as to Johnson's surprise, such maritime plants as thrift *(Armeria maritima)*, and sea campion *(Silene uniflora)*.

Despite the fact that Johnson had a local man for a companion, during this visit the party nevertheless decided to hire the services of a hill farmer's boy to guide them to Snowdon. This is the first published record of a guide being hired in Snowdonia, and the success of the venture must surely be attributed partly, if not wholly, to the guide who led them to the habitats of the rare plants.

These early mountaineers were ordinary hill farmers whose forefathers had tended their flocks, dug for peat and hunted on the same wild mountain terrain for generations. History and folklore had been passed down among them from father to son in the customary oral tradition and with it, in some instances came the specialised knowledge needed to prepare herbal medicine. It would therefore have been essential for certain members of these isolated communities to know the habitats of the plants used for medicinal purposes. The mountain plants were believed to contain healing qualities equal to, if not stronger, than those of the lowland species; for instance the Welsh name for roseroot is *'pren y ddannoedd'*, meaning the toothache plant, which suggests that it was used to relieve toothache. Localities such as Clogwyn Du'r Arddu, Clogwyn y

Garnedd, Cwmglas Mawr and Cwmglas Bach on Snowdon, and Cwm Idwal and the cliffs around the Devil's Kitchen on the Glyder were noted for their variety of flowers from the earliest times. It must also be remembered that these early herbalists and apothecaries could identify plants from foliage alone, a necessary skill during out of season botanical excursions.

Later during their mountain excursion the party halted, and to quote Johnson's words (in translation): 'But when we got to such a point on the ridge that we could not proceed any further, we sat down in the midst of the clouds, and first of all we arranged in order the plants we had, at our peril collected among the rocks and precipices, and then we ate the food we had brought with us' (Thomas, 1908: 8). One can easily imagine a group of dark cloaked gentlemen sheltering among the summit rocks, reflecting on the day's events, sifting through their plant collection probably carried in candle boxes or baskets, and enjoying their refreshments.

They returned to Glynllifon after the mountain excursion and on the following day Thomas Glynne led them over to Anglesey. Like other travellers from the southern part of Caernarfonshire wishing to cross the Menai Straits to Anglesey in those days they would have crossed from Abermenai. They visited Llanddwyn Island and Newborough recording such plants as rock sea-lavender *(Limonium binervosum)* and the sea spleenwort *(Asplenium marinum)*. Johnson also notes how the local people of Newborough wove mats and made ropes from marram *(Ammophilla arenaria)*. This local industry continued until the 1930s. An invitation from Richard Bulkeley of Baron Hill took Johnson and his party to Beaumaris, at the eastern corner of the island, and here they were informed: 'that there was no spot in all that country where rarer or more plants grew than on the high mountain, not more than four miles from Bangor' (Thomas,1908: 9). The site referred to was, most probably, the Ysgolion Duon cliffs between Carnedd Dafydd and Carnedd Llywelyn, a locality still favoured by field botanists today. It is interesting that the site was known to the local inhabitants of Beaumaris as long ago as the 17th century. A guide was hired at Llanllechid, and previous authors have often repeated as to how this local Carneddau mountaineer failed to live up to the standards set by his Snowdon counterpart. Johnson records:

Here we hired a guide, but after advancing in heavy rain we were none the better off, for after we had come to the ridge of the mountain we were taken round it by the guide, enveloped in dense wet clouds, but we failed to persuade him to take us to the precipices, where alone the rarer plants grew; for the hills, clothed with common grass, furnished very welcome pasture for sheep and cattle. Our rustic guide feared the eagles nesting there, for they were accustomed to swoop crosswise on swift pinion before the faces of the cattle feeding on the precipices, and by suddenly frightening them, make them fall down the rocks and become their prey (Thomas, 1908: 9-10).

The disillusioned party then decided to abandon their quest, in view of the adverse weather conditions and the conduct of their guide, and returned to Bangor for the night before returning to Glynllifon the following day. Two days later Johnson's party left north Wales and returned to London via Machynlleth, Ludlow, Gloucester and Oxford. A year after he published his *Mercurii Botanici Pars Altera* war broke out between Charles I and the Parliamentary forces under Oliver Cromwell. Johnson joined the King's Army and was promoted to the rank of Lieutenant Colonel, but was wounded during an engagement near Basing House, Hampshire in 1644 and he died soon after.

We are indebted to Thomas Johnson, not only for the account he wrote of his early botanical tour of north Wales, but also for giving us the names of two of the earliest Welsh botanists, Thomas Glynne of Glynllifon and Edward Morgan of the Westminster Physic Garden.

According to Glyn Roberts writing on the Glynne and Wynne families of Glynllifon in the *Transactions of the Caernarvonshire Historical Society* (1948: 28) Thomas Glynne 'was a man of no outstanding qualities' but he makes no mention of his botanical interests. Thomas Glynne was elected M.P. for Caernarfonshire in 1624 and again to the 'Short Parliament' of 1640. He was Constable of Caernarfon Castle from 1646 until his death in 1648 and supported the Parliament, but before 1646 he served as 'Commissioner of Array' and was a Colonel in the King's Army. The late W. Gilbert Williams (1874-1966) of Rhostryfan, a highly respected local historian, mentions briefly in his book *Arfon y Dyddiau Gynt* (n.d: 114) that Thomas Glynne was a noted botanist and that a plant had been named after him, but no proof to substantiate this claim has as yet been found, as none of his botanical papers seem to have survived.

Edward Morgan left the Garden and Westminster about 1678 and was succeeded there by a Mr Rusholm who held the post until the end of 1687 when the garden was closed and the plants dispersed.

By 1680 Morgan had returned to Wales and was living at Bodysgallen near Llandudno, the seat of Robert Wynne whom he had visited with Thomas Johnson during the botanical excursion to north Wales in 1639. During this period it appears that he was also being employed at Llanforda near Oswestry, at the home of Edward Lloyd, father of the famous Welsh naturalist Edward Lhuyd. While working at Llanforda he introduced Lloyd to a seedsman called Fuller, and Lloyd in return acted for Morgan during a legal transaction which permitted him to retain his interest in the plants in the Physic Garden at Westminster. Brynley F. Roberts, in his published lecture on Edward Lhuyd mentioned earlier, notes the fact that Morgan, who had taken pupils earlier at Westminster, also had some under him at Llanforda. A letter to Dr Morison dated 3 December, 1680 refers to:

> 'two pupils yt have last year taken a gt deal of pains in Briddin hills, snowden fforest, severall mountains rocks Cliffs by ye sea side, sea shore in many places, wee searched for ye solidago sarasenica but wee were ill directed (Roberts, B.F., 1980: 15).

There can be no doubt that Edward Lhuyd held Morgan in high esteem, a respect that could have been nurtured by an earlier teacher and pupil relationship. Lhuyd, in a letter to David Lloyd in 1695 compliments Morgan by saying that he was 'one that, in his way has deserved as well as any in England; a man equally commendable for his good life, and indefatigable industry'.

Morgan could well have been the teacher of Edward Lhuyd, as Roberts' lecture points out, for Lhuyd had listed plants and localities in one of his note books which match those mentioned by Morgan in his letter of 3 December 1680 '. . . Snowdon hils, Breiddin hil . . .' etc. (Roberts, B.F., 1980: 16).

Edward Morgan died in 1689, and his collection of plants, 2000 in all, went to the Ashmolean Museum, Oxford and are now kept at the Bodleian Library, Oxford. He also possessed a fine study of books, which according to Lhuyd was 'worth abt 10li wch he has told me several times he would leave me.' The fate of this library remains unknown.

John Ray and Edward Lhuyd

John Ray (1627-1705), the most celebrated of English naturalists, journeyed through north Wales in 1658 and 1662. He was born the son of a village blacksmith at Black Notley, near Braintree, Essex, on 29 November 1627. It was during his time at Braintree School that his outstanding qualities and exceptional talents were first noticed by the master, a Mr Love, and also by Samuel Collins, the Vicar of Braintree who encouraged him to further his education. Ray went up to Catharine Hall, Cambridge on 28 June 1644 following his admittance on 12 May; ironically this was the year when the first of the botanical travellers into Wales, the London apothecary Thomas Johnson, died.

Ray was ordained in London in 1660, but his strong beliefs made it impossible for him to accept Charles II Act of Uniformity, and so he resigned his office at Cambridge in 1662.

John Ray began to take an interest in plants while recovering from a bout of illness he suffered at Cambridge. He was no physician and studied plants merely so that he could learn more about them, unlike the herbalists and apothecaries of the same period who studied plants for medical reasons. During the years that spanned the lifetimes of Thomas Johnson and John Ray, botany began to emerge as a separate subject. Cambridge in the 1650s was slowly recovering after the upheaval and disorder caused by the Civil War. This was the period that saw an increase in the studying of science, and this clashed with the classical traditions of the Universities. Up until this time botany had received no official recognition as a subject, and when Ray and others went out to the countryside to study plants, they were ridiculed by their fellow students and others who supported the 'traditionalists'. Despite this he continued pursuing his chosen subject, and in 1660 he published a list of the plants he and his friends had recorded in the vicinity of Cambridge under the title *Catalogus Plantarum circa Cantabrigiam nascentium*. It was the first published flora, albeit in Latin, of an English region. The first flora of a Welsh county did not appear until 1813, when Hugh Davies published his catalogue of the plants of Anglesey entitled *Welsh Botanology*.

In 1658 John Ray entered north Wales by way of Chester, Holywell, St Asaph, Conwy and Bangor. He was at Caernarfon on 31 August and on the following day hired a guide for Snowdon but: 'it rained so hard that I was forced within a mile of the town to take shelter in a small cottage . . . This night I lodged at Bethkellart' (Raven, 1986: 112). On 2 September Ray hired another guide for Snowdon and found the summit in cloud but 'Divers rare plants I found on the top and sides of the hill which were then strangers to me' (Raven, 1986:112).

It is interesting to note that at the time of John Ray's visit guides to Snowdon could be hired at Caernarfon, and it is equally important that his is the first record of a Beddgelert mountain guide being hired. Incidentally, on his return journey home through Bala and Shrewsbury Ray heard about the death of Oliver Cromwell.

John Ray returned to north Wales in 1662, this time in the company of two other botanists Francis Willughby (1635-1672) and Phillip Skippon (fl. 1640-1674). They entered north Wales once again through Chester, but this time they arrived in the heartland of Eryri by a route which took them through the mountains via Wrexham, Mold, Denbigh and Betws-y-coed, arriving at Bangor on 19 May. On this second visit Ray had come to Snowdonia at a better time of the year for seeing the mountain plants at their best. He had made his first trip during September when the ferns and mosses are at their best, but most of the flowering plants are well and truly over.

On the day following their arrival at Bangor, the party visited Carnedd Llywelyn, but had no better luck than Johnson did twenty-three years before. They also crossed over to Anglesey, visited Puffin Island and then rode across the island to Abermenai, where they found cottonweed *(Otanthus maritimus)* and sea stock *(Matthiola sinuata)* on the sea shore near the Ferry. They spent Sunday at Caernarfon after crossing the Menai Straits back to the mainland. On 26 May they went to Llanberis and on to Beddgelert recording Welsh poppy *(Meconopsis cambrica)* by the wayside and the small-white orchid *(Pseudorchis albida)* near Dolbadarn Castle: an orchid hitherto unknown to science. This plant is now very rare as a result of changes in agricultural methods, habitat destruction and the overgrazing of lowland sites since 1930. However it is a plant that is easily overlooked and may well be under-recorded from mountainous areas.

On the following day the party ascended Snowdon, although it is not clear whether or not they gained the summit. They probably went up from Beddgelert, and recorded parsley fern *(Cryptogramma crispa)* mossy saxifrage *(Saxifraga hypnoides)* roseroot *(Sedum rosea)* and four of the club-mosses. There is no mention of a guide being with them during this field trip.

After the Snowdon excursion the party left Snowdonia and visited Bardsey Island but only found plants that were already known to Ray. At Harlech he records sharp rush *(Juncus acutus)* and the following week they rode southward to Aberdyfi, recording mountain everlasting *(Antennaria dioica)* 'on the top of Plimllimon-hill' (Raven, 1986: 126) which they must have climbed on their way to Cardigan. They then continued their journey to Pembroke and crossed the southern part of Wales to Kidwelly and Caerwent before leaving for Gloucester on 14 June.

The plants which Ray recorded from his two excursions into Snowdonia are listed in the following works: *Catalogus Plantarum Angliae* (1670) *Fasciculus Stirpium Britannicarum* (1688) and the book which was for generations of botanists the most consulted work on British plants, the *Synopsis Methodica Stirpium Britannicarum*, which was first published in 1690, with a second edition in 1696, and a third in 1724.

It is not known if John Ray and Edward Lhuyd ever met, but they began corresponding during the summer of 1689, and it is clear that Lhuyd thought highly of England's foremost scientist '. . . he is a man of the most agreeable temper imaginable, Mr Ray is doubtless the best acquainted with Natural History of any now living' (Carter, 1955: 55).

Edward Lhuyd rose to become one of the most eminent Welshmen of his time and in 1706 Hans Sloane, who later became President of the Royal Society, described him as 'the best naturalist now in Europe' (Emery, 1970: 54).

Lhuyd was the son of Edward Lloyd, Llanforda near Oswestry, (whom we have already discussed) and Bridget Pryse, the daughter of Thomas Pryse, Glanfred, near Aberystwyth. Being an illegitimate child there is a tradition that Lhuyd was born in Cardiganshire, but his actual birthplace according to records appears to be 'Loppington Parish' and most of his early life was spent in the Welsh part of Shropshire, near Oswestry.

He entered Jesus College, Oxford in October 1682 to study law, but even at this early stage in his career it became increasingly evident that his true interests lay in other matters. His name gradually came to be connected more with the Ashmolean Museum than with Jesus College, and following his matriculation he was appointed assistant to the Keeper, Dr Plot. When the post of Keeper became vacant in 1691 following Plot's retirement, Lhuyd succeeded him, and remained Keeper of the Ashmolean until his death in 1709.

Between the years 1691 and 1695 he was engaged in arranging and cataloguing his collection of British fossils and preparing notes on the Welsh counties for the publishers of the new edition of Camden's *Britannia*. He travelled the Celtic countries between 1695 and 1701, and from 1702 until 1707 he remained at Oxford writing his *Archeologia Britannica*, the first part of which entitled *Glossography*, was then published. From 1707 until the time of his death he busied himself with arranging his notes and worked on historical matters. He did not live to complete his great work and died in June 1709, being buried in St Michael's Church, Oxford.

Lhuyd had begun to visit Snowdonia around 1680, and during the summer of 1688 he discovered over forty new plants; this list was published by John Ray in his book *Synopsis Methodica Stirpium Britannicarum* (1690). Ray described the discoveries as the 'greatest ornament' to his book. The most important discovery, and the one which will always be associated with the name of Edward Lhuyd, did not appear in print until the second edition of the *Synopsis* was published in 1696. On the high cliffs above Cwm Idwal, on a site that was known in those days as 'Trigyfylchau Rocks', Lhuyd discovered the small white lily which was firstly listed and described as *Bulbosa Alpina juncifolia, pericarpio unico erecto in summo cauliculo dodrantali* (Ray, 1696: 233). [a rush-leaved erect bulbous Alpine plant having one pericarp three quarter way up the stalk] The name was later changed by Linneaus to *Anthericum serotinum* before it was realised that it was sufficiently distinct from other species of *Anthericum* to merit the formation of a new genus. The decision was taken to honour the finder and the plant is known today as *Lloydia serotina* (Snowdon lily).

Lhuyd's extraordinary powers of observation become evident if one considers that when he first found the Snowdon lily it was not in flower. He saw only the leaves, and these could easily be taken for a clump of *Festuca* grass, a mistake that most botanists unfamiliar with the plant could make. Lhuyd approached problems in a rational manner, and solved them systematically. For instance, earlier travellers wrote of the snows that covered Snowdon throughout the year, but Lhuyd, with his personal observations, and with the help of the local inhabitants soon proved them wrong. 'Generally speaking, there's no snow here from the end of April to the midst of September . . . It often snows on the tops of these mountains in May and June; but that Snow, or rather sleet, melts as fast as it falls; and the same shower that falls then in Snow on the high Mountains, is but Rain in the Valleys' (Camden, 1695: 668). In 1696 he prepared questionnaires which were distributed to various parishes in Wales where they were to be completed by an eminent local resident. The response formed Edward Lhuyd's 'Parochialia' which was later published in supplements to *Archeologia Cambrensis* (Morris, R.H., (ed) 1909-1911).

The Vicar of Llanberis during this period was Thomas Evans, and on receiving one of the questionnaires of Edward Lhuyd set about writing a report on the weather of the Llanberis district during the years 1697-98. The original manuscript is now kept at the National Library of Wales, Aberystwyth. Thomas Evans was but one of the many who, around Wales, compiled the data for Lhuyd's 'Parochial Queries'. (Emery, 1985: 5-7).

He was also a botanist, and had provided visiting botanists with accommodation during their visits to the wilds of Snowdonia. Dr Richard Richardson (1663-1741) of North Bierley (now part of Bradford), Yorkshire, was a highly accomplished botanist and had the finest collection of British and foreign plants in the north of England, being the first to record finding the rare Killarney fern *(Trichomanes speciosum)* in England. Richardson accompanied Edward Lhuyd during some of his trips to the Glyder mountains, and Thomas Evans probably went along by virtue of his local knowledge. Another local man, William Griffith, acted as guide to Richardson during visits made to the Devil's Kitchen area of the Glyder, and it was also noted that Lhuyd had shown the site of the Snowdon lily *(Lloydia serotina)* to Richardson at this time.

Edward Lhuyd also benefited from the local knowledge of William Rowlands, another native of Snowdonia, who collaborated with Lhuyd in similar work in 1693. Rowlands wrote several letters to Lhuyd in 1694 from Hafod y Llan near Beddgelert with directions that all communications be sent to 'W.R. near Beddgelert to be left with Mr Hugh Jones in Caernarfon, or at his house in Caernarfon' (Emery, 1985:7). William Rowlands' letters deal in an authoritative manner on subjects ranging from mountain plants to fossil shells and they suggest that he had a close relationship with Lhuyd. When Lhuyd held the post of keeper of the Ashmolean Museum, Rowlands had aspired to be his protégé and Lhuyd had hoped that this promising young man would accompany him during his forthcoming tour of the Celtic countries in 1697. The notes Rowlands compiled were used extensively by Lhuyd. They were published in the revised edition of *Britannia* which appeared in 1695 and which includes the etymology of place-names, age of the inhabitants, their illnesses and causes of death, ancient stone monuments and different branches of natural history. Rowlands' communications concerning the weather of Snowdonia agree with those of Thomas Evans, which dispel once and for all the old belief that snow lay on the mountains throughout the year. Equally interesting and conclusive are his revelations regarding eagles on Snowdon in the context of the Welsh name for eagle, *eryr*, and *Eryri*, Snowdonia, the abode of eagles. Rowlands does not say that he had seen any eagles there himself, but emphasises the fact that most of the older inhabitants testified as to the presence of eagles in Snowdonia up until 1690 or thereabouts. There remains some doubt whether eagles did in fact once inhabit Snowdonia. The Welsh for Snowdonia, Eryri, can in fact also be taken to refer to high ridges or highlands (Huws, 2005: 1).

Rowlands did not accompany Lhuyd on his travels through the Celtic countries in 1697, and there is no evidence of any further involvement in matters of natural history; in 1701 he became Vicar of Conwy.

One of Edward Lhuyd's most loyal supporters was his close friend John Lloyd of Blaen y ddôl, Corwen (1662-1725) a keen botanist and a knowledgeable antiquary who possessed a wealth of knowledge about the history of his native locality. Lhuyd was related to John Lloyd and often referred to him as his 'kinsman' in his letters. John Lloyd went up to Oxford about the same time as Lhuyd, and his name later appears in the Subscription Book of the Diocese of St Asaph after being ordained Deacon on 18 December 1686, and Priest on 4 September 1687. By 1689 he was Rector of Llangar, but he moved to Ruthin in 1691 where Lhuyd addressed his letters to him thus: 'John Lloyd, scholemaster of Ruthyn.' According to *Pedigrees of Anglesey and Carnarvonshire Families* John Lloyd was buried on 27 February 1725, having died at the age of sixty-three (Griffith, 1914: 220).

John Lloyd visited Snowdonia during the summer of 1686 in the company of John Wynne (1667-1743; Bishop of St Asaph 1716-27). The journey is described in a letter John Lloyd later wrote to Edward Lhuyd. The passage between Llanrwst and Llanberis must have been quite harrowing, and the land over which they had to travel was described as 'ye Divels bowling green'. Snowdon itself was 'one of ye nearest places to Heaven yt is in this world. Llanberris afforded us but cold entertainmt our fare being next to ye worst of a Souldiers. Their best bread being black, tough & thick oat-bread wch we had not been much accustom'd to' (Roberts, B.,1971: 96). John Lloyd hired one of the local guides who had served Edward Lhuyd to lead him to the summit of Snowdon, and the journey most probably began at Nant Peris, which in those days was called Llanberis. The plants which had been collected on the way up are described using the long winded pre-Linnean fashion, but some of the names are not difficult to recognise however; Gramen Parnassi = the grass of Parnassus *(Parnassia palustris)*.

Mist and cloud hung over the mountain that day and the guide was reluctant to let the party wander more than a foot's distance from the path for fear of them getting lost. Somewhere along the way they recorded the stag's-horn clubmoss *(Lycopodium clavatum)*. When the guide informed the party that they were about a mile from the top and directly above a 'great pool', they persuaded him to allow them to search the surrounding area for plants to within earshot of the guide. Handicapped by poor visibility and the restriction imposed upon them by the guide, the number of plants seen amounted to a surprising forty, and among this rather vaguely described total a single sea-plant is noted. Then the cold damp mountain mist began to affect John Wynne and the guide, and John Lloyd himself had to keep warm by rigorous exercise. 'That was ye highest degree of cold yt ever I felt', he complained, and John Wynne had to remove his boots so that he could rub some circulation back into his numbed feet. The guide also advised John Lloyd not to drink from the spring about a mile from the summit in case the coldness of the water caused his teeth to drop out. After the day on Snowdon the party must have been glad to reach the valley once again, but it was plain to them that the inhabitants of Snowdonia were used to a way of life that was far below the standards to which they were accustomed. 'I need not describe Llanberrys parish unto you, in wch ne're miller, fuller & and any other trades-man but one taylor lives; there [...] a cock, hen, or goose, nay, ne're an oven in ye Parish' (Roberts, B.,1971: 97).

John Lloyd made another interesting observation during this visit. He mentions a low circular wall built on the very apex of Snowdon, the purpose of which was to give shelter to those who had walked to the top. 'There is a wall rais'd on ye top of ye Hill, made like a sheep fold, where we shelter'd for a while, & carved our names in stones as several others had done before us, for we were as willing to be famouse as they' (Roberts, B.,1971: 97). There is no conclusive evidence to show when the practice of walking the hills of Snowdonia first began, but it is very likely that the custom of climbing to the summit of Snowdon to see the view or the sunrise began quite early in history. According to John Lloyd's testimony, the names carved on the stones of the low circular wall dated from an earlier period than 1686, and this custom was mirrored in the visitors books of the 19th century, by which time wooden cabins had been erected on the summit to provide visitors with food and shelter. R. H. Newell in his book *Letters on the Scenery of Wales* describes a visit to Snowdon undertaken several years before the first cabins were built and notes this curious habit visitors have of wishing to leave their names behind on the summit: 'It is amusing to observe the anxiety of the adventurers to record their exploit: scraps of paper are carefully packed among the stones at the top, with their names, and the date of their excursion' (Newell, 1821: 160-161).

Some of the pressed plant specimens of Edward Lhuyd which are preserved in the Morisonian Herbarium at the University of Oxford are signed 'D. Lhwyd', and this might be taken as an error for 'E. Lhuyd', but John Lloyd of Blaen y ddôl had two brothers, David, the eldest, and Robert. The eldest of the three brothers stayed at Blaen y ddôl while John went up to Oxford, and Robert moved to London as an apprentice apothecary, practising later at Wrexham. Following his plant hunting excursions into Snowdonia during the 1680s Edward Lhuyd left instructions for David Lloyd to carry on the work, so could this then be the reason for the 'D. Lhwyd' which appears on the Herbarium sheets? It would appear not. 'D' was an abbreviation of *Dominus*, the Latin for either Lord, Master, College Professor, or perhaps 'learned gentleman', a term of respect. It could therefore, be read not as an initial, but rather as an abbreviation synonymous with mister, (Mr). David Lloyd proved to be a quick learner and in a letter to Edward Lhuyd, John Lloyd has this to say in praise of his brother. 'I found my Brother David a greater proficient in plants yn you or I ever expected. He knows most of the common plants (like myself) by sight if not by their names' (Roberts, B., 1971: 98).

This is how Edward Lhuyd gave plant hunting directions to David Lloyd:

> It's observable yt on most of these high hills, ye rarest plants & greatest variety are to be met with, by the rivulets of water that descend through the rocks from ye tops of 'm. In goeing up to most of 'm you must make use of a Guide; who must not direct you the easiest way of goeing up; but must bring you to all the steep & craggie cliffs, yt are (tho but [with] difficulty) accessible.

> You must have a pretty large simpling Book with a stif cover; & be sure of half a dozen patterns of each plant you meet with on these high Hills, in what posture soever you finde 'm. I judge it better worth a mans while goeing to Snowdon alone; than if he search'd all other Hills in North Wales (Gunther, 1945: 69).

David Lloyd also collected fossils and shells as well as plants for Edward Lhuyd, who collated all this information from local naturalists for inclusion in his great work.

Of all the botanists who worked in Snowdonia pride of place must surely go to Edward Lhuyd for his outstanding contributions to the botanical exploration of Snowdonia. He was also far in advance of his time in his archaeological, philological and palaeontological thinking as well.

The Diary of Samuel Brewer
and the lost Manuscript of William Morris

It is interesting how knowledge of the localities of the plants of Snowdonia has been passed on from generation to generation. This has been a tradition from the earliest times when the Druids and the monks and later the herbalists and apothecaries went out into the countryside collecting plants for medicinal purposes; the botanists studied them for more scientific reasons. It was thus transmitted as part of our folk-tradition.

Thomas Evans was Vicar of Llanberis parish from 1680 until 1723 when he drowned while returning home late from a Christening ceremony. He was caught in a fierce storm while rowing across one of the Llanberis lakes and the boat overturned: his body was never recovered despite repeated searches.

Evans had guided Richard Richardson and probably Edward Lhuyd, both mentioned earlier, to the plant localities on Glyder and Snowdon. William Griffith was another who acted as guide. During the month of August 1726 the German botanist Johann Jacob Dillenius (1684-1747) who was the first Sherardian Professor of Botany at Oxford, 1734-47, came to Snowdonia primarily to study the lower plants, such as mosses, liverworts, fungi and algae. Samuel Brewer (1670-1743) accompanied Dillenius on this visit. Brewer, whose woollen manufacturing business in Trowbridge, Wiltshire, had become unsuccessful, turned his interests to natural history and was ranked highly by Dillenius as a plant collector. 'I am sure I shall never meet with a better searcher, especially for mosses. When we travelled together in Wales in all the badness and violency of weather and rain he would stop and pick up mosses' (Turner, 1835: 290). Brewer stayed in north Wales for twelve months following Dillenius' departure.

Richardson had been informed of Dillenius' forthcoming journey into Wales by William Sherard (1658/9-1728), founder of the Sherardian Chair of Botany at Oxford, and Richardson responded by writing a letter giving details of plants and their localities and directions for finding them.

Armed with Richardson's letter of directions, Dillenius and Brewer entered Wales near Newtown, and rode to Dolgellau via Llanidloes. Here they climbed Cadair Idris. They then spent six days on Anglesey and crossed the Menai Straits back to Caernarfon, then proceeded towards Snowdon, making Llanberis their base.

On 20 August they ascended Snowdon by way of Cwmglas Mawr and

Snowdon summit circa 1850
Reproduced from print by Artist/Publisher: T. Catherall: author's collection

Guide on Miner's Track, Snowdon: author's collection

33

Clogwyn y Garnedd, Snowdon
Photo: author

Llyn Bochlwyd at the base of Y Gribin ridge
Photo: author

Tryfan and Glyder Fach from Braich y Ddeugwm
Photo: author

Cwm Idwal from the split boulder near the outlet of Llyn Idwal mentioned by Charles Darwin (CUL Darwin 27 fol. 9) Photo: author

35

Ruins of Llwyn y Forwyn, by Llyn y Dywarchen, Rhyd-ddu, where according to tradition, Margaret Evans spent her childhood years. Photo: author

Ffynnon Doctor Mynydd (The Mountain Doctor's Spring) also known as Ffynnon Dŵr Oer (The Cold Water Spring) Photo: author

Clogwyn Du'r Arddu, Snowdon
Photo: author

'Altar stone' at Mur Murianau by the Rhyd-ddu path to Snowdon
Photo: author

Moel yr Ogof from the south-west
Photo: author

Forked spleenwort (Asplenium septentrionale)
Photo: Roger Vaughan

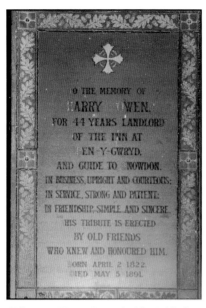

Tribute to Harry Owen inside Beddgelert Church

William Williams (1805-1861) 'The Botanical Guide' Courtesy of Gwynedd Archives

Beautiful hawkweed (Hieracium holosericeum) Photo: author

Snowdon lily (Lloydia serotina) Photo: author

Alpine saxifrage (Saxifraga nivalis)
Photo: author

Alpine woodsia (Woodsia alpina)
Photo: author

Holly fern (Polystichym lonchitis)
Photo: author

Oblong woodsia (Woodsia ilvensis)
Photo: author

continued towards the summit from Bwlch Coch by traversing Crib y Ddysgl. Water lobelia *(Lobelia dortmanna)* and quillwort *(Isoetes lacustris)* were recorded from the lakes of Cwmglas Mawr, and mountain sorrel *(Oxyria digyna)* parsley fern *(Cryptogramma crispa)* lesser clubmoss *(Selaginella selaginoides)* alpine meadow-rue *(Thalictrum alpinum)* and moss campion *(Silene acaulis)* from the cliffs further up. The alpine mouse-ear *(Cerastium alpinum)* was then, as now, a rare flower in Snowdonia, but the party recorded this during their ascent, most probably from the north-east facing cliffs of the main Snowdon peak where the plant has been occasionally found by later botanists. When they reached the summit of Snowdon they found the misnamed Iceland 'moss', which is in fact a lichen *(Cetraria islandica)* and which still grows among the rocks near the summit. It appears that the weather which had been fine for most of the day suddenly took a turn for the worse, and they returned to Llanberis after a long day out.

The two botanists went up Glyder Fawr on 22 August and Dillenius' account confirms the use that was made of Richardson's letter. 'According to the directions we could not find the *Hieracium* said to grow there, nor the *Virga aurea*, but instead of this *Lycopodium foliis juniperini* and *Lichenastrum argenteum'*. (Hyde, 1931: 4). The plants here referred to are most probably the beautiful hawkweed *(Hieracium holosericeum)* and goldenrod *(Solidago virgaurea)*. What they did find however, turned out to be the rarest clubmoss in Snowdonia, the interrupted clubmoss *(Lycopodium annotinum)*, a plant that has not been seen in the area since the first half of the 19th century. It was first found by Edward Lhuyd and recorded in *Britannia* (Camden,1695: 701). On 23 August the two botanists rested and sorted through the plant specimens they had gathered on Snowdon and Glyder. According to Richard Pulteney's *Historical and biological sketches of the progress of botany in England* (1790) the two botanists then left Wales and went to Ireland, but Samuel Brewer decided to stay for the greater part of the following year in north Wales, based mainly at Bangor (Hyde, 1931: 4).

Brewer botanized extensively in Caernarfonshire and Anglesey between 26 February and 24 September 1727, and his activities are recorded in a personal diary. He climbed Snowdon thirteen times and made seven excursions to the Glyder mountains collecting plant specimens and forwarding them to Dillenius who had agreed to name them in exchange for keeping a full set and duly returning the remainder to the collector.

It is not known whether Samuel Brewer's original diary still exists, but a manuscript copy in the hand of Hugh Davies (1739-1821) is kept at the

Department of Biodiversity and Systematic Biology, National Museum, Cardiff, and a similar transcript with slight variations in the hand of Sigismund Bacstrom is in the Department of Botany, Natural History Museum, London, bearing the signature of Sir Joseph Banks (1743-1820) on the title page. Another transcript of Brewer's diary complete with a copy of Richardson's letter is kept in the library of the Earl of Derby at Knowsley Hall. It was formerly owned by William Hudson, author of *Flora Anglica* (1762).

Another eminent Welsh botanist of the period, John Wynne Griffith (1763-1834) of Y Garn, Henllan near Denbigh is known to have had a copy of Brewer's diary with him when he came on a botanizing visit to the Llanberis area during the 1790s. The custom of borrowing and copying from botanical manuscripts dated back to the time of the herbalists when remedies were noted and circulated in a similar manner.

The home of Thomas Evans had been vacant following his tragic death, and Dillenius and Brewer did not have the benefit of staying with the hospitable local Vicar, as Richardson and others had done during their visits to Llanberis. The pair had therefore to put up at 'a very hard and uncomfortable lodging at the alehouse, and got with difficulty a young man to be our interpreter and guide' (Turner, 1835: 263).

Conditions improved considerably for them when William Evans, the late Vicar's son, who was at the time living in Bangor, heard about the visitor's predicament and he immediately made available his old home at Llanberis and provided food and fuel for them. William Evans at a later date succeeded his father as Vicar of Llanberis.

Following Dillenius' departure from north Wales, Brewer appreciated even more the support of William Evans, who in turn introduced him to William Jones of Llanfaethlu, Anglesey and Reverend William Green; these two men were Brewer's most constant companions during his botanical excursions. Another of Brewer's guides was Richard Parry who led the botanist to Clogwyn Du'r Arddu to search the cave there for ferns, but unfortunately this guide did not come up to the mark, as the following passage from the diary shows: 'I was forced to part with R. Parry who would not follow me upon the rocks' (Hyde, 1931: 16).

The rarer species of flowering plants and ferns which Brewer records from the Eryri mountains had been observed by earlier botanists, but many of the commoner species noted in the diary appear to be first records. The reason for this is that the earlier travellers were only interested in plants which were new to them, and subsequently the ones that they were already familiar with were not noted. The mosses and lichens collected and listed by Brewer, many of which were previously unknown, are very difficult to identify and translate into modern terminology. Brewer, when noting all the plants, used the cumbersome pre-Linnean practice by which each species is described in full. For instance the alpine saxifrage *(Saxifraga nivalis)* was written thus: *'Saxifraga foliis oblongis rotundis dentatis, floribus compactis'* and quotes the abbreviated title of the work to which he refers (i.e. 'R.S.' = Ray's *Synopsis).* Students wishing to identify the flowering plants and ferns referred to by Brewer are able to do so by consulting the Dillenian Herbaria at the Department of Plant Sciences, University of Oxford.

On 17 August Brewer, accompanied by William Jones and William Green, walked up Snowdon and gathered seeds from the choice plants they found which were ripe. The diarist states that he met with no plants that were not already known to him except the *'Filix alpina pedicularis rubrae folio, subtus villosa',* which in modern terminology is known as the alpine woodsia *(Woodsia alpina),* one of the rarer ferns. The site of this fern, which grows on the cliffs of Clogwyn y Garnedd, Snowdon, is extant today but can only be reached with some difficulty. Brewer also experienced difficulties in trying to obtain specimens of the fern:

> which was first observed by Mr Green on a high rough rock that standeth perpendicular and faceth the head of the lake called Llyn-cwm-y-ffynnon-las, 'tis about the middle of Clogwyn-y-Garnedd, and the said rock is as high as it is hardly possible for a man to climb up to; it grew very much exposed to view, and hardly any grew lower than ten feet, so that we were forced to take them down with a pole twenty feet long with a radicator at it's end (Hyde, 1931: 24).

Brewer describes the specimen taken as being 'past its beauty and mostly in a withered state'. The *Woodsia* ferns normally remain in good state throughout the summer and autumn but will begin to wither when the first frosts of winter attack them. During a prolonged dry spell, however, the fronds will shrink causing the plant to appear lifeless, but a shower of rain will soon revive them.

Brewer credits William Green as being the first member of the party to find the *Woodsia* on the day. William Green (d. 1782) was curate at Bodedern, Anglesey during the years 1725-6 and was later rector of Llanfair Dyffryn Clwyd. He was the son of Jeremiah Green of Dublin and Ann, the daughter of William Williams, owner of Castellmai near Caernarfon. Details of the family's genealogy appear in *Pedigrees of Anglesey and Carnarvonshire Families* under the heading 'Plas Pentir' (Griffith, 1914: 255).

Ten plant specimens collected by William Green are preserved in the

Synopsis Herbarium, and one in the *Historia Muscorum* of the Dillenian Herbarium, at the University of Oxford. The species represented are listed below using the names that appear in *The Dillenian Herbaria*, Druce and Vines (1907).

Himanthalia lorea (43.11) Found by Mr. Green growing upon ye rocks washed by the sea a little beyond Gardd y fedd yyes [Gardd y feddyges], in English the Woman Physician Garden in ye parish of Llan Rhydled [Rhuddlad] near Llanfaethley in Anglesea.

Delesseria alata (44.20) Anglesey coast from the Rev. Mr. Green, Mr. Brewer. *Ascophyllum nodosum* (48.41) Mr. Green brought it from . . . ye coast of Llan Rhyddled.

Brachythecium plumosum (80.2), var. minor are specimens from Mr. Green & Brewer gathered at Perfeddgoed Bangor.

Gentiana amarella (275.3) From Anglesey by Mr. Green.

Myriophyllum verticillatum (316.11) from ye river a little above ye Mill called Melin Wen, which signify's White Mill, within a mile of Newbrough in Anglesey, Mr. Green & Mr. Brewer. (Flowerless specimens, which are the first record for Anglesey of Myriophyllum verticillatum, L).

Habenaria albida (381.23) from ye meadows at Nant Francon, Mr. Br(ewer) & Mr. Green.

Lolium temulentum (395.1) Yeed Meddw which signify drunken corn . . . The first record for Carnarvon of the awned form of Lolium temulentum.

Limonium occidentale (App. 202/793) Found by Mr. Brewer in company with Mr. Green upon ye rocks near Porth Dafarch.

Gentiana campestris (App. 275) In a meadow calld Talgai near & south from Llanberis church in ye stony ground where ye river formerly ran. (The earliest Oxford record of Gentiana campestris, L.). *Ulota phyllantha* (Hist. Mus. 433.11) Brought from Anglesey by Mr. Green.

There are four specimens from William Jones in the Dillenian Herbarium of the *Synopsis* and all are species of algae collected from Anglesey:

Plocamium coccineum (2 sheets 37.1 No. 16 & No. 67) From ye rocks call'd Llechn [Llechi] llyfnion . . . in ye Parish of Llanfaethly found by Mr. Will. Jones. *Delesseria alata* (37.1 No 33) . . . found by Mr Will Jones upon ye old rotten stalks of Fucus arboreus polyschides at Llanfaethley.

Chylocladia ovatus (45.21 No 63) Not hitherto recorded from Wales. No

63 from ye rocks near Trefadog at Llanfaethly in Anglesey by Will. Jones.

William Griffith guided Brewer on 10 July to the unidentified 'Trigyfylchau Rocks' to look for the Snowdon lily *(Lloydia serotina)*, but despite the fact that they followed the instructions set by Richardson in his letter the plant was not found. William Griffith, who had previously guided Richardson to the site swore that they were on the very rock where the *Lloydia* grew. Normally this plant is only in flower in Snowdonia for a couple of weeks between late May and mid June, and for a brief period after that time only the long rush like leaves remain, which as previously stated could easily be overlooked or mistaken for a clump of grass.

Samuel Brewer is credited as being the first to record the spotted rock-rose in Britain, and he was duly honoured in the earlier name of the plant *Helianthemum Breweri*. The true finder of the plant was in fact William Green, who gathered specimens of it from Holyhead Mountain and sent them to Brewer, who in due course passed them on to Dillenius at Oxford. The true circumstances under which the plant was found were never revealed, and Dillenius upon receiving the specimens from Brewer decided to name the plant in honour of its 'discoverer'. Proof that the spotted rock-rose (now named *Tuberaria guttata*) was a new plant for Britain appears in a letter from Dillenius to Brewer dated 31 May 1727 where the Professor requests that William Green looks for more specimens of the flower and concludes, 'It is a Cistus and seems to be new'.

The last entry in Samuel Brewer's diary is that of 24 September, and by November he was staying with Dr Richardson at his home in North Bierley, Yorkshire which suggests that he had taken the advice of Dillenius in a letter dated 30 September to 'get out of the difficult country before the bad weather set in.'

Samuel Brewer, unlike most of the visiting botanists to north Wales, was not of a high station in society, but his contributions to botany were certainly held in high regard by Dr Richardson and other contemporary botanists. According to the *Dictionary of National Biography*, on the authority of Nichols (1817: 288), Brewer later became head gardener to the Duke of Beaufort at Badminton, following a period of his life when he fell on hard times. His valuable collection of plants and seaweeds which had been pressed and dried by himself was purchased for £20 shortly before his death by Richard Richardson, which proves how low his circumstances were; previously he had refused an offer of £100 from Sir Hans Sloane for his collection. The same authority stated that he died in 1743 at Bierley, and was buried at Cleckheaton; the precise date is not known.

William Morris (1705-1763), one of the famous Morris Brothers of Anglesey was a notable botanist who belonged to the same period as that which has been discussed. The Morris Brothers had a remarkable range of interests which are reflected in their correspondence; these letters were published in parts by J. H. Davies between 1907 and 1909 and by Hugh Owen through the Honourable Society of Cymmrodorion in 1947 and 1949. The letters provide an informative picture of life in Anglesey and other parts of north Wales during the 18th century.

William Morris refers to his botanical interests in his letters and his garden at Holyhead is constantly mentioned:

> I don't remember whether ever I told you that I've for upwards of three years been a-studying botany. I've made a catalogue in English, Welsh, and Latin of the plants growing in and about Holyhead, where we have a great many pretty rare ones, and likewise made a kind of a dry garden, or specimen of each plant. I've lately taken in hand and finish'd (with a design of adding the same to Dr. Davies' Botanologium) a catalogue of all the plants (in Latin, Welsh and English) out of Mr. Ray's Synopsis Stirpium Britannicarum, Dilenius Edition (Davies, J.H., 1907, i: 37-38).

William Morris was appointed Deputy Comptroller of the Customs at Holyhead in 1737, to which he later added other duties, and unlike his brothers Lewis, Richard and John, who left the island to earn a living, he remained in Anglesey. Lewis became a surveyor engaged by the Admiralty to survey the coasts of Wales, and in 1746 he was appointed Deputy Steward of the Crown Manors in Cardiganshire. Richard lived in London where he worked as an accountant, looking after the interests of prominent citizens of the capital, and through the influence of his clients he later obtained a post in the Admiralty. John enlisted in the Royal Navy as 'master's mate' and was killed aged thirty-four while serving on board the warship *Torbay* during an unsuccessful attack on Cartagena in 1740.

William Morris must have inherited his mother's natural flair for knowing the native plants of Anglesey. Margaret Morris was known throughout the island as a knowledgeable herbalist and she had a Welsh name for all the plants. William too had quite a reputation as a local doctor, and his services were called upon frequently as were his mother's before him. Several names of famous botanists appear in his letters, names such as John Ray, James Lee, Benjamin Stillingfleet and Phillip

Miller, the curator of the Chelsea Physic Garden, and many notable naturalists and members of the local gentry came to see his garden.

He published a book entitled *The Kitchen, Fruit and Flower Gardens Complete* in Dublin in 1751; the only known copy was in a private collection in Cardiff, and in the 1979 issue of the *Transactions of the Honourable Society of Cymmrodorion* the book, together with the 18th century manuscripts that were bound with it, were published by William Linnard and Robin Gwyndaf. The volume was first brought to the attention of the writers in 1976, and it was evident to them upon examination that it was a very rare work. The printed book is anonymous, with no indication as to how many copies were published, and no mention is made of the book in any of the letters that passed between the brothers. There can be no question that the manuscripts were written by William Morris, and it would appear that the book is by the same author.

The information compiled in the book has been divided into four parts and presents advice on the Kitchen Garden, the Fruit Garden, and lastly two equally divided parts on the Flower Garden. The nineteen manuscript pages which were bound into the front part of the volume consists mainly of a gardener's calendar and thirteen pages of the twenty-one that were bound to the back form an index to the work.

As already stated, there is no mention of this gardening book in any of the Morris Brothers' letters, but William Morris informed his brother Richard in a letter written on 2 January 1746 of a local 'flora' he had been preparing which he calls '*Botanologium*'. (Davies, J.H., 1907, i: 98). This, most probably, is the 'catalogue' mentioned in the quotation above. The names of plants would appear he says in Welsh, Latin, English and Irish, and when the first edition of this book was published, the present author had no further information to note, but since that time new evidence has emerged which might throw some light on the matter.

Sixty-seven years later another Anglesey botanist, Hugh Davies (1739-1821), acknowledged William Morris in his book *Welsh Botanology*:

In the neighbourhood of Holyhead I see much done in that way in the hand-writing of that good practical botanist, and proficient in the British language, Mr William Morris, some time ago Comptroller of his Majesty's Customs at that place; and especially in a MS by him which bears the title 'A Collection of Plants gathered in Anglesey (Davies, H., 1813: vii).

In a later letter to his brother Richard William Morris expressed his desire to compile a Herbal:

Pe bai'r gallu mal yr ewyllys, rhoddwn allan lysieylyfr iawn, nid enwau

llysiau yn unig, ond hefyd eu rhinwedd, a'u hamser, a'u cartref, etc., etc., –
bynnag par fodd, nid mynych mae wythnos yn mynd dros fy mhen na bwyf
yn casglu at eu gilydd ryw faterion, a hynny er's 10 neu 12 o flynyddoedd
tuag at y perwyl hwnw. Nid hwyrach mai gadael hebeu gorphen y byddis I
ryw genedl goeg sychu eu ----- a hwynt (Davies, J.H., 1907, i: 187-8).

Providing I had the will, I would produce a proper herbal, not just
plant names, but also their uses, their season and habitat etc., etc., –
whatever, scarcely has a week gone by during the past 10 or 12 years
when I have not collected some material to that end. I daresay that
they will be left incomplete for some vain generation to wipe their ----
with.

This work was never published and the original manuscript came, it is
thought, into the possession of William Morris' daughter who lived in
Beaumaris at the same time as Hugh Davies. Further evidence, however,
suggests that the manuscript, or perhaps a copy of the original, had been
at one time in the possession of Caernarfon apothecary William Williams,
who was also a keen collector of manuscripts. William Williams is
mentioned in the letters of the Morris Brothers and referred to as
'Williams y Potiau'; he was also known to Iolo Morganwg who visited
Caernarfon in 1772. According to Robert Hughes (Robin Ddu yr ail o Fôn,
1744-1785) a poet who was living in Caernarfon at the time, Iolo
Morganwg (Edward Williams,1747-1826, poet and antiquary) borrowed
some manuscripts from Williams the apothecary but never returned
them. In a letter written to Owain Myfyr (Owen Jones, 1741-1814) Iolo
Morganwg mentions some of the apothecary's collection of manuscripts,
which included William Morris' manuscript, and other rare literary
works:

Yr oedd amryw bethau da gantho, un a ba rai ydoedd Llyseulyfr Cymraeg a
saesoneg gan Wm. Morris brawd yr hên Lywydd, ag yn rhagori'n ddirfawr ar
yr un o eiddo'r Dr. Dafis , amryw lyfrau Barddoniaeth a welais hefyd gantho
(Jones, G.P., 1962: 80).

He had many good things, one of which was a herbal in Welsh and
English by Wm. Morris, the brother of the old President, and it greatly
excelled that by Dr. Davies [probably Dr John Davies of Mallwyd], I
saw many poetry books that were also in his possession.

William Williams the apothecary was married in 1749 to Lucy
(Griffith, 1914: 213), the daughter of Dr Thomas Knight of Caernarfon, a
medical man who was admitted an Extra-licentiate of the Royal College
of Physicians and spent the whole of his professional life in that town
(Jones, G.P., 1962:80). Thomas Knight's sister Mary was the mother of

Hugh Davies (Griffith, 1914: 213) and therefore it is fair to assume that the rector would, through this family connection, have had access to William Williams' manuscript collection and may have inherited the William Morris herbal following the death of Williams in 1789.

The middle years of the 18th century saw a major development in the science of botany. John Ray and Edward Lhuyd had previously tried to perfect a system of naming plants by grouping those which were related, but the system remained awkward and complicated. Botany was in dire need of a simple method by which they could sort into order, identify and name plants. Carolus Linnaeus (1707-1778) created such a system. His book *Species Plantarum*, published in 1753, includes all the plants then known to science, and they are listed in order of the new classification scheme based on number and arrangement of the sex organs of the flower. In addition he gave each plant a name consisting of two words only. The long descriptive Latin phrase by which plants had been named up until this time was retained as a description but replaced as a name by two words, the genus which the plant belongs to first, followed by a descriptive name to distinguish it from all other species of the same genus – a system analogous to our use of forenames and surnames. Botany benefited as a result of the Linnean System, and the cataloguing of the flora of a country became much easier.

William Morris visited Snowdon on 17 June 1741 and listed seventeen plants that he saw there; worsening weather conditions however, made any further searching impracticable. He was accompanied on this trip by several friends, some of whom rode from Anglesey with him while the others had arranged to meet them at Hafodty in Cwmbrwynog at the foot of Snowdon. His companions are named as being Reverend Thomas Ellis of Holyhead, Reverend Henry Williams of Caernarfon, Mr Phillip Quellyn (d. 1782, a customs officer at Caernarfon) of Cwellyn, Betws Garmon, Mr Richard Owen of Isallt (Holyhead?) and Mr Hugh Jones (1706-1757) of Cymunod, Bodedern, Anglesey. The name 'Rolant o Gwm Brwynog' is also included with the above and this local man could well have acted as guide to the party. The above names have been extracted from a manuscript kept at the National Library of Wales, Aberystwyth (NLW MS 6666D) in which William Morris has copied a lengthy list of alpine plants which were published in Camden's *Britannia* (1695) with the following note: 'This catalogue I drew out to assist me finding out the Plants therein mentioned when I went a Simpling a top of Snowdon 17th June 1741 & may serve future searches'.

The name Snowdon lily *(Lloydia serotina)* does not appear among the plants which William Morris lists as having been seen on Snowdon, but he can claim to be the first to give it the Welsh names of 'brwynddail y mynydd' and 'y bryfedog'. The first name signifies 'rush-leaved mountain plant', and the second is a loose translation of the old English name 'spiderwort'. These names are to be found among a long list of Welsh plant names which were written by William Morris on the margins and plain pages of the *'Botanology'* section of his personal copy of Thomas Richards' dictionary entitled *Antiquae linguae Britannicae thesaurus* (1753). It would appear from reading an annotation on the first page of the *'Botanology'* part that William Morris had offered to make the necessary corrections to the work prior to it being printed, but Richards had declined the offer. The amendments and additions which William Morris made are considerable and appear on every page in this particular chapter. Such a wealth of plant names was most certainly collected for the purpose of forming his *Botanologium*. William Morris' personal copy of Richards' dictionary which is preserved at the British Library (BL Additional MS 14947) possibly contains most of the information recorded in the lost manuscript, apart from any plant localities that the botanist may have added.

It is known that William Morris made at least one more visit to Snowdon. In a letter to his brother Richard dated 23 August 1754 (Davies, J.H., 1907, i: 304) he notes his disappointment at not being able to go botanizing in Snowdonia that summer with his friend Owen Holland (1720-1795) of Plas Isa, Conwy, who was also a keen botanist. Another letter to Richard dated 2 March 1756 confirms William Morris' second botanical excursion to Snowdon:

> Had a letter from him [Thomas Pennant] last Saturday, and at the same time from Mr. Lysons of Hemsted, in Gloucestershire; an ingenious gentleman, who was with us at Snowdon last summer.' (Davies, J.H., 1907, i: 405).

Botany remained one of William Morris' main interests throughout his life and in June 1763 he was considering an invitation by Owen Holland to accompany him on a visit to Snowdonia that summer. William Morris died six months later on 29 December, 1763.

According to a 19th century Welsh journal another William Morris of Anglesey was the author of a manuscript Herbal in 1514. The note in the journal entitled '"Wiliam Morus" Enwogion anghofiedig Cymru gan Gwilyn Lleyn' states that 'Wiliam Morus' was a doctor in Anglesey who left a manuscript containing advice and directions for treating various ailments which had been written in 1514. The title of the manuscript is given as: *'Guilelmus Moris medicus Monensis hume Librum scripsit consumanavit idem Vicesimo quinto maii 1514'*. It was offered on a booklist by Kerslake, Caerodor (Bristol) for £3:13:0. (Lleyn, G.,1862-63: 271-2).

John Wynne Griffith of Garn and his Contemporaries

Dawson Turner (1775-1858), published the *Extracts from the Literary and Scientific Correspondence of Richard Richardson* in 1835. He says in a footnote on page 237 how he wished he could have had a copy of Richardson's letter of directions to Dillenius and Brewer with him in 1802. Turner was probably referring to a visit to Snowdonia he made in that year to collect plant records for a book he and Lewis Weston Dillwyn (1778-1855) published in 1805 entitled *The Botanist's guide through England and Wales*. This book, which consists of two volumes, was probably the first to appear in print dealing exclusively with plant distribution in England and Wales on a county by county basis. Some counties were better recorded than others; the *Botanist's Guide* was not based upon the observations of the authors alone, but rather on the work of local botanists so that if any county was lacking in active field botanists, then the plant list for that particular county was poor. The authors also relied on plant records which had been previously published, but in the introductory note on Caernarfonshire they were fortunate in having two of the leading botanists of the day who had done a lot of recording work in north-west Wales:

> Carnarvonshire, in a botanical point of view, may certainly be considered the best cultivated, as well as the most interesting of the Welsh Counties. Its mountains surpassing in height every other in the Principality, afford inexhaustible fields for discovery; . . . For the greater part, however, of what we know respecting their Botany, especially in the Class Cryptogamia, we are indebted to two Naturalists of our own time, Rev. Hugh Davies and John Wynne Griffith, Esq. the latter whom in particular, joining to a most acute mind an ardour that cannot be surpassed, continues to explore the Botany of this and the neighbouring Counties; and it is to be hoped, will shortly favour the public with observations upon the British Lichens, which his situation and knowledge so well enable him to illustrate (Turner and Dillwyn, (i) 1805: 77).

As the introductory note states the Caernarfonshire plant list were to a large extent entered on the authority of two of the leading Welsh botanists of the period, namely Reverend Hugh Davies (1739-1821) and John Wynne Griffith (1763-1834). Hugh Davies is well known for his work in compiling his personal botanical observations in Anglesey and publishing them in his *Welsh Botanology* (1813); John Wynne Griffith, on the other hand, had none of his work published, but permitted other writers to make known his findings. Reverend William Bingley published a number of Griffith's records in the appendix of his book *North Wales including its Scenery, Antiquities Customs &c* under the heading 'Flora Cambrica', but only once is Griffith's name mentioned by the author, when discussing the identity of a plant he calls 'Alpine Hedypnois':

> Mr. Griffith of Garn, whose judgement on botanical subjects is of great weight, informs me that he believes this plant to be nothing more that a variety of *Leontodon autumnale* of With. 680. *(Hedypnois autumnalis,* Smith, 826). He compared his specimen taken from the bank of Llyn y Cŵn, with those of Dr. Withering, that had been sent from abroad, and they exactly agreed. Mr. G. had, however, the precaution to take one of the roots; and the plant, on cultivation, became much changed. The stalk, which had hitherto been simple, became much branched, and the calyx lost nearly all its woolliness, whilst the leaves remained unaltered, – Under these circumstances he cannot suppose them distinct species (Bingley, 1804: 406).

John Wynne Griffith was born on 1 April 1763, at Wig, Abergwyngregyn, Caernarfonshire. He was the son of John Griffith of Garn near Denbigh and Jane the daughter of John Hughes of Wig and of Cae'r Berllan near Llanrwst. John Wynne Griffith was at Trinity Hall, Cambridge in 1781. He was married in 1785 to Jane, the daughter of Robert Wynne, Garthmeilo and Plasnewydd, and they had thirteen children. In 1806 he supported Robert Biddulph as candidate against his brother in law, Frederick West, and in 1812 led the Whig faction supporting Biddulph in the election, but without success. He was returned to Parliament in 1818 as M.P. for Denbigh and remained a staunch supporter of the Whig opposition. He was a keen supporter of any agricultural improvement, but was not prominent in debate. He retired in 1826 and died on 20 June, 1834 (Thorne, 1986: 113).

Griffith, as already mentioned, assisted other botanists by providing them with details of his own observations. William Withering acknowledges Griffith's help in his book *An Arrangement of British Plants* and besides noting his various plant records in the work states: 'J.W. Griffith whose numerous and instructive specimens and observations have greatly enriched the catalogue of Mosses and Lichens' (Withering, 1796 (i): ix).

Griffith, whose great speciality was lichens, had also a keen interest in the 'tall' plants and is credited with being the first to record the wild cotoneaster (*Cotoneaster cambricus*) from the Great Orme, Llandudno in 1783 (Glenn, 1934: 133) and also the tufted saxifrage (*Saxifraga cespitosa*) from Cwm Idwal (Turner and Dillwyn, (i) 1805: 84). According to one source Griffith 'discovered S. cespitosa ... "on alpine rocks above Lake Idwell" . . . in 1778' (Carter, 1955: 57). This would mean that he made this discovery when only 15 years of age. A hitherto unknown moss which he found on Snowdon in 1790 was named in his honour and the *Oedipodium griffithianum* still flourishes on the eastern side of the summit where it was first discovered (Hill, 1988: 459). A locality for this moss on Moel yr Ogof has been known to the present author since 1998.

In 1830 John Williams (1801-1859), doctor and naturalist published a list of plants, animals and birds which are found in the parish of Llanrwst in the Conwy Valley under the title *Faunula Grustensis*. The author dedicated the book to John Wynne Griffith of whom he wrote:

> The last mentioned Gentleman, who is still living (at Garn near Denbigh) I have had occasion to name him frequently in the Catalogue of Indigenous Plants; as he in his younger days explored the productions of all the mountains and valleys in North Wales, and therefore he is acquainted with the habitats of the rare plants: Although he has the genius of Pennant, yet instead of imitating him, he communicated the fruit of his labours to other writers (Williams, J., 1830: 3-4).

It would therefore appear that John Wynne Griffith did not wish to make a name for himself as a politician or a botanist.

John Wynne Griffith visited Snowdon in 1804 accompanied by his friend William Withering (1775-1832), the son of W. Withering the author of *An Arrangement of British Plants*, who edited and partly illustrated the 4th, 5th and 6th editions of his fathers work.

They made an entry in the Capel Curig Inn's visitors book on 24 October describing a rare phenomenon they experienced whilst ascending the mountain:

> 1804, Oct 24th
> Arriving half past six evening; at half past seven the following morning we set off for Cwm Dyli which we reached by nine, after resting half an hour we began to ascend Snowdon, the summit of which we attained by half past one . . . what chiefly deserves to be recorded was a beautiful natural Phenomenon hitherto we believe seen by few which repeatedly presented itself. This curious spectacle is known to Philosophers by the name of Glory and is . . . described by Dr Haygarth late of Chester but now of Bath in a paper published a

few years ago. It consists of a beautiful and splendid prismatic annulus in the centre of which your own figure, considerably larger than life is presented. This unusual appearance as may be supposed produced the most awful and sublime Ideas. We experienced every civility from the Host and Hostess. N.B. The want of bells was the only thing we had to complain of (GAS., XM5171/1).

John Wynne Griffith was introduced to Sir Joseph Banks (1743-1820) in 1783 by means of a letter written by John Lloyd (1749-1815), a member of the families of Wig-fair and Hafodunnos in Clwyd.; Lloyd had been corresponding with Banks regularly between 1778 and 1790, chiefly discussing geology and botany. The letter of introduction reads: 'a very near neighbour of mine, a very good natured young man of family and a decent fortune, now at Cambridge, quite an enthusiast in Botany and very desirous of being introduced to you and your Hortus (Banks Corr. iii. 162)' (Britten, 1923: 225). The letter is headed 'Wickwar' which is undoubtedly an error in transcription for 'Wig-fair', the residence of John Lloyd near St Asaph.

The only letter from Griffith in the Banksian Correspondence is dated 12 July 1802 and is concerned with the discovery by the writer of a shell fish called Periwinkle which: 'is only the first state of a small species of Lobster', and he goes on to say that the discovery will 'astonish the world'. There is no mention of botany and the letter is written in a very formal manner which suggests that Griffith did not have a prolonged or close relationship with Banks. Griffith became a Fellow of the Linnean Society on the recommendation of James Dickson and Thomas Markham; the certificate is dated 24 May 1795.

Griffith sent plant specimens in a tin box to James Sowerby (1757-1822) together with a letter dated 28 May 1797. Sowerby was a botanical artist who, among other things, engraved the plates for J.E. Smith's *English Botany*, a work published in thirty-six volumes between 1790 and 1814, and he also illustrated Smith's *Exotic Botany* 1804-5. The Sowerby material is kept at the Natural History Museum in eighty-five large boxes, and the one letter from John Wynne Griffith is rather interesting:

Garn near Denbigh,
May 28th 1797

Sir. I have sent you at the request of Dr Smith by this Days Mail the following Plants as numbered below to be engraved for the English Botany. They are packed up in a tin Box, & I hope they will come safe to hand.

I am Sir Your obedt servant
J.W. Griffith.

No 1. Cerastium latifolium [Arctic mouse-ear *(Cerastium arcticum)*]
No. 2. Cerastium alpinum [Alpine mouse-ear *(Cerastium alpinum)*]
No. 3. Draba incana [Hoary whitlowgrass]
No. 4. Saxifraga petraea* [perhaps a variety, or an error for S. hypnoides]
No. 5. Saxifraga perhaps near, or a variety of S. hypnoides]
No. 6. Cardamine petraea [Northern rock-cress *(Arabis petraea)*]
No. 7. Sax. nivalis [Alpine saxifrage *(Saxifraga nivalis)*]
No. 8. Serratula alpine [Alpine saw-wort *(Saussurea alpina)*]
No. 9. Rhodiola rosea [Roseroot *(Sedum rosea)*]
No. 10. Salix herbacea with catkins [Dwarf willow]
And Sax hypnoides unlabelled.

8 & 9 are not come into flower, but I hope you will be able to flower them in water. When you have done with the specimens I shall be obliged to you if you will present them to the person who has the care of the Hortus Siccus of the Linnean Society to whom they may perhaps be acceptable. Pray excuse haste & you may expect to hear further from me concerning their Habitats &c but if in the mean time you are desirous of any information in my Power to communicate, you will please to address J.W. Griffith, Garn near Denbigh, N. Wales.

answered June 22nd 1797 [in another hand]

(NHM Sowerby Correspondence vol. 23: letter no. 143).

* William Withering acknowledges Griffith's new discovery:

'We are indebted the indefatigable researches of J. Wynne Griffith Esq. for this beautiful addition to our Flora. He found it on the rocks of Cwm Idwell, above Llyn Idwell, near Twll Du, and favoured me with recent specimens. It is a very scarce plant (Withering, vol iii,1796: 890).

D. A. Jones (1861-1936)

J. E. Griffith (1843-1933)

The Church at Nant Peris reproduced from Sketches in Wales *by G. J. Freeman (1826)*

Glynllifon, prior to it being destroyed by fire in 1836. The original house, where Johnson stayed in 1639, stands on the left hand side, behind the 18th century mansion.
Photo: courtesy of Gwynedd Archives, Caernarfon

Frontispiece of Flora Londinensis (1777) by William Curtis

Reverend Peter Bailey Williams (17363-1836)

John Wynne Griffith FLS (1763-1834) courtesy of Michael Griffith FLS, Denbigh

Richard Edwards, 'The father of Guides' Reproduced by courtesy of the National Library of Wales

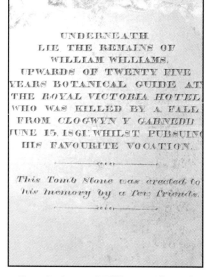

Inscription on William Williams' tombstone in Nant Peris Churchyard

Herbaria specimen of oblong woodsia (Woodsia ilvensis) collected by J. Lloyd Williams from Moel yr Ogof in 1893. E. F. Linton Herbaria

Title-page of John Hughes' pocket-book. Reproduced by permission of O. G. Hughes, Llanberis

Johann Jacob Dillenius (1684-1747)

§. Filix faxatilis Tragi *J. B. Park.* Adiantum &c. feu furcatum *Thal.* Filix faxat. V. feu corniculata *C.B. Horn-ed or forked Maidenhair. Obferved by* Tho. Willifel *upon the Racks in* Edinburgh *Park.* Ad cacumen montis *Carnedh-Lhewelyn* propè *Lhan-Lhechyd* in agro Arvonienfi invenit D. *Lhwyd.*

         Herbæ Capillares foliis femel fubdivifis

§. 1. Filix mas vulgaris *Park.* Fil. non ramofa dentata *C.B.* vulgò mas dicta, feu non ramofa *J. B.* mas non ramofa, pin-nulis latis denfis minutim dentatis *Ger. emac. Common mak-Fern.* In aggeribus fæpium, præfertim umbrofis, paffim. Filicis maris vulgaris radix rachitidi morbo dicto mede-tur, mulieribus inimica cenfetur, ftirilitatem enim facit, conceptionem impedit & abortum caufat. *Theophr. Diofc. Plin* Floridæ feu Ofmundæ radix ad hernias & ulcera exploratiffi-mi commodi eft. Rachitidi morbo remedium præftantiffi-mum & quafi proprium aut fpecificum cenfetur, cui percu-randæ vel fola fufficiat. Confervâ hujus Afparagorum in hoc morbo

Annotation in Richardson's personal copy of Ray's Synopsis *(1696) Courtesy of the National Museum and Galleries of Wales*

The Dolbadarn Hotel, Llanberis
Reproduced by courtesy of Gwynedd Archives, Caernarfon

Snowdon summit in mid Victorian era
Reproduced by courtesy of Gwynedd Archives, Caernarfon

Snowdon summit in late Victorian era
Photo: author's collection

Edward Lhuyd (1660-1709) from
a portrait by W. Roos

Hugh Lewis (1827-1886) reproduced
from Hobley's Hanes Methodistiaeth
Arfon *(1921)*

V. C. vereq; Generoso

D. THO. GLYNNÆO

D E

GLYNN-LHIVONA

Armigero,

Тно. ЈОНNSON S.P.O.

M *Agis & inusitatis a te V. C. affectus beneficiis jam ... obticui, quoniam digna ... manitate, digna gente tua oratio m.. non contigerit. Gentem tuã Antiquæ* Britanniæ *reliquias, nullos nisi Gener... continere, a nostratibus* Anglis ...go jactatum esse omnes norunt, sed ..usce rei veram rationem*

Thomas Johnson's tribute to Thomas Glynne in Mercurii Botanici Pars Altera *(1641)*

J. Lloyd Williams with his sister Elizabeth Williams
Photograph reproduced from original in possession of Mel Williams, Llanuwchllyn

Llanberis in 1852 reproduced by courtesy of the National Library of Wales, Aberystwyth

Royal Victoria Hotel, Llanberis
Reproduced from The Book of Snowdon, *n.d., McCorquodale & Co Ltd*

Hugh Davies (1739-1821) reproduced
from Y Casglwr, *Haf 1999*

J. Lloyd Williams
Photo reproduced from Popular
Lectures *(Bangor c. 1900-1914)*

Sir James Edward Smith (1759-1828) purchased Linnaeus' collections in 1784 and founded the Linnean Society of London in 1788; he published *Flora Britannica* in three volumes between 1800 and 1804, and wrote the text for *English Botany* to which Sowerby, mentioned earlier, provided the plant drawings. The Smith Herbrium at the Linnean Society contains only one specimen from John Wynne Griffith: 'Saxifraga hypnoides North Wales J.W. Griffith 1796', but there are no specimens of hoary whitlowgrass *(Draba incana)* or alpine saxifrage *(Saxifraga nivalis)* or any of the plants which Griffith sent to Sowerby, according to the microfiche of the Smith Herbarium which is available at the Natural History Museum.

Sowerby's plate of a drawing of the Snowdon lily *(Lloydia serotina)* which appears in *English Botany* (Smith: 793) was taken from a specimen collected in Snowdonia by John Wynne Griffith and sent to Smith. There is also a sheet of *Lloydia* in the Banksian Herbarium at the Natural History Museum endorsed by Joseph Banks: 'Trig-y-fylichan, [Trigyfylchau] part of the Glyder Range on the N. side of Llanberris in the County of Carnarvon, found by J.W. Griffith of Garn Esq., the 23rd of June 1794' (Britten, 1923: 225).

John Lloyd had also sent a specimen of *Lloydia* to Banks and the latter replied and stated that he was not convinced about the identity of the plant in question. Lloyd's answer written on 1 October 1778 reads:

> I was much surprised to find that you were not satisfied of the bulbose plant I sent being Bulbocodium *[Lloydia serotina]* I do not recollect ever before having seen any plant with a bulbose root near Llanberris; and the leaves answered the description very exactly, so I hope, upon the whole, you may be mistaken; it grew deep betwixt a cleft in the rock which was moist facing the north, with a great deal of earth about the root, which lay 4 inches under the splinter of the rock (Britten, 1923: 225).

John Wynne Griffith had also acquired a copy of Brewer's diary and had spent some time in the neighbourhood of Llanberis in 1790 when he found all the plants that were recorded in the diary by the old botanist. Griffith, however, found many of the place names changed or forgotten since Brewer's day, although he managed to locate the habitats of the rare plants by consulting the journal and by seeking local help. According to John Lloyd, writing to Banks on 28 November 1790, Griffith 'had made a very fine and plentiful collection now in his garden' from the plants he had gathered during this excursion, of which the rare *Lloydia* was one.

John Lloyd was a regular visitor to Snowdonia during the latter part of the 18th century; he was known as 'the Philosopher' and was one of the many 'dilettantes' of the time. Among his many interests were geology and botany, and whenever he went on one of his field trips to Snowdon he took Hugh Jones of Cwmglas Bach with him as guide. It is also said that John Lloyd publicised the name of Hugh Jones in the newspapers of the period as a guide who could be relied on to give satisfactory service (Williams, 1892: 61). This same guide probably served John Wynne Griffith.

Joseph Banks' interest in obtaining specimens of *Lloydia* first becomes apparent in a letter that Reverend John Lightfoot (1735-1788) wrote him on 19 June 1773. Banks and Lightfoot visited Wales during the summer of that year, but Lightfoot was at first doubtful if he would be free to make the journey. 'If I should be so unfortunate as not to have it in my Power to accompany you, I will take the Liberty to rely on you for a specimen of the *Bulbocodium serotinum* [*Lloydia serotina*] which I have no doubt of your finding' (Riddelsdell, 1905: 292).

Lightfoot's journal gives an account of the journey made through Wales by the two botanists. The transcript of the original was made by Daniel Carl Solander (1733-1782) and this is kept at the Natural History Museum.

They arrived at Llanberis at the beginning of August and ascended Snowdon on the 2nd, gathering various specimens of flowering plants, mosses and lichens. The ease by which the visiting botanists found rarities such as the alpine saxifrage *(Saxifraga nivalis)* arctic mouse-ear *(Cerastium arcticum)* and the alpine saw-wort *(Saussurea alpina)* suggests that they were led to the localities either by a local botanist or by one of the botanical guides. This is verified in a letter written by John Lightfoot to Sir John Cullum on 19 June 1774 in reply to a previous letter giving directions and advice concerning that gentleman's proposed visit to Wales:

At Bangor it will be proper for you to lay in Provisions & hire a Guide, if you intend to visit Snowdon. I would also recommend it to you to take up your Lodgings in Llanberys Vale, in one of the Cottages at the Foot of Snowdon. Mr. Banks & our Companions were at the House of one John Close [Closs], & we had a Man whose Name is Hugh Jones [? Cwmglas Bach] to conduct us about the Mountains & carry our Viaticum [luggage]. Ray & Hudson with Hugh Jones or some other Person in his Stead, will now be your Guide to almost every Plant we found. I must observe to you that we were not fortunate enough to find either Bulbocodium serotinum, Thlaspi hirtum [*Lepidium hirtum* (L.) Sm.], or Schoenus ferrugineus . . . (Bowden, 1989: 88).

Sir John Cullum had already started on his journey to Wales before the letter reached him, and wrote to Lightfoot describing his visit. Lightfoot replied on 28 September 1774 enquiring whether or not he had found the Snowdon lily:

> Snowdon is highly worth a Visit to a Naturalist in every View. Other Plants, as well as the Statice Armeria [*Armeria maritima* (Mill.) Willd.], are common to the Sea Shores & the Summits of the highest Mountains. The Plantago maritima is another, & some few more . . . [Postscript:] You do not tell me whether you found the Bulbocodium on Snowdon. Yr. Silence makes me suspect the worst (Bowden, 1989: 89).

Lightfoot and Banks also failed to find the Snowdon lily on the 4th and 5th of August when the party went firstly to Glyder and then to Clogwyn Du'r Arddu in the company of John Williams, Rector of Llanfairynghornwy in Anglesey, who is mentioned by Hugh Davies in his *Welsh Botanology* (Davies, 1813: 53). The flowering time of the *Lloydia* was well over by this time and as with other plant hunters before them the elusive lily had foiled them also.

The botanists then crossed over to Anglesey finding the Isle of Man cabbage *(Coincya monensis* subsp *monensis)* and marram *(Ammophila arenaria)* near Abermenai Ferry, and Portland spurge *(Euphorbia portlandica)* at Llanddwyn. On the shore at Llanfaelog they found small quantities of cottonweed *(Otanthus maritimus)* and then continued their journey to Llanfairynghornwy and Cemlyn Bay, before returning to the mainland; they then followed the coast to Conwy and Gloddaeth, near Llandudno, where they stayed with Sir Roger Mostyn before continuing their journey to Chester.

Banks and Lightfoot's Welsh Tour was mentioned in a letter by the latter to Gilbert White on 13 September 1773 where he notes:

> Wales in general behaved to us with great politeness. We had fine weather through the whole journey; we found the greatest hospitality, a multitude of plants, and five or six not before discovered in South Britain, though I had seen them in Scotland. Snowdon was very complaisant; three times we scaled his highest top, once enveloped so in clouds that we could not discern each other at twenty yards' distance; but no sooner had we refreshed ourselves with our necessary *viaticum* than the clouds withdrew, and gradually discovered to our wondering eyes the most glorious prospects we ever beheld. The clouds all settled about the midway on one side of the hill, appearing like great volumes of snow in various grotesque figures, one behind

another. The sun tinged their edges with silver, and darting his rays now and then between them discovered the rugged precipices, the limpid lake, the trembling cascades, and distant vallies beneath us. Over them appeared the British Alps, the Irish Sea, and coast of Ireland, almost all North Wales; the coasts of Lancashire and Cumberland, with the Islands of Anglesea and Man, appeared at one view, like a great map spread beneath us. In short, we seemed as if we had been snatched up into the clouds, and were taking a peep on the little world below . . . (Bowden, 1989: 92).

Banks' Welsh tour followed his voyages of discovery, and he will always be associated with Captain Cook's voyage around the world on the *Endeavour* between the years 1768 and 1771. His journey through Wales with Lightfoot is considered to be the last of the historical botanical expeditions to north Wales the original plan of which was to follow in the footsteps of John Ray in 1662, but in reverse order. However, due to having spent too much time in Pembrokeshire they had to abandon their plans to visit Cadair Idris so that they could have enough time to explore Snowdon. The journey from St David's through Hereford and Chester to Bangor and eventually Llanberis took exactly seven days; this was considered good going and was done in much less time than it would have taken had they followed the rough terrain of the western coast of Wales.

Hugh Davies, The 'Welsh Linnaeus'

Reverend Hugh Davies, who was mentioned earlier as having a transcript of Brewer's diary, was one of the most knowledgeable Welsh botanists since Edward Lhuyd. Among the local people he was known as 'Davies y dail' (Davies the leaves) but to his fellow British botanists he was 'the Welsh Linnaeus' (Williams, J.L., 1944: 144). He was born on 3 April 1739, the son of Lewis Davies, the Vicar of Llandyfrydog, Anglesey, and after attending Beaumaris Free Grammar School he went up to Oxford, residing at Jesus College. He was still at Oxford when he was ordained deacon in 1763, having graduated B.A. the previous year. In 1764 he was ordained priest by the Bishop of Bangor and in 1768 took his M.A. It became evident from quite early in his career that natural history was to play a major part in his life; indeed, if it was just for his work as rector and curate, he would hardly be remembered.

In 1774 he visited the Isle of Man in the company of Thomas Pennant and other gentlemen of standing. Proof of Davies' dedication to botany is noted by the great author:

> I should accuse myself of a very undue neglect, if I did not acknowledge the various services I received from the friendship of Mr Davies, at different times, since the beginning of our acquaintance. I will in particular mention those which resulted from his great knowledge in botany. To him I owe the account of our *Snowdonian* plants; to him I lie under the obligation for undertaking, in *June* 1775, at my request, another voyage to the *Isle of Man*, to take a second review of its vegetable production. By his labours a *Flora* of the island is rendered as complete as possible to be effected by a single person in one season of the year. The number of plants he observed amounted to five hundred and fifty. (Pennant: 1793: 22).

Davies is also known to have assisted Pennant with his *Indian Zoology*, a work published in 1790.

Hugh Davies, it would seem, had ample free time to carry out his botanical researches. During the late 18th century it was customary for rectors, providing they had the means, to pay a curate to carry out the duties of the parish and during his twenty nine years at Aber near Bangor, where he held the living from 1787 following his time at Llandegfan, Anglesey, he had no fewer than six different curates. He knew the plant distribution of his native Anglesey well, and as Pennant testifies, he was an authority on the alpine plants of Caernarfonshire; like John Wynne

Griffith, Davies supplied Turner and Dillwyn with plant records which they incorporated into their *The Botanists Guide to England and Wales* (1805).

Davies carried out his botanical work at a time in history that was both uncertain and dramatic. The country was troubled by the effects of the French Revolution while other religious denominations were beginning to cause problems for the Church. He is known to have spoken out in no uncertain terms against Nonconformity, but it does not seem to have caused him any major worries. While Sir Thomas Wynn of Glynllifon formed the Caernarfonshire Volunteers and built Fort Williamsburg and Fort Belan on his land in order to combat a possible French invasion, Hugh Davies roamed the mountains of Snowdonia and the extensive fens of Anglesey looking for plants.

In 1813 he published the fruits of his labour in a two part volume, the first Welsh county flora to appear in print. This followed a two-year leave of absence granted him by the Bishop of Bangor during which he busied himself preparing his *Welsh Botanology*. The first part of the book is a catalogue of the native plants of Anglesey, where each plant listed is classified in the Linnean System starting with the genus, and then the specific name, English name and the Welsh name, and in some cases as many as three or four synonyms for the one plant. The names follow the text set by Smith in his *Flora Britannica*. In the Appendix to the first part of the book he listed the 'British Generic Names of those Phænogamous Plants in Flora Britannica, which are not of spontaneous Growth in Anglesey' (Davies, 1813: 133).

Davies included several of the Snowdonian species in this list and for the first time in print the Welsh name of the Snowdon lily *(Lloydia serotina)*, '*brwynddail y mynydd*', appears. This he no doubt copied from the manuscript *Botanologium* of William Morris mentioned previously. He listed the mountain avens *(Dryas octopetala)* as *Derig* a name derived from '*derw*', (oak), on account of the leaves of the plant being likened to oak leaves. The roseroot *(Sedum rosea)* is called *Pren y ddannoedd* which implies that the plant was used to cure toothache, and globeflower *(Trollius europaeus)*, was called '*Cronell*' the Welsh word for globe.

Following the common names, Davies gives the type of habitat, and names actual localities where some of the more uncommon species are to be found. Each entry then concludes with the flowering time. The flora was produced years before the first Ordnance Survey maps in north Wales appeared, and the introduction of the grid line system which made the job of pin-pointing any locality relatively easy and far more precise. These old books however, are of special interest to the local historian, as the localities named, and the comments which follow them, are much more informative in that respect than the modern county floras which replaced them. Here are a few examples:

> *Lithospermum arvense*; Corn [field] Gromwell ... in Baron Hill and Red-Hill demesnes, on each side of the road which leads by the Almshouse (Davies, 1813: 19-20).
>
> *Paris quadrifolia*; Herb Paris. "Near Carreg y forwyllt, on the west side of the river near Llangefni." This account I have taken from an old, elegantly-written manuscript ... I have walked the ground but once in search of this plant; let not my disappointment, in not finding it, discourage the botanist from future searches, for Dr. Pulteney observes, that at one time he failed of seeing a single plant on a spot of ground, which, in the preceding year, was thickly overspread with it (Davies, 1813: 39).

The awlwort *(Subularia aquatica)* is a plant that grows in lakes and pools and occurs in highland Snowdonia as well as at some lowland sites. Hugh Davies' early record from Anglesey is worth quoting:

> In the dry summer of 1798, as I walked the bed of a lake called Llyn Llywenan, in the parish of Bodedern, whence the water had retired about two months before, I very unexpectedly discovered this plant in great abundance. Notwithstanding its appearance was very different from what I had been used to see in the Arvonian Alpine lakes, where it always blossoms and seeds at the bottom, under water of considerable depth, yet it did not seem to regret the privation; the foliage was spread, the leaves somewhat reclining, and the flowering stems procumbent; the calyx and corolla were fully expanded; the petals, which are white and of an obovate form, were horizontal, the seed vessels and seed quite perfected; and, on the whole, it seemed to indicate a quite different plant (Davies, 1813: 61-62).

The plant was again recorded from Llyn Llywenan by J. E. Griffith (1895: 13), but there have been no recent sightings of it in Anglesey. It still grows in Cwmglas Mawr on Snowdon where it was first noted by Edward Lhuyd during the late 17th century and published in *Britannia*: 'A Spindle-leav'd Water-Sengreen-like Plant, growing in the bottom of a small Lake near the top of Snowdon-hill, call'd Phynon vrêch, &c' (Camden, 1695: 702).

Hugh Davies in his note on the habitat of the cottonweed (*Otanthus maritimus*), confirms the use he made of his transcript of Samuel Brewer's diary: 'This plant is now become very scarce below Llanfaelog, where Mr.

Brewer "found it in great plenty for a mile together" on Sept. the 5th, 1727' (Davies, 1813: 76). A note in Davies' transcript of Brewer's diary reads: *'Gnaphalium maritimum [Otanthus maritimus]* doth not grow anywhere about Abermeney or Llanddwyn . . . whatever it did formerly' [cf. Ray's statement, "We found it plentifully on the Sand near Abermeney-Ferry, in the Isle of Anglesea" R. Syn., 180] (Hyde, 1931: 27). Lightfoot however, during his visit with Banks in 1773, records having seen cottonweed on 7 August 'among the Sands at Llanfaelog on the west Side of the Island, but only a few plants and those not yet in Flower. It flowers in Sept.' (Riddelsdell, 1905: 305).

Brewer's diary is again mentioned following his notes on the sea stock *(Matthiola sinuata)*. Davies includes the plant on the strength of the records of Lhuyd and Brewer, but it was in fact John Ray who first recorded the plant in Anglesey during his tour through north Wales in 1662. There have been no subsequent records for this plant from Anglesey.

Despite the fact that the mistletoe *(Viscum album)* was not actually seen by him growing wild on the island, Davies nevertheless decided to include it in his flora in the belief that the Druids, whose stronghold was Anglesey, held the plant in very high esteem and made extensive use of it in their ceremonies and as a medicine. The mistletoe is normally found growing on apple trees, but the Druids believed that if it was found growing on oak then it was especially sacred. Davies adds:

I have not seen this plant; but we can scarcely suppose that the Druids had fixed upon, as a favourite residence, a spot that did not produce this highly venerated plant; add to this, that there is a place in the parish of Llangeinwen which is supposed to take its name from it (Davies, 1813: 93-94).

The juniper is listed on the strength of the fact that a place bears the Welsh name for Juniper: 'I venture this as once an inhabitant, from the name of a place, Cefn y Ferywen, the Juniper Bank, in the parish of Llanidan' (Davies, 1813: 95). In 1978 the dwarf juniper *(Juniperis communis* subsp. *nana)* was found growing on sea cliffs near Holyhead and the record appears in *The Flowering Plants and Ferns of Anglesey* (Roberts, 1982: 5).

Griffith (1895) and Roberts (1982) in their respective floras of Anglesey both record the Scots pine *(Pinus sylvestris)* as being 'frequent in old plantations'. Davies, however, does not include this species on the same grounds, but only on evidence which proves that the tree did at one time grow on the island. He states that the timber remains dug up with peat, and the tree stumps that were found while deepening the outlet of Llyn Llwydiarth near Pentraeth proved to be that of Scots pine: 'as the sylvestris is the only species of Pinus indigenous in Britain' (Davies, 1813: 91).

The rusty-back fern *(Ceterach officinarum)* according to Davies, was being gathered from caves on Holyhead mountain and used for bait in rock-cod-fishing, and as a result its numbers had been greatly reduced.

The *Welsh Botanology* includes a wealth of Welsh plant names which had either been collected locally from the eldest inhabitants and the writings of William Morris and others, or coined by the author. We are indebted to Hugh Davies for collating and publishing these old 'British' names, as he calls them, and they have formed the basis upon which modern Welsh plant name collectors have built.

One of the Welsh plant names of the dwarf elder *(Sambucus ebulus)* is given as *'Gwaed y gwyr'* (Blood of the warrior), as is tutsan *(Hypericum androsaemum)*, but Davies in a footnote favours the latter as being the most worthy:

> . . . that if the yellow flowering tops are bruised between the fingers, they will immediately communicate a deep crimson stain. The Ebulus claims it on the strength of a fabulous tale, that the plant originally sprung from the blood of the Danes, who were slain in Britain, whence it has also obtained the English name Dane-wort (Davies, 1813: 72-73).

Davies names two local botanists whose records he includes in his *Welsh Botanology*. Reverend Evan Lloyd recorded finding meadow clary *(Salvia pratensis)* on Cwirt Farm in the parish of Llangeinwen (Davies, 1813: 4), but Griffith (1895:108) dismisses this as an error for wild clary *(Salvia verbenaca)* which he found near Penmon Priory, as did Davies. In Griffith's opinion the plant specimens labelled *'Salvia pratensis'* in Davies' Herbarium was in fact *'Salvia verbenaca'*. There have been no recent records of either of these plants from Anglesey (Preston, Pearman & Dines, 2003: 530). Evan Lloyd can be credited with the first discovery of the meadow saxifrage *(Saxifraga granulata)* in Anglesey which he found on the sandy pastures of Rhuddgaer Farm near Llangeinwen. Davies confirms the find by adding that he, later, had found the plant in abundance at the same site (Davies, 1813: 41). More recent accounts (Roberts, 1982: 21) show that it still flourishes in various sites at the southern corner of the island.

The other local botanist named by Hugh Davies was Reverend John Williams, rector of Llanfairynghornwy who found the rare spotted rock-rose *(Tuberaria guttata)* in his home parish:

> Found by the Rev. Mr. Williams, Rector of Llanfairynghornwy, on a hill in that parish called y gader; by myself many years ago, plentifully, N.

73

west of, and near Amlwch, and on Holyhead Mountain; and lately, near Brewer's Habitat, on Holyhead Mountain, by the Rev. Mr. Lloyd, Minister of that parish (Davies, 1813: 53).

John Williams is mentioned by John Lightfoot in a letter to Joseph Banks dated 24 August 1773, and he accompanied the two visiting botanists to Glyder and Clogwyn Du'r Arddu on Snowdon during that year.

The common wintergreen *(Pyrola minor)* is recorded for Anglesey by Davies on the testimony of William Morris of Holyhead who was mentioned earlier as having prepared a list of the island's plants in a manuscript which is later believed to have been used by Davies:

> This is one of the very few which I take upon hearsay: I find it in a list of Anglesey plants, which was made by that ingenious man, and skilful naturalist Mr. William Morris, whom I have had occasion to mention in my preface; he says he found it in Lligwy wood (Davies, 1813: 40).

In 1955 R. H. Roberts of Bangor found the round-leaved wintergreen *(Pyrola rotundifolia)*, for the first time in Anglesey, in Newborough Warren, and since that time the plant has been seen in other parts of the island (Roberts, 1982: 39).

It seems hardly credible that even in those far off days plants could suffer due to industrial pollution. Davies, however, points out that the purple melic-grass *(Melica caerulea)* had withstood the sulphurous fumes of the copperworks at Amlwch, 'where every other vegetable, within a certain distance, even the crustaceous lichens, have been destroyed' (Davies, 1813: 9-10). This grass is now known as purple moor-grass *(Molinia caerulea)*.

The exploitation of the earth's natural resources was well under way during Davies' lifetime, and experiments in land improvement and reclamation were also imminent. It would appear that he was not as keen as his contemporary, John Wynne Griffith of Garn, on modernising farming methods and the utilization of land. Davies possessed a very intimate and thorough knowledge of his native island, and when out on his botanical rambles he would inquire into the past use of a piece of land when he felt a reason was needed for to the appearance of a plant that he had not previously seen there; plants that would today be referred to as 'aliens'. The following comment is added to his record of thorn-apple *(Datura stramonium)*: 'This plant was produced abundantly on cutting up a piece of old ground in the demesne of Maes y Porth [Dwyran] it is known that this land has undergone no process in agriculture within a century, prior to this'(Davies, 1813: 23). At a time when conservation as we know it today was unheard of, Davies was noticing the changes that were taking place around him, and this becomes clear in another of his comments in the book which he inserts while dealing with the smooth-stalked sedge *(Carex laevigata)*:

This species I discovered many years ago on Tyfry demesne; it has been totally destroyed in a meadow which once abounded with it; but is still found on the side of a deep glen, which lies about south of the mansion, where it is likely to bid defiance to the ruthless hand of improvement, both imaginary and real (Davies, 1813: 88).

These are the words of a man who had foreseen the rape of the Industrial and Agricultural Revolutions and the effect it was bound to have on the habitats of the plants he had studied during his lifetime.

Davies was quick to point out any errors he found in the work of other natural history writers but he would always explain his objections and disagreements in his own particular style. He disagrees with Edward Lhuyd on the Welsh name of the darnel grass *(Lolium temulentum)*, which, according to Davies is given as *'Ller'* in the *Archeologia Britannica*. The full name of *'Pawr-wellt Ller'* is given in *Welsh Botanology* for the rye brome grass *(Bromus secalinus)* as it has 'none of the noxious qualities of the other' (Davies, 1813: 11). The attention given by Davies to finding both the correct Welsh plant names and the uses to which plants were put becomes evident in his note on the sea plantain *(Plantago maritima)* where nearly a whole page is dedicated to the agricultural value of the plant. The author points out how names like *'llys y defaid'* (sheep's vegetable), *'sampier y ddafad'* (sheep's samphire) and *'bara can y defaid'* (sheep's favourite morsel) proves that it was regarded as an important grazing plant, and also as a cure for common ailments in cattle. In the same note Davies mentions an error in Withering's *An Arrangement of British Plants* where the rock samphire *(Crithmum maritimum)* is credited with the medicinal qualities which should have been attributed to the sea plantain. Withering gives the following uses: 'Poor people on the sea coast eat it as a pot-herb, and gather it for sale, it being much used as a pickle. – Sheep and cows eagerly feed, and are said to grow fat, upon it' (Withering, ii, 1796: 295).

The second part of *Welsh Botanology* was, to quote the full title, 'an alphabetical catalogue of the Welsh names of vegetables rendered into Latin and English with some account of the qualities, economical or medicinal, of the most remarkable.'

The plants are listed in alphabetical order with the Welsh name first, followed by the scientific and English names. The introduction, and the details for preparing the medicinal cures, are written in Welsh, and this part of the book was intended as a herbal that might benefit families who lived many miles from the nearest doctor in scattered farms or remote villages. In his introduction Hugh Davies pays tribute to Dr John Davies of Mallwyd, Meirionnydd (c.1567-1644), who published up to a thousand Welsh plant names in his Welsh-Latin Dictionary, and also to the manuscripts of '*Meddygon Myddfai*' the well known mediaeval physicians of Myddfai in Carmarthenshire. It may be interesting to note that Dr John Davies' list of Welsh plant names was copied from the manuscripts of Thomas Wiliems (1545/6-1622) of Trefriw, mentioned previously, the priest, scribe, lexicographer and physician who compiled a Latin-Welsh Dictionary that was never published. In effect the lineage of the derivation of some Welsh plant names can be observed from Salesbury's Herbal through the works of Thomas Wiliems, and the *Botanologium* of the *Dictionarum Duplex* of John Davies (1632) to William Morris, accumulating steadily in the course of time.

The *Welsh Botanology* is both a county flora and a family Herbal. It bridges the gap between the old traditional herbal botany and the modern study of plant distribution. It is the first complete catalogue of plants listed for any of the Welsh counties, and perhaps even more importantly for its author, it provided him with an opportunity to publish the vast collection of Welsh plant names that he had so diligently amassed during his lifetime.

Conflicting views of Snowdonia

Conrad Gesner, a 16th century Zurich naturalist made an early ascent of Pilatus in the Bernese Alps, and could well be the first botanical mountaineer. His feelings towards mountains was unique for his period as he climbed mountains for much the same reasons that we do today. The following is a passage translated from a Latin tract which Gesner wrote in 1543:

> I have resolved for the future, so long as God suffers me to live, to climb mountains, or at all events to climb one mountain every year, at the season when vegetation is at its best, partly for the sake of studying botany, and partly for the delight of the mind and the proper exercise of the body. For what, think you, is the pleasure, what the joy of a mind, affected as it should be, to marvel at the spectacle of the mighty masses of the mountains, and lift up one's head, as it were, among the clouds. The mind is strangely excited by the amazing altitude, and carried away to the contemplation of the great Architect of the Universe . . . Cultivators of philosophy will proceed to contemplate the great spectacles of this earthly paradise; and by no means the least of these are the steep and broken mountain-tops, the unscaleable precipices, the vast slopes stretching towards the sky, the dark and shady forests (Gribble, 1899: 52).

It is often said that the early travellers who visited Snowdonia did not appreciate the wild grandeur of the mountainous scenery and were more attracted to the historical antiquities found in towns and cities than to the natural delights of the countryside. This however was not always the case, and Thomas Johnson, the London apothecary mentioned earlier, certainly had an eye for natural views and a high opinion of the inhabitants of north Wales. Johnson had some unique theories in the forward of his book *Mercurii Botanici Pars Altera* (1641), a portion of which was translated into English under the title *The Itinerary of a Botanist* in 1908. According to Johnson the Welsh people were the remnants of a noble British race who inhabited the south-eastern corner of England prior to the Roman occupation, who had to flee their lands during the invasion and found refuge in the mountains of Wales where they settled:

> And this part of the island, up to the present day, produced men famous in war, and in the pursuits of peace. Nor will you anywhere easily find men who are well-born, magnanimous, upright, loyal and hospitable, and if true nobility derives its origin from manliness, it

must be confessed that this nation is truly noble
(Thomas, 1908: 2).

To Johnson, the Welsh language is the 'language of ancient Britain', and he proved that he was aware that it was still the language of the people by bringing along Edward Morgan to act as interpreter. Johnson, being a naturalist, appreciated picturesque scenery, and differed from other early visitors by actually enjoying the views of the mountains from the grounds of Glynllifon where he stayed:

> On one side St. George's Channel can be seen, and not far off the island of Mona and even Ireland can be seen in fine weather; on the other side our British Alps, the highest mountains in the whole island, rear themselves up, so that wheresoever you go there is something worth seeing (Thomas, 1908: 7).

The main purpose of Johnson's visit was to collect rare and interesting plants, but his writings leave us in little doubt that the journey itself also gave him pleasure.

Many of the early travellers were botanists, and some of them were so preoccupied with their subject that it made them quite oblivious both to the surrounding scenery and to the perils of the localities they visited. Samuel Brewer was such a botanist. He dismissed his guide on Clogwyn Du'r Arddu because he refused to follow him up to the rocks, and on Anglesey he explored the swampy bogs of Cors Llechylched: 'for a mile together in water above our knees, and the earth shaking under us' (Hyde, 1931: 28). Brewer's obsession with his plant hunting was paramount, and although the weather is sometimes referred to in his diary, he makes no mention of the scenery. One gets the impression that he would have been just as happy conducting his searches inside an enormous greenhouse, or a laboratory, and that he most probably would never have noticed the difference.

Some of the comments that the early scientists made regarding mountains were quite remarkable, as the following passage from an early edition of *Britannia* testifies: 'On the interior parts nature had reared groupes of mountains as if she meant to bind the island fast to the bowels of the earth' (Camden, 1586).

Another early traveller who found mountain scenery aesthetically pleasing was George Lyttleton; unlike Thomas Johnson, he was a politician and not a naturalist. Lyttleton's itinerary to north Wales in 1756 differed, however, from those of his contemporaries in as much as he chose to climb Moel Hebog and not Snowdon, and this he did by a western route as opposed to the more normally used Beddgelert track.

Here are some selected passages from his 'letter to Mr. Bower' from 'Bryncir, in Carnarvonshire, July 6, 1756':

This morning (July 7) being fair, we ventured to climb up to the top of a mountain, not indeed so high as Snowdon, which is here called Moel Guidon, i.e. the nest of the eagle; but one degree lower that that called Moel Happock, the nest of the Hawk . . . The hill we stood upon was perfectly clear, the way we came up a pretty easy ascent; but before us was a precipice of many hundred yards, and below, a vale, which, though not cultivated, has much savage beauty; . . . I am perfectly well, *eat like a horse, and sleep like a monk* so that I may by this ramble, preserve a stock of health, that may last all winter, and carry me through my parliamentary campaign (Lyttleton app. to Wyndham, 1781: 235-237).

Turning to Samuel Johnson, we find that he was certainly no mountaineer; in fact he seemed to be quite unaccustomed to any excessive bodily exertion and his walk up to Dolbadarn Castle near Llanberis left him quite breathless. The natural beauties of Snowdonia made little impression on him, compared to that of the Peak District of which he wrote:

We saw Hawkestone, . . . and were conducted by Miss Hill over a large tract of rocks and woods; a region abounding with striking scenes and terrific grandeur. We were always on the brink of a precipice, or at the foot of a lofty rock; but the steeps were seldom naked: in many places, oaks of uncommon magnitude shot up from the crannies of stone; and where there were no trees, there were underwoods and bushes.

Round the rocks is a narrow path cut upon the stone, which is very frequently hewn into the steps; but art has proceeded no further than to make the succession of wonders safely accessible. The whole circuit is somewhat laborious; it is terminated by a grotto cut in the rock to a great extent, with many windings, and supported by pillars, not hewn into regularity, but such as imitate the spots of nature, by asperities and protuberances.

The place is without any dampness, and would afford an habitation not uncomfortable . . . though it wants water it excels Dovedale by the extent of its prospects, the awfulness of its shades, the horrors of its precipices, the verdure of its hollows, and the loftiness of its rocks: the ideas which it forces upon the mind are, the sublime, the dreadful, and the vast. Above is inaccessible altitude, below is horrible profundity.

Ilam has grandeur, tempered with softness; the walker congratulates his own arrival at the place, and is grieved to think he must ever leave it. As he looks up to the rocks, his thoughts are elevated; as he turns his eyes on the vallies, he is composed and soothed.

He that mounts the precipices at Hawkestone, wonder how he came thither, and doubts how he shall return. His walk is an adventure, and his departure an escape. He has not the tranquillity, but the horrors, of solitude; a kind of turbulent pleasure, between fright and admiration (Johnson, 1816: 38-42).

It was probably the fertile greenery and gentle beauty of the Peak District that motivated Johnson to write these words, the craggy wild greyness of Snowdonia failing to elicit any comment from him such as his beloved English hills did. First impressions usually count with mountaineers. The same could be said of Dr Johnson, who favoured the 'pretty' as opposed to the 'awe inspiring'.

There was a marked difference in the attitude of the travellers who visited Wales from the last quarter of the 18th century onwards, and during that period fifty individual tours through Wales were published. Before that time some of the comments made by tourists on Wales and the Welsh were offensive. In 1670 Charles Cotton wrote of 'hills and valleys uncouth and uneven' where he was forced to crawl on all fours in the company of a guide who had: 'a voice like a cricket, a look like a rat: the brain of a goose and the heart of a cat'. The Welsh language suffered similar abuse: 'Their native gibberish is usually prattled throughout the whole of Taphydom except in the market towns, whose inhabitants being a little raised do begin to despise it.'Tis usually cashiered out of gentlemen's houses, there being scarcely to be heard even one Welsh Tom (sic) in many families so that (if the stars prove lucky) there may be some glimmering hopes that the British language may be quite extinct and may be English'd out of Wales' (Hughes, 1924: 45). These were quite different comments to those made by Thomas Johnson the apothecary earlier that century.

However, when Joseph Craddock published his *Letters from Snowdon* in 1770, he wrote passionately and with an enthusiasm for scenery, a fashion which came to be adopted by most of the contemporary authors of the Welsh 'Tours'. Craddock stayed in Snowdonia as the guest of the curate of one of the parishes, the name of which is not given but which, from the description and proximity to Llyn Cwellyn, could have been Beddgelert or Betws Garmon.

The curate is a venerable clergyman, on the eve of threescore. He wears his own natural grey locks, and still retains a ruddy bloom in his countenance, acquired by health and exercise. He has lived among

80

these mountains for nearly forty years, upon a curacy and a little paternal estate, which he cultivates with his own hands. His whole revenue amounts not forty pounds per annum, and yet that exceeds his expences (Craddock, 1770: 53).

The curate was also his guide to Snowdon, which they ascended from a 'hut' near Llyn Cwellyn; the views completely overwhelmed Craddock, as did his stay among the hills. 'O my friend', he wrote, 'why should we return to the busy haunt of men? Why were we doomed to drag an existence in populous cities and the crowded forum! O that it had been our lot to live among these mountains, unenvied and unknown' (Craddock, 1770: 59). Craddock also enjoyed the company of the local inhabitants, and he took the trouble to learn a few Welsh words which, together with a few coins given in gratuity, helped him to gain their trust. While spending the evening in a 'small thatched hut' prior to their ascent of Snowdon, 'a poor blind harper' was sent for and a number of 'blooming country girls' entertained them with singing and dancing. Craddock enjoyed the music. 'There is something very plaintive and affecting in the Welsh music, and the manner of their singing symphonious and responsive to the notes of the harp, renders it exceedingly melodious.' His comments on Welsh poetry, however, were quite the opposite and one detects that old aloof imperialistic attitude influencing his opinions: 'The poets, or such as pretend to be such, arrogate to themselves a most unwarrantable poetical licence of coining words, for the sake of sound; and this they will seldom scruple to do, whenever they want a word for rhyme. Hence the greatest part of their poetry, is nothing more than melodious nonsense, a perfect jargon of harmonious sounds. And when translated, scarce reducible to common sense' (Craddock, 1770: 88-89). Craddock formed these opinions of Welsh poetry during his short stay in Snowdonia, and sadly he failed to understand or appreciate the rule that permits a bard to coin words for use in rhyme. When he asked for the meaning of a certain word he was given the translation literally, which did not always make sense, and what he failed to understand he chose to ridicule. His comments on the Welsh language also illustrate a self-opinionated character, with no previous knowledge of the country. He sees the Welsh as a nation which had benefited but little from the improvements of the civilized world. The overall impression one gets, however, is that his judgments, although based on an imperialistic view of life, are nevertheless and at the same time compassionate.

In conclusion, perhaps it is Arthur Aikin, who toured north Wales during the summer of 1796 in the company of two friends who best sums up this issue: '. . . but the requisite knowledge of a sufficient number of circumstances from which to deduce a national character is not to be acquired without long residence and much intercourse with the inhabitants' (Aikin, 1797: viii)

Arthur Aikin (1773-1854), who was a chemist and interested mainly in mineralogy, also made botanical observations and contributed a list of Shropshire plants, plus a few Caernarfonshire plants to Turner and Dillwyn's *Botanist's Guide* &c (1805). He entered Snowdonia through Aberglaslyn Pass, recording such plants as white water-lily *(Nymphaea alba)*, royal fern *(Osmunda regalis)*, bog myrtle *(Myrica gale)* and beaked tasselweed *(Ruppia maritima)* on the way. Aikin passed this way before Madocks' embankment was built across Traeth Mawr and at a time when the sea reached up to Aberglaslyn, and he found the beaked tasselweed 'in the pools and ditches of the marshes covered by the tide ... the fruit are formed by an elastic spiral line, contracting or elongating itself according to the depth of the water' (Aikin, 1797: 93).

Aikin ascended Snowdon from Llyn Cwellyn, along the Snowdon Ranger path which in his day started near Bron y Fedw, a hill farm long associated with the old Snowdon guides. Aikin failed to hire the services of a guide because it was a Sunday, but nevertheless took advantage of the fine weather and set out with his colleagues for the summit. He gives no record of the plants he saw, but dismisses them as being the same as he found on Cadair Idris, which suggests that he did not visit the localities of the rarities due to the absence of a local guide. His comments are on the whole to do with the geology of the area, and he was also impressed by the black cattle and the sheep that were left unattended to graze on the lower parts of the mountain. Aikin described the views in fine prose, as is often the case with the writers of the 'tours', but without the lengthy over-dramatic style of most of his fellow writers. As a scientist he was interested in the varying temperatures recorded on the summit in comparison with that of the valleys, and he must have made a night ascent in 1795 as he was on the summit of Snowdon watching the sunrise on 5 July of that year and recorded the temperature as being 34°F at that time and 48°F at the same place at 1 o'clock in the afternoon. The temperature recorded for him at Beddgelert at 7 o'clock on the same morning was 62°F.

While on the summit during his 1796 journey he saw three ring ouzels 'amid the thickness of the clouds' and goes on to say that the eagle was also an occasional visitor to the loftiest crags. (Aikin, 1797: 100). On the day following the Snowdon trip, Aikin and his friends set out from Beddgelert bound for Llanrwst; a walk of about twenty miles which they took amid showers of heavy rain. The unusually wet weather of that summer had all but destroyed the hay crop as he noted while passing the enclosures of land near Llyn Dinas and the hill farmers had taken the precaution of placing slabs of stone on top of each stack to keep it from being washed into the lake by the mountain torrents. Aikin describes the enclosed land around Llyn Dinas as being better than average, as 'mosses, orchids, and asphodels, with a small proportion of grass which was mown to serve for the winter provision of the cattle and sheep' (Aikin, 1797: 103). On arriving at the head of Llyn Dinas they continued along the road towards Llyn Gwynant, but failed to ford the river due to the ferocious rush of water. They therefore took to a narrow footpath which eventually brought them to the head of Llyn Gwynant, after having 'forced their way through a steep swampy wood'. The 'road' up to Bwlch Ehediad from Llyn Gwynant is described as 'a continued series of rude broken steps, very narrow and winding, ascending the steep face of a craggy mountain that overlooks the lake, without any parapet wall, or the slightest barrier, in places where the descent is all but perpendicular' (Aikin, 1797: 104). After reaching the top of the 'Bwlch' they crossed the wide boggy tract in torrential rain, and on descending the other side they could make out the form of Dolwyddelan Castle through the clouds. On arriving at Dolwyddelan they managed, with some difficulty arising from language problems, to obtain refreshments before continuing their journey to Llanrwst in the Conwy valley. Aikin records that the 'number of neat little farmhouses and gentlemen's seats give an air of plenty and civilization to this valley, ... Here we found no difficulty in inquiring our road, for we have invariably found the English language understood in the fertile and populous parts' (Aikin, 1797: 106-107).

Aikin, like Craddock before him, was much impressed with the singing of harmonious melodies to the accompaniment of the Welsh harp, a custom popular in the inns and public places of north Wales. J. Lloyd Williams (1854-1945), botanist and musician, writing of his childhood days in Llanrwst recalls how his father used to sing old Welsh ballads to the accompaniment of the harp around the inns of the town. (Williams, J.L., 1941:17).

Observations concerning the lead mines at Gwydir and the copper mines of Llanberis take up most of the chapter that records the journey from Llanrwst to Caernarfon, and is of great interest to students of mineralogy. On enquiring after lodgings at Capel Curig they found the houses deserted and the inhabitants gone to Llanrwst Fair, so they continued their journey in the direction of Llanberis but missed the junction of the horse track at Penygwryd and subsequently found themselves approaching Llyn Gwynant. In order to avoid retracing their steps the party then decided to climb directly from the hollow of Cwm Dyli and managed to gain the Llanberis track at the top of the pass. Their appetites were soon satisfied at a 'hovel of an inn' at Llanberis (now Nant Peris) and the list of plants seen *en route* though small in number, is nevertheless interesting. Near Capel Curig they saw venus'-looking-glass *(Legousia hybrida)*; a plant of arable fields in south-east England, and not recorded since from Snowdonia. The tiny filmy-fern *(Hymenophyllum)* was noted as being collected 'near Llanberis', but it is impossible to say whether it was the *Hymenophyllum wilsonii*, or the *Hymenophyllum tunbrigense*, as the two British species were not distinguished until after Aikin's day. Parsley fern *(Cryptogramma crispa)* was and still is a common fern in Snowdonia, as is also the lemon-scented fern *(Oreopteris limbosperma)*.

The 'Classic Tours'

Thomas Pennant (1726-1798) naturalist and antiquary had, according to Samuel Johnson, 'greater variety of inquiry than almost any man, and has told us more than perhaps one in ten thousand could have done in the time he took. He has not said what he was to tell, so you cannot find fault with him for what he has not told' (Pennant, 1883, i: xiii). Pennant's much acclaimed *Tours in Wales* are considered accurate and informative sources of information and are frequently consulted by historians. He was not, by his own admission, a botanist but he nevertheless noted a number of plants while on his mountain excursions, and is credited with the first record for Caernarfonshire of the alpine meadow-grass *(Poa alpina)* which he saw while ascending Snowdon under the guidance of Hugh Shone (Pennant, 1883, ii: 323). Pennant's guide was in fact probably Hugh Jones of Cwmglas Bach, pronounced 'Huw Siôn' by the local Welsh, which would to a stranger's ear sound like 'Hugh Shone'.

They began their ascent from Llanberis and after the climb past Ceunant Mawr, the much visited Llanberis waterfall, they crossed the lower meadows of Cwmbrwynog and joined the Snowdon Ranger track after crossing Bwlch Maesgwm and descending a short distance on the Betws Garmon side. The plants mentioned during this trip are mainly grasses and rushes and Pennant explains the term *'gwair y rhosydd'*, as being the local term for a mixture of rushes, sedges and grasses which are still the dominant plants on the lower moorland slopes of Snowdonia. Literally translated *'gwair y rhosydd'* means moorland grass. Like most of the other travellers he noted the sheep and cattle high on the mountain during the summer months and also the *'hafotai'*, or summer dwellings, where the hill farmers stayed to be nearer their stock before herding them back to the *'hendre'*, or winter dwelling in early autumn; Pennant compares this custom to that practised by the farmers in the Swiss Alps and their *sennes*. These summer dairy houses are described as consisting 'of a long low room with a hole at one end, to let out the smoke from the fire which is made beneath,' where the family lived in Spartan style using stones for stools and hay for beds. Their homespun clothes were dyed using lichen gathered off the mountain rocks; the lichen was named by Pennant as *'Lichen omphaloides'*, and William Withering notes the following uses of the plant as a dye:

> It dyes wool of a brown reddish colour, or a dull but durable crimson or purple, paler but more lasting than that of Orchal. It is prepared by the country people in Ireland by steeping it in stale urine, adding a

little salt to it, and making it up into balls with lime. Wool dyed with it and then dipped in the blue vat becomes of a beautiful purple. With rotten oak it makes a good dark brown frize. Wool dyed with red wood, or sanders, and afterwards in corker, becomes of a dark reddish brown (Withering, 1796, iv: 34).

The substance was also used to check the bleeding from a wound, and it was known by the common names, cork, corker, arcell, and according to Pennant, as *'cenn du y cerrig'*, meaning 'black lichen of the stones' in Welsh.

Pennant climbed the Glyder from 'Pont y gwryd', where the servants were directed to proceed to Llanberis with the horses, and after reaching the summit of Glyder Fach he descended via the Gribin Ridge to Cwm Bochlwyd and on to Nant Ffrancon. His trip to Cwm Idwal, Glyder Fawr, Llyn y Cŵn and down to Llanberis was undertaken on another day, and he describes the way as passing 'beneath that vast precipice Castell y Geifr, or The Castle of the Goats'. The Devil's Kitchen, or Twll Du, is described as *'a stupendous roche fendue'* and 'Klogwyn Du Ymhen y Glyder' is as 'dreadful a precipice as any in Snowdonia'. Pennant was aware that this area was much frequented by botanists, and names the alpine saxifrage *(Saxifraga nivalis)*, Snowdon lily *(Lloydia serotina)* and *Lichen islandicus (Cetraria islandica)* as being among the plants found here, but he does not say whether or not he saw them there himself. The *Lichen islandicus (Cetraria islandica)* was used by the people of Iceland and is thus described by Pennant:

A decoction of the fresh leaves in water serves them in the spring as a powerful cathartic; and yet, when dried, changes its quality, and, if grinded to powder, is a common food, either made into bread, or boiled with milk, or water (Pennant, 1883, ii: 316).

It was also used as a cure for coughs and consumption. Llyn y Cŵn is also noted by Pennant as being a spot worthy of a visit by botanists. The lake he declares to be devoid of any fish, and questions the claim, made by Giraldus in his *Itinerary through Wales &c.* in 1188, that the lake yielded trout, perch, and eels, all of which were wanting a left eye. It must be noted that Giraldus does not actually name Llyn y Cŵn as being the lake connected with the folk-tale of the one-eyed fish, and Pennant most probably saw the reference to it in Gibson's edition of Camden's *Britannia* which states:

The lake wherein he [Giraldus] tells us there's a wandering island, is a small Pond, call'd *Lhyn y Dywarchen* (i.e. *Lacus cespitis,*) from a little green moveable patch, which is all the occasion of the Fable of the wandering island; but whence that other of monocular Fish (which he says were found also at two places in Scotland) took beginning, I have nothing to say, but that it is credibly reported that Trouts having only one eye are sometimes taken at *Lhyn ykwn* near Lhan Berys (Camden, 1722: 797-798).

Edward Lhuyd, who contributed substantial additions to this edition of *Britannia*, probably heard the folk-tale during one of his visits to Snowdonia just as Giraldus had five hundred years earlier.

The plants recorded from in and around the lake are water lobelia *(Lobelia dortmanna)* awlwort *(Subularia aquatica)* and quillwort *(Isoetes lacustris)*. It was also in this area that he made the first record of the three-flowered rush *(Juncus triglumis)*, a notable find for a man who stated of himself: 'botany is not within my province' (Pennant, 1883, ii: 331). This might suggest that he was shown these plants either by the guide, who would have known about the locality previously, or by a companion. He also notes the alpine hawkweed *(Hieracium holosericeum)* from the same area and it is interesting that the first record of this plant is credited to Sir Joseph Banks who with the Reverend John Lightfoot undertook a botanical tour of Wales in 1773, the same year in which Pennant made his first tour.

Thomas Pennant came from Downing in Flintshire, and he was proud of his Welshness, something clearly illustrated in his writing: 'we sustained our independency . . . against the power of a kingdom more than twelve times larger than Wales', he wrote 'and at length had the glory of falling, when a divided country, beneath the arms of the most wise, and most warlike of the English monarchs' (Pennant, 1883, i: 4).

Pennant's travels in north Wales were undertaken in 1773 and 1776 accompanied by Moses Griffith, the celebrated artist from Bryncroes, Lleyn, who illustrated the published works, and also Pennant's Scottish tours, as well as the author's books on natural history which contain a large number of illustrations of animals, birds and fishes.

Pennant enjoyed his mountain walks and favoured traversing the hills and returning by a different route to that which was used to ascend. It will be remembered that the guide Hugh Shone [Hugh Siôn] led Pennant up Snowdon along the Snowdon Ranger path, which they had reached via Bwlch Maesgwm from Cwmbrwynog, they then came down the pony track, which is known today as the Llanberis path. Hugh Siôn 'was a most able conductor' according to Pennant and this testimonial would have been considered useful by the guide and kept for showing to future potential clients.

The poet William Sotheby was also pleased with his guide, and in his book entitled *A Tour Thro' Parts of North and South Wales, Sonnets Odes and other Poems . . .'* gives the following account:

Thee, Snowdon! King of Cambrian mountains hail!
With many a lengthened pause my lingering feet
Follow the experienced guide; a veteran maimed
With glorious wounds, that late on Calpe's height
Bled in his country's cause; though time has marked
With graceful touch his silver hair, yet health,
The child of temperance, has fixed the rose
Of youth upon his cheek; keen beams his eye
Beneath his hoary brow, and firm his foot
Springs on the steepness of the rough ascent.
Proud of his native land the veteran points
To every mountain, wood and winding stream,
That by tradition sacred made records
His great forefathers' deeds: for not derived
Of simple lineage the brave warrior boasts
Hereditary blood of British Chiefs (Sotheby, 1794: 33-35).

The anonymous guide, a soldier wounded on active duty in Gibraltar, knew his native mountains well and took delight in telling to his charge the legends and folklore related to them. It is sad that the poet did not pass on to us the name of this wounded 'warrior' so that he, along with the poem, could have achieved a measure of immortality.

There is further evidence of wounded ex-servicemen acting as guides in north Wales. In 1794 Robert Clutterbuck left Dolgellau under the guidance of an old sailor who had lost an arm in the service of his country, and two years later Sir Christopher Sykes wrote: 'Our guide Henry Roberts was an old soldier wanting an arm aged 67. His mother living aged 88, his father died 7 years ago, aged 87. They had been married 67 years and lived about two miles up the mountain. He [Henry Roberts] now keeps a turnpike gate at Dolgellau'(NLW MS 2258).

In addition to the highland guides who operated in the mountain areas there were also lowland guides who were hired by travellers to lead them across the remote and often trackless terrain between towns and villages. One such tract of land which led many a traveller astray was that which lay between Harlech and Penmorfa, and prior to the completion of the embankment across the mouth of the river Glaslyn in 1811 guides were employed to cross the notoriously treacherous sands of Traeth Mawr and Traeth Bach when the tide was out.

Henry Penruddocke Wyndham toured Wales and Monmouthshire in 1774 and 1777 and his comments on the guides of this area are not very complimentary: 'In order to avoid the goat track of our morning ride,' he writes, 'we returned over the sands of the Traeth Bychan, which are only passable at low water. It is remarkable, that we had hitherto never deviated from the true line of our route, when alone; and that we seldom failed of doing it when we employed a guide.' Wyndham's guide from Tan y Bwlch lost his way twice while leading the party to and from Harlech, 'and we were obliged to have guide upon guide, before we ventured to cross the sands, which are by no means difficult when known, but which, from their shifting and quickness, are intricate and dangerous to strangers.' He goes on to accuse Welsh guides of blundering through the country, preferring to make a mistake rather than stopping to ask the way, which would give away their lack of knowledge; 'till he himself is really alarmed, at which time he becomes more terrified, than those he pretends to conduct.' Wyndham's Harlech guide refused to admit his mistakes until the party were led to the verge of a steep cliff down which it was impossible to descend. This was the fourth incompetent guide whom Wyndham had the misfortune to hire during his Welsh tour, and this induced him to use horse drawn carriages on his second journey. He nevertheless found it necessary to revert to guides to attend to the horses whenever they wanted to travel beyond the range of the coaches and even this caused problems: 'and it would appear incredible, if I was to repeat, how, consequently, we were almost bewildered between stage and stage' (Wyndham: 1781: 118-121).

The guides who led travellers across the treacherous sands of Traeth Mawr and Traeth Bach continued to operate until 1820. Traeth Bach was crossed at the estuary of the river Dwyryd by a route connecting Talsarnau and Penrhyndeudraeth, while Traeth Mawr, the Glaslyn estuary, was undertaken from either Penrhyndeudraeth or Llanfrothen across to Penmorfa. John Lloyd or Siôn Llwyd, who kept an inn called 'Ceunant' at Llanfrothen during the 1740s served as guide during this time, and his son, of the same name, took over from him until 1820. Another of the known guides from this district was William Jones of Abergarfan, Penrhyndeudraeth who died in 1830. There are several entries in parish burial registers which testify to the number of strangers unfamiliar with the area who ventured alone onto the sands and were drowned. Wiser travellers would look for an ash tree which once stood close to the edge of the sands near Rhos, Penrhyndeudraeth. This tree bore a sign in the shape of a white horse on which were displayed the words 'Guide for the Sands' (Owen, 1943: 98).

Bron y Fedw, 'The Guide's House'

Several references are made by travellers during the latter part of the 18th century to the 'guide's house near Llyn Cwellyn', as the starting point for the ascent of Snowdon. This was Bron y Fedw in Betws Garmon, and traces of the old farmhouse can still be seen by the side of the stream above the present Bron y Fedw Isaf, close to the path connecting Nant y Betws and Llanberis (Hobley, 1913:192). This is the path that can also be used to reach the summit of Snowdon by turning off and following the Snowdon Ranger path where the two paths cross higher up the hillside.

An old manuscript written in 1775 refers to climbing Snowdon from 'Bronfedow the Shepherd's House' but the author met his guide on his arrival at Caernarfon. It is not clear if he came there to meet him or if the guide was actually from the town. Reverend J. Poole and Charles Joseph Harford also had difficulties finding the guide during their tour through north Wales in 1798:

> Soon after breakfast we quitted Caernarvon by an excellent Road lately made by subscriptions which soon led [through] the Mountains . . . passing a very pretty Lake in about 6 miles we came to Bettws a little beyond which is the Guide's House which for want of a direction first we passed but having heard it was before we came to the bridge we turned back and found a Cottage on the side of the hill about two fields out of the road on the left hand. It is only to be discovered by some white washed stones on the top. Griffith the Guide encouraged us with hopes at having a clear view from the top though it was then covered with clouds, but as they had been gradually rising as yesterday we resolved on making the attempt which as soon as our conductor had put on his shoes and stockings and best coat we began. The path from his house was rather steep and passing large fragments of stone for nearly a mile when we came to a large plain of Peat Moss which might with little difficulty, be drained and converted into excellent pasture. On this stands a large isolated rock called Maen mawr (the great Slab) crossing this inclined plain we came to the foot of a rather steep ascent which when we had surmounted we arrived at the base of the first ridge of Rocks whence we enjoyed a fine view of Anglesey before us and below the Black Lake we had before observed . . . from hence the path became very steep . . . with a precipice on each side and I began to [wonder] if I could venture . . . Our path now varied sometimes leading over Grass, Bogs detricia masses of Rock, but very steep 'till we came within about a mile of the top. When we

rested at a [most] delicious spring which flows from the side of the mountain. An upright stone which marks it had long complemented with eager wishes I never felt so pleased at getting refreshment as this spring afforded . . . adopted my normal mode of gargling my throat some time before I swallowed any of the delicious liquid and then with a slight mixture of Brandy our repast was rather scanty . . . thinking of dining on Snowdon. Our Guide had gathered most of the Alpine Plants for which he had ventured on the Rocks and Cliffs with the intrepidity of the Goats some of whom we saw (UWB MS 31).

Other tourists have noted Ellis Griffith's goat-like agility and these talents were often put to more practical uses than just plant collecting. Mrs Griffiths and Miss Bell visited north Wales during the 1790s and whilst journeying from Caernarfon to Tan y Bwlch they ascended Snowdon from Bron y Fedw under the guidance of Ellis Griffith:

Soon after six leave the Boot Inn [Caernarfon] where there is an obliging and intelligent landlord, but who has not been able to introduce much order or [...] into his family: the confusion of the time (it being the Assize-week) must be allowed for in some measure. After a pleasant road of 7 miles between Moel Eilion on the left, & the vast mountain Mynyth vaur [Mynydd Mawr] on the right, wch on this side presents to us a scooped hollow of an immense size of circular form, the rock wch compases it being almost perpendicular & fluted as it were by the rain, we arrived at a neat little cottage at the foot of Snowdon, where the guide lives who conducts travellers to the summit. The name of this place is Bronyveddo [Bron y Fedw]; beneath it lies Llyn Gwethlan [Cwellyn] famous for its Char wch   is only caught in the Winter; . . . We now ascended a hill not very steep of about a mile & half, till we came to the side of a small lake from whence Snowdon properly so called begins to rise. We had the mortification the find the top of the mountain completely covered with clouds wch seemed rather inclined to thicken & descend lower, we marched on however in hopes it might clear up; The wind increased to a violent gale & as we advanced higher made it almost impossible to stand. After climbing about half a mile with frequent rests under the shelter of the rocks, we all were of opinion that the wind was too violent to venture any further. The guide assured us we were passed the most difficult part of the enterprise, but did not suppose if we were to reach the Wyddfa that we wd enjoy any prospect at all. The ladies often lost their legs; handkerchiefs flew out among the rocks, and our guide skipped like a goat to the very verge of the precipice to recover them. One fair Lady had her hat & nightcap wch they had the precaution to tie close to their heads [...] blown off & her hair "screamed like a meteor to the troubled air". Many often ludicrous accidents happened in the storm too tedious to mention. This man [Ellis Griffith] told us he paid £28 per ann. for his farm; kept about 19 little cows & lived almost intirely on the produce of the dairy as their beverage was nothing but milk or whey. His demesne was pretty extensive reaching from Llyn Gwethlan to the Wyddfa, that is about 3 miles & a half long by one mile broad. The family consisted of a man & his wife a son & 2 daughters; one of whom handsome was most industriously kept out of sight.

For the honour of female resolution it must be recorded that the Ladies advanced some yards further than the Gentlemen thought proper to do. But the whole company were unanimous that the attempt in calm weather would be not very difficult or dangerous. From [...] we got up to, the prospect of the surrounding hills & lakes was very grand; Ireland & the Isle of Man appeared like clouds at a great distance. The descent was rather alarming. At one place where a precipice overhangs the vale of Llanberis, it was with difficulty we prevented [...] from showing us the nearest way down. By the aid of shrub, (not what grow on the mountain for there was not even a sprig of heath) but the shrub we carried with us in a bottle, we descended the steep, & made our repast on the provisions we had brought with us from Caernarvon, by the peat fire in the friendly cottage of our guide Ellis Griffith (NLW MS 9352A).

During the summer of 1794 the author of another 'Tour' called upon the services of Ellis Griffith. He was a young Cambridge graduate aged twenty-three called Joseph Hucks, who together with Samuel Taylor Coleridge the poet and two others arrived in Beddgelert by the Caernarfon road. Hucks and Coleridge had begun their tour by entering Wales from Gloucester, continued northwards to Welshpool, Bala, Wrexham, Denbigh and Holywell before turning westward, joining up with two Cambridge students on the way. At 11 o'clock on a stormy night the party set out from Beddgelert to look for the guide's house which they had learned was a distance of five miles from the village. Hucks notes that 'Bethkelert' was the usual place from which tourists made their ascent of Snowdon; but they became quite lost in the dark on the way to Betws Garmon. They eventually saw a faint light on the hillside above the road and, directing their steps in this direction they came to a 'small hut' where they found that the family had retired for the night. It was some time before an elderly man appeared at the door, and like most local people in

Snowdonia at that time neither spoke nor understood English. After some difficulty the party succeeded in making themselves understood, and on hearing the words 'Ellis Griffith' and 'Snowdon' frequently repeated, the old man agreed to lead them to the house of the Snowdon guide. After a half hour's walk they arrived at another cottage to which they were admitted by a young man of about seventeen years of age who turned out to be the man they were looking for. The guide firmly advised against any attempt at climbing Snowdon that night, so the party decided to wait until morning in the hope that the weather might improve by then. Hucks spent the night reading an old Welsh dictionary by rush-light while his friends lay on the benches on either side of the open fireplace, from which the dying embers of the peat fire gave comfort against the sound of the wind and rain and the roar of a nearby waterfall in full spate.

Hucks records waking the household at 4.00 a.m. the following morning; although the weather had not improved very much, the other members decided to attempt the excursion while Hucks returned to the inn at Beddgelert to wait for them; they did not arrive until 4 o'clock in the afternoon. This ascent of Snowdon was undertaken mainly to find plants rather than for the view from the top: Hucks had stated earlier that: 'One of my companions was a very skilful botanist, and his botanical furor [sic] induced him at all times to despise danger and difficulty, when in pursuit of a favourite plant . . .' (Hucks, 1795: 43). The party seems to have suffered similarly at the hands of this 'skilful botanist' during their stay at Caernarfon when he expressed a desire to cross the Menai Straits to Anglesey in order to see a rare plant. Soon after coming off the ferry at Abermenai it began to rain very hard and they made their way back again as it began to grow dark. The two-mile crossing was very rough and the rain, together with the spray of sea-water, thoroughly soaked them.

There is no evidence to show which member of the party was the botanist; the two Cambridge students who accompanied Coleridge and Hucks, joining them at Conwy, were John Brooke (1773-1821) and Thomas Berdmore and neither one is known to have been a botanist. Hucks met the only person who could have been described as a very skilful botanist when they attempted to cross the Menai Straits to Anglesey from Aber, near Bangor:

> The village of Abber Conway, usually called Abber, ... is situated upon the straits of the Menai, that at high tide is there about four miles across; but when the water is out, it appears perfectly dry; for the sea retires so far back, that it only leaves a channel of a quarter of a mile, . . . all the rest is a complete flat, and consequently the tide overflows it very rapidly. There are stated times to pass this ferry, which one

should be very exact in observing, for ten minutes may be of the utmost importance. The clergyman of the place accompanied us to the boundaries of this wilderness of sand; he gave us the necessary directions for our passage, which were only to keep a white house in view that belonged to the ferryman on the Anglesea shore, . . . (Hucks, 1795: 34).

The clergyman who gave directions to Hucks and his party was probably Hugh Davies, author of *Welsh Botanology* and rector of Aber during this period, but there is no evidence to substantiate the suggestion that he was the 'skilful botanist' mentioned.

Ellis Griffith was baptized on 1 January 1778, and on 19 October 1804 at Beddgelert he married Ann Evans, the daughter of Dafydd Evans of Talymignedd Farm in the Nantlle valley. They had three children, Ellis, Ann and Jane. The couple went to live at the present Bron y Fedw Uchaf soon after the wedding; this farmhouse became the home of the local Methodist Sunday School until a chapel was built in 1825. Ellis Griffith died on 26 August 1810 aged thirty-two, and his wife Ann on 18 July 1860 aged eighty-three; they were buried at Beddgelert.

Evans the Botanist and Richards the Guide

Reverend John Evans (fl 1768-1810s), originally from Lydney in Gloucestershire, made his botanical tour of north Wales in 1798 and on entering Wales from Shrewsbury he travelled by way of Newtown, Bala, Dolgellau, Barmouth, Harlech and northwards into the heart of Snowdonia. Harlech is described as 'a few miserable cottages on the top of a bare rock', where he records, probably among the sand dunes, the sharp rush *(Juncus acutus)*, wild cabbage *(Brassica oleracea)* – which used to grow on the cliffs below the castle but has not been recorded recently – and enchanter's nightshade *(Circaea lutetiana)*, which was seen inside the castle and which is accorded the following footnote: 'This plant called Enchanters Night Shade, was, in ages of ignorance, celebrated in the mysteries of witchcraft, and for raising the Devil' (Evans, 1802: 124-125).

Since the inn at Harlech offered no sleeping accommodation such as the botanist had been accustomed to, and sleeping on a bed of rushes laid on a bare floor did not appeal to him, he decided to move on to Tan y Bwlch. While enquiring about a guide to lead him there he had the good fortune to meet John Richards, a local man who could speak English fluently, which was then uncommon in those parts, and after learning that the normal guide was absent he agreed to lead them to Tan y Bwlch. Richards proved himself to be a competent and reliable leader whom Evans had no regrets of having hired 'as some have done before us, that after employing a guide, they were obliged to give him information of the way'. Evans in his work provides an interesting account of Richards' career, and the reasons for his resorting to working as a guide.

John Richards was a native of Harlech, and had learned from his father a trade which combined that of a skinner, breeches maker and glover. When hard times affected the industry the family was forced to seek other means of earning a living, and they turned to the wool trade, probably on account of having sold wool remnants at the skinners yard. When he received a bequest of a few hundred pounds from his father in law, Richards' business flourished and the annual returns gradually increased, connections having been formed with London dealers. His dream of eventually being able to acquire a small estate became more realisable as he grew more able to provide a better standard of living for his family which was, by then, regarded as among the most prosperous in the area.

In an attempt to expand the business, Richards began to change his former London connections for others whom he thought would be more advantageous to him; for a time this increased the demand for wool from the local farmers. The situation then took a turn for the worse, however; delays in receiving payments forced Richards to try and obtain credit wherever he could, while at the same time the local farmers who supplied the wool were waiting to be paid. On demanding an explanation for the decline in trade from the London businessmen they told him about the failure and closure of a business concern in Europe, and said that when that affair had been properly dealt with he would receive the dividend he was entitled to, as would the other creditors. He was now faced with the collapse of his business plus constant demands for payment made by a number of poor farmers, and, should he be prosecuted, the gloomy prospect of life imprisonment. He called a meeting with the farmers and laid before them all the correspondence explaining the reasons for his business collapse. After much discussion they realised that the problem had not arisen as a result of any dishonesty on the part of John Richards and the farmers unanimously decided that he should retain his furniture and stock of leather, so that he could continue with his glove making trade and in addition they promised to give what support they could to the family.

The once booming glove making trade had for some time been on the decline in north Wales as a result of English glove makers buying up all the leather and manufacturing a superior and cheaper glove by using more modern methods. 'Richards', wrote Evans, 'was therefore reduced to the precarious emolument arising from the few journies he took in the summer months as a mountain guide, and the low profits upon a few strong country gloves, made during the winter, to support a sick wife and five children (Evans, 1802: 132).

Evans engaged Richards to guide him to Tan y Bwlch that evening and the path they took started steeply up the hillside behind Harlech; it was by all accounts 'a difficult stair-case path, up the steep side of a craggy mountain, and took a North-easterly direction over the trackless plain, known to our guide by several upright stones, called Maen hirion [Meini Hirion], and concentric circles of stones, many of them pebbles, said to have been formed for religious purposes in the ages of Druidism' (Evans, 1802: 134). The route took them past Llandecwyn where the moonlight reflected the waters of the lake and by following a track through a deep glen and crossing a stream near Felinrhyd they finally emerged on the turnpike road close to the village of Maentwrog. Here they crossed the bridge over the Dwyryd and arrived at the inn at Tan y Bwlch at 2 o'clock in the morning.

After spending the night at the inn at Tan y Bwlch, and the following day resting the horses, Evans, under the guidance of John Richards set out to complete the journey to Beddgelert, described by the botanist as 'eight miles of the worst road in the Principality'. They arrived soaked to the skin after experiencing a severe mountain storm. Evans, like Aikin, records observing the royal fern (*Osmunda regalis*) on the way, and he also notes the virtues of the bog-myrtle (*Myrica gale*):

> The poor inhabitants are not inattentive to its virtues; they term it Bwrli, or the emetic plant, and use it for this purpose. An infusion of the leaves as tea, and an external application of them to the abdomen, are considered as a certain and efficacious vermifuge. It is made a substitute for hops, in brewing: a decoction is used in the *morbus pedicularis*, and in the vulgar species of herpes. It furnishes a yellow dye for woollen cloth; and by its powerful odour is fatal to moths and bugs (Evans, 1802: 149).

Carolus Linnaeus is quoted as suggesting that camphor could be had from this plant, and the cones if gathered in sufficient quantities and boiled to produce a waxy substance could be used to make candles. Withering (1796, ii: 208), quoting from Pennant's *Tours in Wales*, mentions how the Welsh people made use of it by laying the branches across their beds to keep away the fleas.

The difficulties surmounted, they finally arrived at Aberglaslyn and it was not long before they came to Beddgelert which was 'a few straggling houses' among which the inn was marked only by a sign reading 'The Guide to Snowdon lives here'. Their clothes were laid to dry before the fire while they ate their meal of fried eggs and bacon in bed, refreshed also by what Evans describes as mugs of 'excellent cwrw', or Welsh beer. Since he merely relates the story of Gelert and how it became connected with the village, and gives a brief history of the Church, Evans appears not to have spent much time at Beddgelert and he is soon on the road to Caernarfon describing Nant Colwyn and the lake of the floating island (Llyn y Dywarchen) the story of which is first recorded by Giraldus in 1188, and which Evans takes great delight in substantiating.

Bron y Fedw, the 'guide's house', at the start of one of the Snowdon paths is dismissed with just a brief reference, but on the road between Betws Garmon and Caernarfon the state of the cottages of Snowdonia induces Evans to give a lengthy and detailed description of them. Compared to the cottages of Meirionnydd, the Caernarfonshire ones were in his opinion much worse, being built with turf or clay and chopped rushes except in the mountainous parts where stones, being more readily available, were used. The shape was described as being 'generally oblong' and consisting of one long room, the walls rising to about six feet above the ground level with a roof made of heath or rushes laid upon rafters of 'maiden poles not even stripped of their bark'. Smoke from the peat fire usually filled the room before it found its way out through a hole in the roof, or through the doorway which in bad weather was blocked by a door made from 'a few watlings and rushes'. Evans goes on to describe the slightly better houses of the farmers, which had in addition a couple of bedrooms built in the loft, and a partition which divided the long room into two parts, but adds 'even here, pigs, asses, and other domestic animals, take up their abode and form part of the family'. The botanist entered one of these hovels out of curiosity, and saw the family gathered around a small fire of peat about to start their supper of potatoes and *'diod griafol'*, a drink made from the berries of the mountain ash *(Sorbus aucuparia)*. Such scenes of abject poverty made a deep impression on Evans, and he makes these feelings of disgust known in his writings:

> Such are the dwellings in which part of the inhabitants of the most opulent and powerful nation upon earth at present live, and in which the Genius of Virtue and Content seems to delight to dwell (Evans, 1802: 161).

Despite these hardships the people that Evans met on his travels were generally cheerful and content, and he concludes his account of his meeting with the following quotation: 'Man wants but little, nor that little long'.

His description of the town of Caernarfon includes a list of the plants he saw while inspecting the various sites of historical interest. On a salt marsh opposite the castle, which has long since disappeared following the growth of the town, he found sea plantain *(Plantago maritima)*, buck's-horn plantain *(Plantago coronopus)*, sea arrowgrass *(Triglochin maritimum)*, brookweed *(Samolus valerandi)*, sea-milkwort *(Glaux maritima)*, Portland spurge *(Euphorbia portlandica)* and, on the shore near Llanfaglan, sea stork's-bill *(Erodium maritimum)*, glasswort *(Salicornia agg.)* and sea campion *(Silene uniflora)*.

Unlike most of the touring botanists of his time, Evans did not climb Snowdon, nor did he succeed in reaching any of the sites which are noted for their variety of plants. Despite waiting a fortnight for the weather to improve, the opportunity did not present itself and so he reluctantly gave up, confining his researches to the lower areas instead. Following the 'vale of the Seiont' as he calls it he records finding the fragrant orchid *(Gymnadenia conopsea)* and the small white orchid *(Pseudorchis albida)*, a plant first recorded from these parts by John Ray in 1670.

Evans came on horseback to Cwm-y-glo from Caernarfon, and took a boat from the lower end of Llyn Padarn to Pont y Bala, the point where the two lakes meet close to Dolbadarn Castle. His botanical finds from this particular habitat included awlwort *(Subularia aquatica)*, white water-lily *(Nymphaea alba)*, quillwort *(Isoetes lacustris)*, branched bur-reed *(Sparganium erectum)* and floating water-plantain *(Luronium natans)*.

The latter-named plant is the rarest and most interesting of the list; an earlier record of it appears in the 1789 edition of Camden's *Britannia*: 'in the great lake below the old castle at Llanberris'. This site must have been well known to the early botanists. John Wynne Griffith of Garn also records it: 'In a small rivulet on the west side of the lower lake at Llanberris, about ½ mile from the old castle' (Withering, 1796 ii: 362). Hugh Davies describes it not as a rarity but as a plant seldom seen in flower, especially so on the Isle of Anglesey. This he attributes:

> to the extreme variableness of the depth of water in a level country, where lakes and rivers have no supply but immediately from the sky. In the month of May or June, this plant may be seen drawn by a stream to the length of many feet, from three to ten, or even more, where, at the end of six or eight weeks after, the water being often so very much reduced as in some places not to cover the bed of the river, we can scarcely perceive any traces of it (Davies, 1813: 36).

Davies records seeing the plant in Llyn Coron and in one of the lakes near Valley, but it is now, according to Roberts (1982: 59), probably extinct in these localities. It was recorded by the present author from Llyn Cwellyn near Betws Garmon in 1989 but has not been seen at its old Dolbadarn site near Llanberis since the building of the Hydro Power Electric Scheme there. Although he does not specify which plants he himself saw, John Evans' list of 'plants furnished by the immediate neighbourhood of Llanberis' include Welsh poppy *(Meconopsis cambrica)*, ivy-leaved bellflower *(Wahlenbergia hederacea)*, scurvy grass, (recorded by Evans as *'Cochlearia Greenlandica)'*, lesser skullcap *(Scutellaria minor)*, the filmy-fern *(Hymenophyllum)*, parsley fern *(Cryptogramma crispa)*, oak fern *(Gymnocarpium dryopteris)*, field gentian *(Gentianella campestris)*, moss campion *(Silene acaulis)*, black spleenwort *(Asplenium adiantum-nigrum)*, wall rue *(Asplenium ruta-muraria)*, spring sandwort *(Minuartia verna)*, holly fern *(Polystichum lonchitis)*, northern bedstraw *(Galium boreale)* and black alpine-sedge *(Carex atrata)* (Evans, 1802: 181). The scurvygrass recorded by Evans as *'Cochlearia Greenlandica'* was, most probably a variety of the common scurvygrass *(Cochlearia officinalis)* which is found growing in a number of localities in Snowdonia. Withering (1796) doubts that the specimens collected from Wales by botanists and named

Cochlearia groenlandica were in fact the true plant. He points out that the common scurvygrass taken from Wales and other mountainous parts of the British Isles and transplanted in his garden produced flowers every year, compared with the true *Cochlearia groenlandica* which was biennial. John Wynne Griffith of Garn, whose opinion Withering sought on the matter had this to say:

> The Cochlearia groenlandica is certainly not an annual. I cultivated it 3 or 4 years, during which time it retained its diminutive state, which gave me reason to suppose it distinct from the C. officinalis; but I have since repeated the experiment, and it became as large as the Cochl. officinalis (Withering,1796 iii: 574).

The scurvygrass *(Cochlearia)* group of plants can still cause problems to botanists and *C. groenlandica* is today included with *C. officinalis* forming a very variable group (Rich: 1991: 127-131). There is a cliff on the Carneddau range of mountains which is named *'Clogwyn Sgyrfi'* (Scurvygrass cliff) and in former days shepherds used to gather the plant leaves and eat them with their bread and butter as a sandwich.

Evans, though unable to climb Snowdon himself, gives a description of the various routes taken by the guides during this period. These routes were related to Evans by a friend:

> Ride to Cwm-y-glo in the parish of Llanrug; take a boat up the lake of Llyn Padarn; land in the little Isthmus, between this and Llyn Peris, near Dolbadarn Castle; there take your guide and ascend by Ceunant Mawr, or the great chasm . . . Climb up along the South side of the ridge, that separates Cwm Peris from Cwm Brwynog; thence ascend in sight of Llyn du yr Arddu, which you must leave on your right. The steep rock over this lake called Clogwyn du yr Arddu. i.e. the black rock above the Arddu, is celebrated for a great variety of rare plants. Ascending a steep and difficult pass, called Llechwedd y Re, you arrive at a cold spring, called Llyn coch, which is within a mile of the highest summit called y Wydd fa [sic] . . . the steep and almost inaccessible crags on the North side of this peak, are termed Clogwyn y Garnedd; and known to Lloyd and Ray for the habitats of alpine plants (Evans, 1802: 190-191).

The second route to the summit of Snowdon named by Evans is in fact the Snowdon Ranger path and although it was not known by its present name at that time, he describes it as the usual ascent.

The 'Bedd Kelert' route is 'extremely steep and dangerous' and the terrors of crossing Clawdd Coch and Bwlch Main are vividly described.

The plants listed by Evans as growing on Clogwyn y Garnedd and Clogwyn Du'r Arddu are included on the authority of the same anonymous friend who gave him details of the Snowdon paths. Of the nineteen plants named as growing on Clogwyn y Garnedd only ten have been substantiated by other botanists. These are the Snowdon lily *(Lloydia serotina)*, alpine saw-wort *(Saussurea alpina)*, alpine mouse-ear *(Cerastium alpinum)*, arctic mouse-ear *(Cerastium arcticum)*, starry saxifrage *(Saxifraga stellaris)*, alpine saxifrage *(Saxifraga nivalis)*, oblong woodsia *(Woodsia ilvensis)*, alpine woodsia *(Woodsia alpina)*, Welsh poppy *(Meconopsis cambrica)* and dwarf juniper *(Juniperis communis* subsp. *nana)*; the latter named is known to grow close to, if not on this cliff. It should also be noted that both *Woodsia* plants have been recorded from Clogwyn y Garnedd in the past, but only the *Woodsia alpina* has been found there recently. The remainder include: alpine catchfly *(Lychnis alpina)*, which in Britain is a very rare plant found only in Cumberland and Angus; forked spleenwort *(Asplenium septentrionale)*, a small fern found in various parts of Snowdonia but not on these particular cliffs; Royal fern *(Osmunda regalis)* recorded from this area but not from either of these two cliffs; mountain pansy *(Viola lutea)*, mountain avens *(Dryas octopetala)* and yellow saxifrage *(Saxifraga aizoides)*; of these the *Dryas* is the only plant confirmed as being currently extant in Snowdonia, but it has not been recorded from any of the above mentioned Snowdon cliffs.

For Clogwyn Du'r Arddu Evans names but two plants, the stone bramble *(Rubus saxatilis)* and northern rock-cress *(Arabis petraea)*, the latter named having being noted on this cliff by Thomas Johnson during his botanical excursion of 1639.

Two other well known botanical hunting grounds mentioned by Evans are Llyn y Cŵn and Trigyfylchau Rocks. The exact locality of the latter is by now obscure, but they were frequently referred to by both Lhuyd and Brewer. The Llyn y Cŵn area still produces such plants as water lobelia *(Lobelia dortmanna)*, beautiful hawkweed *(Hieracium holosericeum)* and the three-flowered rush *(Juncus triglumis)*. The cliffs around Cwm Idwal, where Trigyfylchau was located, are the stronghold of the rare Snowdon lily *(Lloydia serotina)*. This appears on Evans' plant list for 'The vicinity of the Glyder, between Llyn y Cŵn and Llyn Idwal' as 'Anthericum serotinum'(Evans: 1802: 193-194). Also included are plants which seem to have been either overlooked by other botanists or inserted erroneously, namely the hoary whitlowgrass *(Draba incana)*, alpine mouse-ear *(Cerastium alpinum)* and spring bulbocodium *(Bulbocodium vernum)*, since there have been no subsequent records of them from this locality.

The latter named plant surely must have been the Snowdon lily

(Lloydia serotina). In John Ray's *Synopsis Methodica Stirpium Britannicarum* Richardson is quoted thus (translation by P. Oswald; personal communication 25 November, 1997):

> Afterwards Master D. Lhwyd, in my company, found this plant flowering on the western side of the mountain *Trigvylchau [sic]* in a very steep place, looking towards the mountain Hysvaë, to which I have given the name: Alpine Bulbocodium, dwarf, rush-leaved, with a single flower, white within [and] a dirty reddish outside. Its flower [is] six-petalled, large for the size of the little plant [usually = seedling], in shape and size somewhat resembling the flower of Lujula; Master *Richardson* (Dillenius,1724: 374).

It is clear, therefore that John Evans relied on other sources for much of the plant information which he published in his book describing a tour through part of north Wales in 1798 and at other times. He graduated at Oxford in 1792 and later became Master of the Academy, Kingsdown; he supplied Turner and Dillwyn with plant references for their *Botanist's Guide* published in 1805. His anonymous friend from whom he received the names of some of the alpine plants of Snowdonia proved an unreliable source, and it is a pity that he did not venture out on to the high places himself to carry out his own observations.

Bingley's Botanical Tours

Reverend William Bingley (1774-1823) who visited north Wales in 1798 and 1801 appended a catalogue of plants to his book as published in 1800 and in the later edition of 1804 entitled *North Wales; including its scenery, antiquities, customs, &c.* The *'Flora Cambrica'*, as he calls it, is a 'Systematic Catalogue of the more uncommon Welsh plants . . .' which included their known habitats and their flowering times (Bingley, 1804, ii: 363).

William Bingley was born in Doncaster, Yorkshire in January 1774 and graduated B.A. at Cambridge in 1799. He became a Fellow of the Linnean Society in 1800 and was curate at Christchurch Priory, Hampshire from 1802 until 1816 when he moved to London acting as minister at Fitzroy Chapel, Charlotte Street until his death in 1823. His first visit to north Wales was undertaken during the summer recess of 1798 while he was a student at Cambridge; after travelling by coach to Chester he began his tour by following 'the great Irish road' through St Asaph, Conwy and Bangor to Caernarfon, where he stayed for a time, making his excursions to the mountains and visiting parts of Anglesey. He then planned and followed a route which took him to Harlech, Barmouth, Dolgellau, Machynlleth, Llanidloes, Newtown, Montgomery, Welshpool, Oswestry, Wrexham and Mold where he turned inland to Ruthin, Llangollen, Corwen and Bala returning to Cambridge via Shrewsbury in September.

This first visit made a deep impression on the young botanist and he returned to stop for four months in 1801, between the months of June and September, during which time he walked around the counties of Caernarfon, Meirionnydd, and Anglesey. 'Previously to my first journey' he wrote, 'I had made several tours through nearly all the romantic parts of the North of England. I can, however, with truth declare, that, taken in the whole, I have not found these by any means so interesting as four of the six counties of North Wales, namely, Denbighshire, Caernarvonshire, Merionethshire and Anglesea. The traveller of taste (in search of grand and stupendous scenery), the naturalist, and the antiquary, have all, in this romantic country, full scope for their respective pursuits' (Bingley, 1804, i: vi).

Bingley made his excursions chiefly as a pedestrian but at times he found it more convenient to use horses or carriages. He is, however, quick to point out the advantages of walking, especially when the places of attraction are inaccessible to carriages and horses. Bingley's companion and guide during most of his rambles in Snowdonia was Reverend Peter Bailey Williams (1763-1836), rector of the parishes of Llanrug and

Llanberis, whose various interests, like the visitor's, included local history and botany. Williams knew the country well, and was able to introduce Bingley to the more interesting characters who dwelt in the two parishes; the latter, being a prolific writer meticulously noted down all these observations for inclusion in his forthcoming book. Bingley was invited by Bailey Williams to visit some of the poorer farms of the area, the first of which lay in Cwm-y-glo, and it proved to be no different to the home which Evans commented on during his journey from Betws Garmon to Caernarfon:

> I entered at a small gate, and first observed a wretched hovel for his cattle: the hay rick was formed by a large slate, placed near one side, with its edge on the ground: the roof was so broken in and damaged, that only one corner afforded shelter to the miserable beasts from the fury of the mountain storms . . . A path between two rude walls, adorned with holly hedges, led me to the dwelling. The door was so low, that I was obliged to stoop considerably to enter; and coming out of a bright sun-shine, it was not till some time had elapsed that I was able to distinguish any thing in this hut, except the gleam of light that came down the chimney. This was at least equal to what the six small panes of glass in the window afforded. On the open hearth were a few peat-ashes, the remains of a fire with which the old man had a little while before cooked his dinner. The frame of the roof was formed by branches of trees fixed to larger timbers by straw or hay-bands. This frame was covered with sods, and the whole with slates, which, in the mountains, are obtained in great plenty. The furniture consisted of an old bed, an oak chest, a range of shelves for such poor eating utensils as were necessary in this lowly habitation, some old earthen vessels, some dingy pewter dishes, and a few other things . . . (Bingley, 1804, i: 219-220).

Bingley on reflection chose a few lines of Goldsmith's: 'Man wants but little here below . . .', which were the very lines quoted by Evans who saw a similar hovel. On the same day Bailey Williams took Bingley to the cottage of a lame old woman, Mary Morgan, who lived close to the farm they had just visited and the traveller's only reason for mentioning her is the fact that she used the chimney of her house as a means of entry whenever she mislaid the key of the door. Both tourists seem to have paid more attention to describing these type of housing rather than commenting on the dwellings and living conditions of the wealthier farmers for comparison.

Bingley, accompanied by Bailey Williams, took a boat from Cwm-y-glo to Llanberis, where the local man related the story of Margaret Evans, who according to tradition spent part of her early years at Llwyn y forwyn (Jenkins, 1899: 165) near Llyn y Dywarchen, close to the present village of Rhyd-ddu, but lived at Penllyn near the lower end of Llyn Padarn during the time of Pennant's visit. Marged uch Ifan (Margaret daughter of Evan) or Peggy Evans, as she was also called, hailed from the Nantlle Valley where she kept an inn called Telyrnia (between Drws y Coed and Nantlle near the present Turnpike cottage) while the copper mines there flourished (Ambrose, 1872: 59). She later moved to the Llanberis area, where she held a contract to convey the copper ore down the lakes, before it was carried onward down to the coast. Margaret was also a blacksmith, shoemaker, boat builder and maker of harps, and the finest hunter in all Snowdonia, keeping a pack of hounds for tracking down foxes; for every fox she killed, she carved a notch on her wooden mantelpiece. She was immortalised by Pennant as the 'Queen of the Lakes' and at the age of seventy-two was the best wrestler in the country as well as being fond of playing the harp and violin. It must be noted that none of the 'tours' writers, Pennant included, actually met Margaret, and therefore the tales of her exploits must have been related to the travellers by the guides and other local people. 'The Queen of the Lakes', however, will always remain part of the rich Snowdonian folklore. An entry in the Llanddeiniolen Parish Register dated 24 January 1793 records the burial of Margaret Evans, aged 91, of Penllyn (GAS XPE/29/3).

There were two houses at Llanberis at that time which provided travellers with refreshments. One belonged to John Closs, a Yorkshireman who had as a young man travelled into north Wales with some cattle and decided to stay. John Closs was a 'grey headed old man' at the time of Bingley's visit and the inn was kept by his son Robert, who, when occasion demanded, took up the role of a mountain guide to supplement the family income. Morris Pritchard, the parish clerk, kept the other house and he too was a competent part-time guide (Bingley, 1804, i: 236).

The inns did not provide any beds for the travellers and the only food available was bread, butter and cheese and bacon and eggs. Bingley called at John Closs' house during his first visit to Llanberis and he relates his novel experience at the dinner table. John Closs, his wife son and daughter sat at one table eating their bread and milk while the botanist sat at another table enjoying his bread and butter and satisfying an appetite brought on after a day among the hills. His meal was soon interrupted by the intrusion of a 'large overgrown old sow' which entered the room and began to devour, rather noisily, her own dinner from a bucket which the daughter had put in front of her. After this experience, Bingley vowed that in future he would bring his own food and enjoy it in the solitude of the countryside.

Bingley does not say whether or not he stayed at the house of Morris Pritchard, but he does speak very highly of his prowess as a guide. 'I found him well acquainted with the mountains, and a much more intelligent man than guides are in general. He does not speak English well, but his civility and attention are a sufficient compensation for this defect' (Bingley, 1804, i: 236).

Morris Pritchard was known to other visiting botanists and he was often employed by them to gather alpine plants from the surrounding mountains, a task frequently undertaken by the guides. Despite Bingley's claim that the parish clerk did not speak good English, Peter Bailey Williams nevertheless wrote to him in English; this letter is dated 'Whitmonday 1794', and reads:

Morris Pritchard,

I understand the parishioners turn cattle into the Churchyard and seem to look upon it as their property, but I shall soon let them know that it is my Freehold, and in the meantime I require and charge you to keep the Churchyard locked and not suffer any one to turn sheep, calves or any kind of cattle into it. Did Mr Morgan keep either cow or horse, I should have suffered him to have the use of it. When Owen David comes up to take tythe lambs I shall give him leave to turn them in for a day or two.

I am, Yours, etc., Peter
Williams.

P.S. Either you or Mr Morgan must keep the key of the Churchyard (GAS XPE/27/15).

Morris Pritchard died on 9 February 1818, leaving a sickly daughter and arrears of rent amounting to £9. Harry David, the old guide's grandson, later applied to be given the tenancy of Gallt y Llan and live there on the understanding that the arrears of rent must be settled (UWB: Porth yr Aur MS 49751).

In his letter Bailey Williams mentiones John Morgan the curate, whom Bingley visited during one of his excursions to Llanberis. Reverend John Morgan came to Llanberis in 1772 and served twenty-nine years as curate. He died at the age of 58 and was buried in the Churchyard on 30 March 1801. Bingley found the curate 'engaged over an old folio volume of sermons' in his small cottage a short distance from the Church. The cottage was divided into two parts, a kitchen and a bedroom, the latter also being used as a study where the curate worked and housed his small library. He was dressed according to the botanist in a 'blue coat that long had been worn threadbare, and in various places exhibited marks of the industry of his wife, a pair of antique corderoy [sic] breeches, and a black waistcoat, and round his head was tied a blue handkerchief' (Bingley, 1804, i: 238-239).

He supported his family on a salary of £40 per annum, together with the produce of his small farm and he was a very contented man, popular and greatly respected by the parishioners. He was a very popular preacher and his reputation spread to other parts of Snowdonia inducing people to travel great distances to hear his sermons.

Bingley's botanical excursion to Clogwyn Du'r Arddu developed into what today would be termed, if not a rock climb, a challenging scramble. Peter Bailey Williams, who led Bingley on most of his mountain walks, suggested that they climb the precipice to look for plants. It could well be that the guide had done this on previous occasions, and all went well at the beginning, but the visitor soon became aware of the dangers involved when he tried to pull himself up and the rock on which he had put his weight gave way. He only just managed to save himself by grabbing at a 'tuft of rushes'. They had climbed about 300 feet up the cliff when they realized that it was too dangerous to try and retrace their steps, so they decided to try to overcome the difficult pitch which lay directly above them. Bailey Williams, who led, had on a pair of strong boots with nailed soles, and with some difficulty managed to overcome the crux to gain a secure position higher up. The local man carried a small basket which was used to carry provisions and the plant specimens they had collected on the way up, and this was held securely to his body by means of a leather belt around the waist. Bailey Williams took off the belt and used it to haul Bingley over the difficult part of the cliff after which they were able to continue to the top of the precipice without further incident arriving 'in possession of all the plants we expected to find'. From there they followed the Snowdon Ranger path to the summit of Snowdon (Bingley, 1804, i: 248-250).

Bingley goes on to list the plants found growing on Clogwyn y Garnedd, the steep cliff which faces north-east directly below the summit of 'yr Wyddfa', a site known to earlier botanists like Ray and Lhuyd for its uncommon alpine plants. Bingley lists twenty-five species as growing on this cliff (Bingley, 1804, i: 253-254), and it is a much more accurate and credible account than the one Evans published. Evans included his plant list on the testimony of his anonymous friend and never ventured to Clogwyn y Garnedd himself. Bingley does not state categorically that he visited the cliff, but stresses the hazards which had to be encountered in doing so. 'There is at all times some difficulty in searching them [the cliffs of Clogwyn y Garnedd], but when the rocks are rendered slippery from heavy mists or rain, this becomes, from the insecurity of the footing, greatly increased. A list of plants that have been found here may not be unacceptable, at least to a young botanist' (Bingley, 1804, i: 253).

Bingley then ascended Snowdon by way of Cwmglas Mawr, a wild hollow high above Llanberis Pass which has the finest variety of plants in the whole district, but the only ones mentioned in this chapter are awlwort *(Subularia aquatica)*, quillwort *(Isoetes lacustris)* and water lobelia *(Lobelia dortmanna)*, which were observed in Llyn Bach on the way up. This lake used to be called Llyn Ffynnon Frech and appeared so in print up to the end of the 19th century (Griffith, [1895]: 117), and the hollow we know today as Cwmglas Mawr would not in Bingley's day have been known by that name. In those days Cwm Glas was the name given to the lower part of the Llanberis Pass from the area around the farm of Cwmglas Bach up to and including the regions below Bwlch Coch. Bingley's plant records for Cwmglas Mawr, which appear in *Flora Cambrica*, would be described as being found on 'rocks above Ffynnon Frech', or, 'on Crib y Ddescil, near Llanberis' and the quillwort was described as growing in 'Ffynnon Frech, a small pool in the mountains betwixt Llanberis and Snowdon', not – as we would say today; – 'in Cwmglas Mawr'. Bwlch Coch is situated between the pinnacles of Crib Goch and the long ridge which culminates on Crib y Ddysgl, the second highest peak in Snowdonia. The route followed by Bingley took him from Bwlch Coch across the southern slopes of Crib y Ddysgl to Bwlch Glas, above the lake of Llyn Glaslyn, which he misnames Llyn y Cwm Glas; this lake was known in those days as Ffynnon Las as well as Glaslyn. He then followed the Pony track from Bwlch Glas to the summit of Snowdon, and returned to Llanberis by descending the steep slope directly above the village of Nant Peris (called Llanberis in Bingley's day), a route so rugged and unpleasant that it made him wish that he had followed the Pony track to Dolbadarn Castle, instead of using the short cut.

The following day saw this intrepid botanist ascending Snowdon once again, but this time from the opposite side of the mountain. Bingley rode from Llanberis to Betws Garmon and began the day's excursion from Bron y Fedw, 'the guide's house' near Llyn Cwellyn. The horses were left in the care of servants near Llyn Ffynnon y Gwas at the foot of the main climb – as was the custom with visitors who used this path – and the party continued on foot up the rocky shoulder towards the summit. Bingley found this path very tiring, either because of the previous day's exertions, or from the ruggedness of the terrain. During the years which followed, the Snowdon Ranger Path, (as it was later to be called) was improved in order to transport the copper ore from the mines near Llyn Glaslyn to Caernarfon. The ore was carried by the miners in bags to Bwlch Glas where it was transferred onto small sledges which were then dragged by horses down to the road at Betws Garmon, there to be carted to Caernarfon. The new sledge-way made the ascent of Snowdon from Llyn Cwellyn much easier for the tourist, but the transporting of copper ore was later transferred to a more convenient route on the northern side of the mountain when the new road connecting Llanberis and Penygwryd was opened, to which the Miners track was built joining it at Gorffwysfa (Pen y Pass).

Bingley had fine weather during the morning and the clear views from the summit more than compensated for the hard toil up the rocky path. The guide, not named by Bingley, but who was most probably Ellis Griffith of Bron y Fedw, quite suddenly gave warning of an approaching storm and advised the party to prepare for an immediate descent of the mountain. Bingley admits to ridiculing the guide's warning at first, but later had enough cause to regret having done so. During the descent the party was overtaken by a severe mountain storm and the botanist was glad to have a moment to reflect upon the day's events as he rested in the guide's 'cottage' while waiting for his clothes to dry.

His aim to climb Snowdon by all the principal routes was fulfilled when he set out from Ffridd Uchaf, a farm on the lower west facing side of the massif, along the old Beddgelert track. The path winds its way towards Llechog before reaching the summit by traversing Clawdd Coch and crossing Bwlch Main. This route is known today as the Rhyd-ddu path. The horses were left at the farm, and the visitors then walked as far as the place where the 'Half-way House', a corrugated iron structure where refreshments could be acquired, was later built. 18th century travellers, however, had to make do with a drink of water from a natural spring among the rocks, the last but one spring between there and the summit.

This site is unique in being the only level patch of ground on a rugged mountainside, and legend has it that it was the site of an ancient temple called *Mur Murianau*. Scattered over the site are the remains of several circular stone huts (*Cytiau Gwyddelod*), built up at a later date to be used as sheepfolds. To the south west a line of rocks form a wall which if followed will be seen to enclose the whole site, and on a rocky elevation at one end a large clog-shaped rock is seen resting on three smaller stones, one at each corner; the whole structure having the appearance of an altar

(Jenkins, 1899: 178-179).

Bingley's guide during this excursion was William Lloyd of Beddgelert who was also the village schoolmaster, and when the Beddgelert Hotel, later to be called the Royal Goat, was built he served there as a waiter. He advertised his summer vocation with the aid of a poster displayed on the door of the inn which read:

> William Lloyd, conductor to Snowdon, Moel Hebog, Dinas Emrys, Llanberis pass, the lakes, &c &c. Collector of crystals and fossils, and all natural curiosities in these regions. Dealer in superfine woollen hose, socks, gloves &c (Bingley, 1804, i: 369).

William Lloyd died in 1804 leaving his wife with a considerable quantity of fossils to sell. (Nicholson, 1813: 114).

There are no rare alpine plants mentioned by Bingley during this ascent, the whole account being dominated by a description of the views and the terrain over which the route passes. Like Evans (whose description of the path, it must be remembered, is given on the authority of another) Bingley's account of passing over the Clawdd Coch – Bwlch Main section is greatly dramatised.

> This narrow pass, not more than ten or twelve feet across, and two or three hundred yards in length, was so steep, that the eye reached on each side, down the whole extent of the mountain . . . in some parts of it, if a person held a large stone in each hand, and let them both fall at once, each might roll a quarter of a mile, and thus, when they stopped, they might be more than half a mile asunder (Bingley, 1804, i: 385-386).

Bingley, however, is quick to point out that he was not at all afraid of crossing this ridge, at least during the day time, but that a night ascent along the same route was a different matter. The chapter also includes stories, probably told to him by the guide, of the terror and fright experienced by other visitors when negotiating the ridge, and of people who having passed over it during the hours of darkness, and thus unaware of the exposure on either side, refused to return the same way when coming back down in the morning. There were also tales of gentlemen who were so alarmed that they had resorted to crawling across on hands and knees.

William Lloyd, having guided the party to the summit, led the party back to Beddgelert by returning over Clawdd Coch and then directly down the South Ridge to Bwlch Cwm Llan, and from there to Nantgwynant. Bingley's only mention of plants on this trip concerns a group of children collecting the berries from the mountain ash (*Sorbus aucuparia)* in Cwm Llan. The guide William Lloyd explained to him that the berries were crushed and left in water for two weeks at the end of which time the liquid was ready to drink. This drink, called *'diod griafol'* after the Welsh name for mountain ash *(pren criafol)*, was mentioned in the previous chapter in the context of Reverend John Evans and his tour of north Wales in 1798.

Guided by Peter Bailey Williams, Bingley completed a traverse of part of the Glyder range climbing Tryfan, Glyder Fach and Glyder Fawr which he claimed was 'by far the most laborious walk that I ever ventured upon in the course of one day'. Their excursion began at Nant Peris at 7 o'clock in the morning and on reaching Llyn y Cŵn they met a group of men digging peat, one of whom was the son of one of the Llanberis guides. The peat was carried by horses to the verge of the steep descent, where it was transferred onto sledges. The men would then push the sledges down to the valley floor, running to gain speed where practicable and braking by moving the sledge from side to side whenever a steeper gradient caused too great a velocity.

From Llyn y Cŵn, the party walked down into Cwm Idwal, passing below the Devil's Kitchen on the way. Bingley refers to the chasm by its Welsh name 'Twll Du', explaining that the small holes in the rocks at its base are known as the 'Devil's Pots', this being the reason why the place was sometimes known as the Devil's Kitchen.

The ascent of Tryfan was undertaken from Cwm Bochlwyd, the steep rocky appearance at first raising doubts in the minds of the two clergymen if such an attempt would be practicable. However, after a scramble of about three quarters of an hour which called for frequent use of hand-holds, the pair eventually stood next to 'Adam and Eve', the two conspicuous columnar boulders that crown the summit. Bailey Williams climbed to the top of one of the rocks, and, as Bingley watched apprehensively, calmly stepped from one to the other. This feat was apparently frequently performed by a 'female of an adjacent parish'. The summit of Glyder Fach, the next mountain visited, compelled the agile Bailey Williams to explore the heaped pile of variously shaped boulders that comprise the summit; one in particular, known today as the 'Cantelever', a long flat projecting rock, moved as he jumped on it.

They crossed the 'Waen Oer' to the summit of Glyder Fawr and continued their way back down to the Llanberis valley arriving at 8 o'clock in the evening after spending fourteen hours among the mountains (Bingley, 1804, i: 266-274). At the end of this chapter Bingley listed fifty-two plants that he had seen around Llyn y Cŵn and the Devil's Kitchen area; and unlike Reverend John Evans' list there were no plants included which were not already known to occur in Snowdonia. It is evident from his writings that Bingley derived great pleasure from walking the mountains of Snowdonia and he was critical of many of his contemporaries for overstating the difficulties likely to be met with during such rambles. He dismisses the carrying of strong sticks with a spike at the end as being unnecessary, and likewise, despite his adventure on Clogwyn Du'r Arddu, the wearing of nailed boots. He advises the tourist to make an early start, 'to be upon the journey by five or six o'clock in the morning', the advantage of this being that there would be sufficient time to stop and rest frequently to admire the changing scenery as height was gained.

To undertake any journey into the mountains without a guide would in his opinion, be foolhardy: 'a sudden change in the weather might render the attempt extremely perilous to a stranger' (Bingley, 1804, i: 258). The local guides, being familiar with the mountains, knew the course of the paths from the shape of certain rocks and the flow of the streams. These natural 'waymarks' had been memorized over the years, and were useful when low cloud and mist covered the route.

Bingley's *Flora Cambrica* consists of fifty-eight pages containing the names of 472 plants as well as several varieties. All the 'classical' habitats of Snowdonia are mentioned when an uncommon plant is dealt with, these being:

Habitat	Number of plants listed
Clogwyn y Garnedd	16
Clogwyn Du'r Arddu	7
Cwm Idwal / Devil's Kitchen	23
Llyn y Cŵn	10

To these are added Glyder Fawr, Snowdon, Crib y Ddysgl, Cwmbrwynog, the two lakes in Cwmglas, Ffynnon Frech and Ffynnon Felen, and the long forgotten sites of Creigiau Hysfa Bengam and Trigyfylchau, which are thought to be situated between Glyder Fawr and the Devil's Kitchen chasm.

A great number of the plants recorded by Evans and Bingley appear in various editions of Nicholson's *Cambrian Traveller's Guide*. By the end of the 18th century most of the interesting flowering plants of Snowdonia had been discovered, and likewise the richest localities, the cliffs and cymoedd of Snowdon and Glyder. These sites had been visited by generations of botanists from the days of Ray and Lhuyd, and each one had amassed records and others had built upon these. Some outlying districts, however, remained botanically unexplored.

Peter Bailey Williams

Reverend Peter Bailey Williams (1763-1836), a native of Llandyfaelog, Carmarthen, (and son of Peter Williams the biblical commentator) became Rector of Llanrug and Llanberis in 1792 and remained there for the rest of his life, being buried in Llanrug Churchyard. He entered Jesus College, Oxford to read law, but decided during his first term to become a Church minister. He was ordained deacon by the Bishop of Gloucester in February 1788 and licensed to the curacy of Eastleach Martin. In November of the same year he was ordained minister; the following month he received a permanent curacy at Swinbrook, Oxfordshire. Early in 1790 he moved to Burford where he remained until his preferment to Llanrug and Llanberis, serving also in Betws Garmon from 1815 onwards. In September 1804 he married Hannah, the daughter of Henry and Ann Jones of Llanrwst; they had one son, who, following his graduation became a curate to his father.

Bailey Williams was a staunch conservative, having no sympathies with the current revolutionary upheaval in France, and was, as would be expected, in favour of retaining the 'tithe' laws. He was a Justice of Peace for the county of Caernarfon, at a time when that office held a much wider range of responsibilities than it does today, yet despite his strong political beliefs he always stood firmly in support of the rights of the poor. He is remembered mainly for his literary and antiquarian interests and was a close friend of local poets like David Thomas of Waunfawr (Dafydd Ddu Eryri 1759-1822), William Edwards (Gwilym Padarn 1786-1857), and his son Griffith Edwards (Gutyn Padarn 1812-1893) of Llanberis, Robert Parry (Robyn Ddu Eryri 1804-1892) of Caernarfon and Owen Williams (Owain Gwyrfai 1790-1874) of Waunfawr, as well as many others. His own poetical compositions left much to be desired, and none of his attempts at translating Welsh poetry into English were successful.

He copied extensively from old manuscripts in the libraries of the county's most prominent families and avidly collected all kinds of old stories, legends and traditions. Most of his manuscripts later came to be in the possession of John Davies (Gwyneddon 1832-1904), the printer and journalist, and these (entitled the 'Gwyneddon Manuscripts') are now kept at the Library of the University of Wales, Bangor. The remainder became part of John Humphreys Davies' large collection. Davies (1871-1926), a bibliographer, man of letters and educationist, was a prominent and recognized authority on Welsh books and manuscripts, and his documents are today kept at the National Library of Wales, Aberystwyth under the title 'Cwrt Mawr Manuscripts'.

Of the travellers who visited north Wales during this period, two are known to have stayed in Bailey Williams' home at Pantafon, Llanrug: Reverend William Bingley with whom we have dealt in the previous chapter, and Richard Fenton (1747-1821), the poet and topographical writer from Pembroke. Fenton made use of Bailey Williams' library at Pantafon, 'to satiate myself with his very curious and miscellaneous collection of Welsh History added much to my stock' (Roberts, G.T.,1948: 77). Another topographical writer who received help from Bailey Williams was William Cathrall who in 1828 published his *History of North Wales*. In a letter to Walter Davies (Gwallter Mechain, 1761-1849; cleric, poet, antiquary and literary critic), Bailey Williams tells how he wrote to Cathrall, 'to point out some mistakes in his history of North Wales,' to which the writer replied that he had received no help from the people from whom he had earlier requested assistance. 'I began to assist him when he was about to commencing the History of Anglesey and I have now gone through the North Wales counties except Montgomeryshire' (Roberts, G.T., 1948: 77), wrote Bailey Williams, who admitted to being in need of Walter Davies' advice before completing his notes and submitting them to Cathrall.

Nicholas Carlisle, author of the *Topographical Dictionary to the Dominion of Wales* was also indebted to Bailey Williams during his preparatory researches for his book.

There can be no doubt that Bailey Williams had a special interest in local history, and in 1821 he published the result of his researches in his book entitled *The Tourist's Guide through the County of Caernarvon containing a short sketch of its History, Antiquities, &c.* The volume is in many ways similar to others already published about the topography of Wales, except that it deals with only one county. It has been said of the book that it lacks the detail needed to be a reliable guide-book for visitors, and is too disorderly in arrangement to qualify as a history book of a high standard, as the sub-title claims. He also wrote an essay on the history of Anglesey, and another on the Monasteries and Abbeys of Wales.

Despite his own local knowledge Bailey Williams relied heavily on the work of Pennant for his guide book on Caernarfonshire. He was also indebted to Leland's *Itinerary*, first published by Thomas Hearne, 1710-12 (with later editions appearing in 1744, 1770 and 1906), and Nicholas Owen's *Caernarvonshire. A sketch of its History, Antiquities, Mountains and Productions* (1792). If one compares pages 14 to 17 of Bailey Williams' *Tourist's Guide* with Pennant's *Tours* (1883, iii: 116-123) the texts are seen to be nearly identical. The chapter in question dealt with Conwy, but Bailey

Williams relies on Pennant even when describing his home parishes of Llanrug and Llanberis. (Volume 1 of Thomas Pennant's *A Tour in Wales* was published in 1778, volume 2 in 1783, and three volumes of the work appeared in 1810). This practice is much in evidence with most other topographical authors of the period, but why Bailey Williams, who had collected so much himself, chose to copy from other writers rather than use his own material is indeed a mystery.

His other interest was botany, and although he makes several references to the plants of Snowdonia and their habitats in his book, he decided to ask another local botanist, John Roberts of Caernarfon, and later Bangor, to prepare a list of plants to be included in the appendix to his *Tourist's Guide*.

Among the 'Gwyneddon Manuscripts' kept at the library of the University of Wales, Bangor, is a list of plants compiled by Bailey Williams entitled 'Botany of Snowdon Plants' (UWB: Gwyneddon MS 6). This consists of the scientific and English plant names with a space left for the Welsh names to be added, and also a section giving the localities of some of the less common species. There are no plants listed which had not been recorded previously for the county and neither are there any new localities.

In Bailey Williams' personal copy of Hugh Davies' *Welsh Botanology*, now in a private collection, there is a list of rare plants copied onto the margins of page xv which has been annotated by the original owner, and on other pages there are more plant names which appear under the heading: 'Indigenous plants in the vicinity of Carnarvon'. Also included are three herbal remedies, one for the cure of ague and the others for migraine and toothache; these were apparently copied from the old manuscript book of Hafod Uchtryd, Cardiganshire. The treatment for the ague consists of a drink made from dandelion *(Taraxacum)* leaves mixed with those of the common fumitory *(Fumaria officinalis)* which must be drunk 'hard during the morning and at noon'. For the migraine it is recommended that primrose *(Primula vulgaris)* roots and the leaves of betony *(Stachys officinalis)* be used to block the nostrils 'each day of the week'. Toothache is said to be cured by boiling holly *(Ilex aquifolium)* leaves in spring water and inhaling the steam rising from the pot.

In a letter dated 27 June 1828 Bailey Williams requests the help of William Wilson of Warrington (1799-1871), another noted botanist, in sending him a list of plants which would be likely to be found on the mountains in readiness for a group of visiting botanists. Bailey Williams thus made arrangements for the visit:

My intention is to employ a man to collect them at the lake, ... at the beginning of next week. Mr. [Newcome] has made a mistake as I am no Botanist . . . If you would have the kindness to give me a list of plants and their habitats. If you care to remain any time longer at Llanberis you would probably allow the bearer Ellis Jones who speaks a little English & attend you up the mountains in order to collect some of the plants best adapted for this purpose' (WWCWL vol 3).

In his *Tourist's Guide* (Williams, P.B., 1821: xxiii) Bailey Williams recommends 'Thomas Williams, Glan y Bala, or the Cottage between the Lakes, Llanberis. Thomas Phillips, Thomas Griffith, and all the Boatmen at Cwm-y-glo, Llanrug' as good guides.

In addition to the Gwyneddon Manuscripts held at Bangor more of Bailey Williams' papers are among the manuscripts at the National Library of Wales, Aberystwyth. Among these writings is the tragic story of the death of young John Closs of Llanberis who perished on Moel Eilio on 17 December 1805 (NLW MS 9177B). John was the seven year old son of Robert Closs, guide and landlord of the village inn at Llanberis (Nant Peris) who went to live with his grandmother at Betws Garmon, his mother walking over occasionally to visit them. During one of these visits the young lad decided to follow his mother home over the mountain, but without making his intention known to her or his grandmother. Snow began to fall, fine blinding snowflakes which soon covered the path and obscured the footprints of his mother. John Closs lost his way and began to wander. His body was eventually found, following a search of two or three days, near the summit of Moel Eilio, where he had perished presumably from hypothermia. He was buried at Nant Peris Churchyard and the poet David Thomas (Dafydd Ddu Eryri) composed the following '*englyn*' which was carved on his tombstone:

> *Oerfel anochel fu'n achos – i Angau*
> *Llym ingol, ymddangos –*
> *Mantell niwl mewn tywyll nos*
> *A dychryniad dechreunos.*

Also preserved in the same manuscript is a list of the various cliffs, hills and ridges that Bailey Williams had diligently recorded from the inhabitants of the Nant Peris district.

Rocks or Eminences on the S. & S.W. of Llanberis Village taking the whole length of the ridge or Buttress & commencing near Cwm Glas Ucha.

Y Gyrn Las
Llechwedd y Re

Brynn Pen y Llyn
Llechog
Clogwyn yr Ysgwydd
Y Bol Du
Y Tryfan Bach
Tryfan Mawr
Pen Carreg y Frân
Y Dderlwyn

Eminences N. of Do.

Y Glyder Fawr
Ysdol Felen
Braich Glas under it
Cwm y Nadroedd under that
Pen y Cerneu – North end of Glyder
Cwm Padrig
Llosgwrn – North of Pen y Foel
Pistill Gwynn between Pen y Foel & Glyder
Bryn Bras between Pen y Foel & Llosgwrn
Esgair y Ceunant
Garn or Pen y Garn.

A few of the names appear on current O.S. maps, while the remainder have been lost or forgotten over the years.

'Cors y Bwrli' was a boggy tract of land near Dolbadarn Castle where bog-myrtle *(Myrica gale)* grew in 'great plenty'. The bog takes its name from one of the Welsh names of this plant, *'bwrli'*. The above is entered by Bailey Williams on a sheet under the heading 'Plants-Habitats'(NLW MS 9177B). He goes on to include the dwarf juniper *(Juniperis communis* subsp. *alpina)* from 'the side of Glydair Fawr mountain & Crib Goch'; floating water plantain *(Luronium natans)* 'in the great Lake below the Castle' (a locality known to earlier botanists); thrift *(Armeria maritima)* which he calls 'Mountain Thrift' on Clogwyn y Garnedd and 'on Clogwyn Du yn yr arddu'; roseroot *(Sedum rosea)* 'on a rock on the North side of Bwlch Glâs near the ascent to the Peak or Summit of Snowdon'; alpine saxifrage *(Saxifraga nivalis)* and starry saxifrage *(Saxifraga stellaris)* 'on Clogwyn y Garnedd i.e. north side of Snowdon'; the water lilies *(Nymphaea alba* and *Nuphar lutea)* 'near Cwm-y-glo in the lower Lake & River'. He concludes the page by saying: 'There are great varieties of plants on the side of Allt Wenn above Mr Smith's Cottage.' This site was probably on the wooded slopes below Fachwen, above Llyn Padarn.

Peter Bailey Williams served the parishioners of Llanrug and Llanberis for forty-four years. He was interested in poetry, collecting and copying old manuscripts, local history and agriculture. He was also an author and translator, and a prolific writer contributing numerous articles for Welsh and English journals on subjects which included religion, poetry and agricultural improvement. Mountaineers remember Bailey Williams as the first man to lead a rock climb in Snowdonia. He and William Bingley climbed the eastern terrace of Clogwyn Du'r Arddu in 1798, describing the use of hands and knees, the sudden grip of fear experienced when a hold loosened, and the use of a belt in the absence of a rope.

John Roberts Penclip, 'A Bygone Welsh Botanist'

The list of plants appended to Peter Bailey Williams' *The Tourist's Guide through the County of Caernarvon* was the work of 'Mr John Roberts, Surgeon, Caernarvon' (Williams, P.B., 1821: xxi-xxii) whose name appeared occasionally in botanical books and journals during the 19th century.

An enquiry appeared in the *North Western Naturalist* under the heading 'A Bygone Welsh Botanist' stating that 'Dr John Roberts, surgeon, of Bangor, seems to have devoted some attention to the flora of North Wales a century or so ago', and after giving a scant account of the facts which were available then, concludes by saying: 'It would be interesting to know if anyone could supply any further information regarding the subject of this enquiry' (Dallman, 1926: 39).

J.E. Griffith (1843-1933) in the Preface of his *The Flora of Anglesey & Carnarvonshire* mentions Dr John Roberts of Bangor as the only person who had taken any interest in the botany of the two counties since the time of Reverend Hugh Davies, author of *Welsh Botanology* (1813). J.E. Griffith goes on to say that John Roberts was a personal friend of bryologist William Wilson of Warrington, and that Roberts' herbarium, which he claimed to have seen, contained no Anglesey plants and only a few Caernarfonshire ones; these he says were given to him by Wilson. J.E. Griffith in his *Flora* erroneously gives 1828 as the year of Roberts' death (Griffith, J.E., [1895]: iii) but the correct date of 1849 appears in his *Pedigrees of Anglesey and Carnarvonshire Families* (1914: 332) in which the family tree is traced.

John Roberts was the son of a Caernarfon blacksmith, Robert Jones of Pen y clip who died 18 May 1829 aged 64. The children of Robert Jones and his wife Elizabeth were named as follows: Dr John Roberts of Bangor, William Roberts Jones, Robert Roberts a smith at Caernarfon, Ann who married Rice Owen, a chemist of Pwllheli, and Elizabeth who married Richard Griffith, a saddler at Bangor. An entry in the Llanbeblig Parish Register shows that 'John Roberts Son of Robert Jones, Smith by Elizabeth' was christened on 28 September 1792. An interesting note on the same subject is that given by John Wynne in his book *Sir a Thref Caernarfon fel yr oeddynt ac fel y meant yn 1860* (County and Town of Caernarfon as it used to be and as it is in 1860) (Wynne, 1861: 49).

Wynne claims that Dr John Roberts of Bangor was the son of Robert Jones, a blacksmith, of Penymaes, Caernarfon. There can be little doubt that both J.E. Griffith and Wynne are dealing with the same family, but the latter named Penymaes as opposed to the former's Pen y clip.

John Roberts served his apprenticeship at the Caernarvonshire and Anglesey Loyal Dispensary, which had been opened in October 1810 and was probably articled to Dr James Roose who was apothecary and secretary in 1813. Roberts later succeeded Roose in this position and he was appointed house surgeon in November 1818. Also attending the Loyal Dispensary during this period were the surgeons Thomas Roberts and Rice Griffith, and physician William Mason, a graduate of Edinburgh University, who was appointed in 1812. A year following his appointment as house surgeon, John Roberts resigned his position announcing his intention through the press of opening a practice at Caernarfon.

During his time at the Bangor Dispensary he became known to Reverend Hugh Davies, but apart from being advised on the proper books on botany and the method of study he gained but little advantage from this acquaintance which came to an end with Davies' death in 1821 (Anon., 1849, i: 657). John Roberts however, despite his announcement of moving to Caernarfon and despite the fact that Bailey Williams describes him as 'Mr J. Roberts, Surgeon, Caernarvon' in the heading of the catalogue of plants which Roberts contributed to his *Tourist's Guide* (1821), remained in Bangor.

A John Roberts of Bangor took his membership examination at the Royal College of Surgeons of England, Lincoln's Inn, on 2 July 1824. The *Medical Directory* (1845: 335) lists John Roberts as an apothecary before 1815 and a surgeon in 1824. He practised at Castle Street (now the lower section of the Bangor High Street), at number 315 on the corner of High Street and Dean Street, which was for many years the premises of Thomas Lewis & Co, a grocer's shop (Ingman, 1950: 70).

John Roberts married Jane, the daughter of Elias Jones of Gorswen, and of The Abbey, near Llanrwst and his wife Jane, daughter of Richard Evans of Llwydfaen. They had five children, Elias John, Jane, Robert, John and Elizabeth. John Roberts' wife Jane died in 1835, and in a letter to William Wilson of Warrington dated 27 December he acknowledges the latter's letter of sympathy (WWCWL). Jane Roberts during that year had, as usual, been managing the domestic affairs of their farm, and had bought a plot of land at Garth, on the northern outskirts of the city, where she was busy supervising the building of a cottage. She caught a cold at the cottage on 7 November, and her condition worsened with headaches and fever; she took to her bed on the 20th and died soon after. It is not known if Roberts ever went to live at the new cottage after his wife's death, nor has the present author been able to find anything further about the farm mentioned in the letter.

Among the correspondence of William Wilson at the Warrington Library are six letters in the hand of John Roberts, all addressed from Bangor. Botany is the prime subject of discussion in these letters, but they also reveal matters of a very personal nature which will be discussed later, showing that the two men were close friends.

According to John Roberts' notice in *The Lancet* (Anon.,1849, i: 657) Roberts had by 1820 formed a considerable collection of dried plants which he had gathered on Snowdon, Glyder and in the districts around Bangor. This is inconsistent with J.E. Griffith ([1895]: iii) who states that Roberts' herbarium contained 'but few Carnarvonshire' plants. One can therefore but assume that the earlier herbarium was either dispersed, lost or destroyed before Griffith's time. It is certain, however, that Roberts communicated plant specimens from his collection, and also gathered plants for other botanists. He took the opportunity to gather plants whilst visiting patients in the country.

A number of very eminent English botanists came to stay with him in Bangor, and he used to accompany them on excursions to Cwm Idwal, Snowdon and parts of Anglesey to look for plants. During one such botanical ramble led by John Roberts the Snowdon lily *(Lloydia serotina)* was rediscovered on the rocks of the Devil's Kitchen above Cwm Idwal. It was thought that this plant had not been gathered by any other botanist from this particular site since the time of John Wynne Griffith of Garn (mentioned earlier) and the fact of its growing there had become merely traditional. It should be pointed out, however, that secrecy has always played a major part in field botany, especially during the period under discussion when the over-collecting of plants from a site could, and did, lead to the extermination of a rare species.

Most botanists kept their knowledge of rare plant localities to themselves and would only share that knowledge with people they trusted. One fine example is that of Owen Rowlands of Blaen y nant in the parish of Llandygái (1742-1817), a skilful herbalist and bone-setter, who knew well the site of the Snowdon lily on the Devil's Kitchen cliffs, but kept the locality secret despite constant badgering from other botanists and plant collectors. He finally divulged his long cherished secret on his death bed (Parry, 1868: 78). A transcript in the hand of William Roberts, Groes Lwyd, Abergele of a manuscript herbal by, or belonging to Owen Rowlands is preserved at the National Library of Wales (NLW MS 21948C) to which extensive notes have been added, mainly in red ink, by William Roberts with additional entries attributed to Griffith Williams (Gutyn Peris, 1769-1838), Hugh Derfel Hughes (1816-1890) and others.

John Roberts undertook a botanical ramble on 19 June 1844 in the company of Joseph Sidebotham (1824-1885) of Manchester, (one of the founders of that city's Field Naturalists Society) an account of which was published by the visitor in *The Phytologist*. On a previous occasion Sidebotham, following a short stay at Beaumaris, had made an excursion through Bangor and along the Holyhead Road to Llyn Ogwen, and from there into Cwm Idwal and the Devil's Kitchen before crossing the mountain from Llyn y Cŵn to arrive at Llanberis. On the following day he ascended Snowdon and inspected the slate quarries on his return. During this visit he was unsuccessful in his main object, since he failed to procure a specimen of the Snowdon lily *(Lloydia serotina)*.

On his second visit Sidebotham was met at Bangor by John Roberts and, taking a conveyance as far as the Penrhyn slate quarries, where Roberts had made previous arrangements for a quarryman to join them, they continued on to Cwm Idwal. While skirting the lake they observed water lobelia *(Lobelia dortmanna)*, quillwort *(Isoetes lacustris)* and awlwort *(Subularia aquatica)*. Rain began to fall heavily as they ascended the rocky slopes to the base of the Devil's Kitchen chasm and from there up the steep 'Llwybr y Carw' (the deer's path) which emerges on a plateau a short distance from Llyn y Cŵn. The following plants were recorded from the cliffs above the path: globeflower *(Trollius europaeus)*, alpine meadow-rue *(Thalictrum alpinum)*, roseroot *(Sedum rosea)*, spring sandwort *(Minuartia verna)*, mountain everlasting *(Antennaria dioica)* and a saxifrage whose identity caused uncertainty and which Sidebotham records as 'I suppose to be S. caespitosa'. This, the tufted saxifrage, is included in the plant list which John Roberts gave to Bailey Williams to be included in his *Tourist's Guide* (1821).

On arriving at the top of the Devil's Kitchen chasm the quarryman, who had brought along a rope, was lowered down the face of the cliff towards the spot where several flowers of the Snowdon lily had been spotted, but climbed back soon after, saying that the rope was too short to reach them. Sidebotham remarks at this point in his account of the incident that: 'I had to act as guide, being the only one of the party who had visited the place before' (Sidebotham, 1844: 1037). This was not so, as the list of plants which appeared in Bailey Williams' *Tourist's Guide* show that John Roberts had been well acquainted with the Devil's Kitchen, and indeed the whole of the Snowdonian range, for at least 24 years before Sidebotham's visit. The party then moved to a lower step which was closer to the *Lloydia* site and from this point John Roberts, after securing the rope around his waist, while the others held fast to the other end at the top, lowered himself down the face of the cliff. He reappeared a few minutes later with a few specimens held in his mouth and more in his hat.

By this time, the mist which had hung low over the mountain was beginning to clear, and before descending the botanists next walked in the direction of Glyder Fawr to search for the oblong woodsia (*Woodsia ilvensis*), a very rare fern. In this they were unsuccessful as the rock on which the oblong woodsia grew was found to be completely devoid of the plant. The *Woodsia* site near Llyn y Cŵn was well known to John Roberts and he had on previous occasions led other botanists there. Sidebotham notes:

> in this we were unsuccessful, although possessing plans of the district, which my friend Mr. Roberts of Bangor favoured me, embracing even the actual rock upon which he and Mr. Borrer had gathered it in plenty (Sidebotham, 1844: 1038).

Sussex botanist William Borrer (1781-1862) wrote to William Wilson on 19 May 1834 and the letter is a fine example of the badgering to which botanists with knowledge of plant localities were subjected to during the 19th century:

> obliged if you can give me such directions as may enable me to find readily some of the rarest plants of which I engage to help myself so moderately as not to endanger their extermination. W. ilvensis most anxious to find, Sax. caespitosa, Anthericum serotinum, at Snowdon, Rosa Wilsonii at Bangor. In Anglesey – Knappia agrostilea Lysimachia thyrsiflora A. guttatus, Brassica moensis, Elatine hydropiper, Potam. Lanceolata, Alisma ranunculoides, A. natans, Callitriche autumnalis, Charra aspera, Carex limosa, Pot. Rupestris (WWCWL: Borrer to Wilson 19 May 1834).

John Roberts was first introduced to Borrer, and his son, when they arrived at Bangor on 11 June 1834 (ANYBG Roberts to Wilson, 15 July 1834). Borrer made a favourable impression on Roberts being described as being friendly and familiar and ready to communicate any knowledge he could. The visitors then made their way across to Anglesey visiting Carreg Onnen, Holyhead, Llanfaelog and Aberffraw. Borrer visited Llandudno on the way to Bangor as Roberts notes that he had found the *Cotoneaster cambricus* which grows on the Great Orme there. Roberts' letter continues:

> Mr Borrer promised to write me an account of his success in Wales which he did on the 25 of June dated Brecon – I made a bet with him that he would not get Anthericum without ropes & that I would give him 5/- [25p] for every specimen, however he says in his letter that he got 3 flowers & bits of others at Twll du & demands 15/- [75p] for

them, but I wrote to say that they were not perfect specimens but fragments . . . He went from here to Carnarvon & Beddgelert & from thence to Cappel Curig & Llanberis where he had nothing but heavy rain most of the time. However he reached Twll du & found Anthericum as before stated. He did not go down to Llyn Idwal as the guide persuaded him "it was as dark as midnight there". He found no *Saxifraga caespitosa* no Woodsia no *Hieracium alpinum* . . . (ANYBG Roberts to Wilson 15 July, 1834).

Borrer is again mentioned by Roberts in a letter to Wilson describing an unsuccessful excursion to the Devil's Kitchen during July 1835 when they failed to find any oblong woodsia, *(Woodsia ilvensis)* forked spleenwort *(Asplenium septentrionale)* or tufted saxifrage *(Saxifraga cespitosa)*. It is noted however that the 'Gymnostomum Griffithianum' *(Oedipodium griffithianum)* was found in fruit at a previously known station near the top of Snowdon. Charles Cardale Babington (1808-1895), who is mentioned in the letter as having gathered 'several hundred' specimens of *Scirpus savii* on Anglesey, was with Borrer and Roberts during this visit. (WWCWL vol 3: Roberts to Wilson, 27 December, 1835).

Babington's visit to north Wales in 1835 is recorded in his diary which was published in 1897. William Borrer met with Babington at Birmingham on 23 July of that year and they were at Llangollen on the 25th. Two days later Babington travelled by coach to Bangor and met John Roberts, and on the 28th he travelled by coach to Caernarfon and Llanberis, and visited the Devil's Kitchen but found very little (Babington,1897: 41-42). John Roberts again joined Babington and Borrer on the 29th when they went to Clogwyn Du'r Arddu finding the northern rock-cress *(Arabis petraea)* before continuing on to the summit of Snowdon where they saw the *Oedipodium*, thereby confirming Roberts' report in his letter mentioned earlier. Borrer and Babington parted on 5 August.

Another rare fern, the alpine woodsia *(Woodsia alpina)*, suffered from over collecting in Snowdonia as the following quotation by Charles Babington testifies:

I was not able to find this plant on Glyder Fawr, Caernarvonshire, July 1835 although in company with J. Roberts, Esq., of Bangor, who knew its station well. It is, I fear, exterminated in that place. I searched for it in the same spot in 1837 and a botanical friend in 1840 but both without success (Francis, 1851: 27).

An interesting note which testifies to the collecting of plants from the Cwm Idwal area appears in the topographical work of local historian and poet Hugh Derfel Hughes (1816-1890) who refers to 'John Roberts Penclip' and other local doctors such as O.O. Roberts, Bangor, O. Rowland, Blaen Nant and John Owen, Pant y Ffrydlas, who visited the Devil's Kitchen cliffs every year armed with ropes and long sticks with small hooks attached which were used to uproot the plants they could not reach (Hughes, H.D., 1866: 28).

Some of the letters John Roberts sent to William Wilson contain family news and current affairs, and as would be expected from two with similar interests, botanical matters. In one letter the medical man advises Wilson to bring his ailing mother to Wales for a holiday during the months of May or June to drink plenty of buttermilk; he was quite convinced that her complaint was purely 'fanciful'. The subject then changes to plants, and a botanical excursion is planned: 'If you can reach Ormshead in May pray let me know of your arrival.' In another letter Roberts urges Wilson to take more physical exercise to combat his varicose veins, which were 'the result of sedentary life causing languid circulation . . . you ought to use as much exercise as you can daily without fatiguing yourself' (WWCWL vol. 3: Roberts to Wilson, 30 March 1831).

In 1833 Roberts expresses deep relief that the cholera epidemic did not reach the city of Bangor:

It was if not singular that we were most mercifully exempted from the ravages of Cholera, not a single case occurred in Bangor although it raged at Beaumaris & Caernarvon to both which places I went to see several cases – I am much obliged for your communication respecting Mr Hale's treatment, but I am convinced of what is now the opinion of the most eminent & candid Physicians that more cases would have done well if left to nature and cold water than under any other treatment whatsoever, no doubt many were killed by experiments; & bleeding in the stage of collapse would prove instantaneously fatal, indeed the blood will not flow in that stage, the best plan is to say that we know nothing at all about it, at least respecting the cure of it – that is my firm opinion – (WWCWL, Roberts to Wilson: 15 July 1833).

In the same letter Roberts thanks Wilson for sending him a copy of ' Mr Winch's Flora'. Nathaniel John Winch (1768-1838) was secretary at the Newcastle Infirmary and with J. Thornhill and R. Waugh was co-author of the *Botanist's Guide through . . . Northumberland and Durham* published in two volumes between 1805 and 1807. He also wrote the *Essay on Geographical Distribution of Plants . . . of Northumberland, Cumberland and Durham* (1819), with a second edition appearing in 1825, and *Remarks on Flora Cumberland*, also in 1825. Roberts notes that 'the old boy must have taken a great deal of trouble to put it together – Cryptogamic portion is all Chinese to me further than the *Jungermanniae . . .*' The letter goes on to say how his work at certain times restricted his botanical rambles to the Bangor district '. . . indeed I am now more completely tied down & confined to certain limits than ever I was before, in consequence of having so many midwifery cases upon hand. If I go far, the Ladies in this country are not always so accommodating as wait my return'. The constant demands of Roberts' profession are frequently mentioned in his letters; being a conscientious doctor, he put his vocation before his botanical interests; most other botanists of his time were gentlemen of private means with more free time to carry out their botanical investigations.

Another correspondent and friend of John Roberts was John Eddowes Bowman (1785-1841) whose chief interests were mosses, fungi and later geology. The letter of 15 July 1833 quoted above also records the visit to Wales of two of Bowman's sons, who came primarily to see Telford's bridge across the Menai Straits; the letter, which was delivered to Roberts by the young men mentions a visit made by Bowman and another botanist to the Devil's Kitchen a month previously with a view to collecting specimens of the Snowdon lily *(Lloydia serotina)*, when they had failed to find a single plant:

> He [Bowman] went with a young friend of his about a month ago to Twll du, chiefly for the purpose of getting some Anthericum [Snowdon lily], but not a single specimen could they find – I received a note a little before this from Mr Trimmer, who now resides at Carnarvon, containing a small fern & desiring to know its name; it proved to be *Asplenium septentrionale* [forked spleenwort], at the time of getting it, he says that he found Anthericum in flower having procured men & ropes to get down to the side of Twll du chasm. I am afraid we shall not be able to get any in future without having recourse to the same plan.

It was evident from comments such as this that during this period all the rare plants found in Snowdonia during any particular flowering season were being gathered. The first plant collector to arrive at any rare plant site would pick all the plants he could reach. None were spared; the acquiring of a complete herbarium was paramount.

Joshua Trimmer (1795-1857) was also interested in geology and his discovery of sands containing marine fossils on Moel Tryfan near Rhosgadfan was published in the *Proceedings of the Geological Society* (Trimmer,1831: 331-332). According to Lindsay (1974: 55): 'Joshua Trimmer, a tile and brick manufacturer of Middlesex, applied to the

Crown for a lease to work the quarries in Llanllechid'. In an essay on the slate quarries of the Nantlle Valley and Moel Tryfan which won at the Rhostryfan and Rhosgadfan Eisteddfod in 1889 a 'Mr Trimer' is named as chief inspector at the Penyrorsedd Quarry and that the house at Nantlle called Plas Baladeulyn was known locally as 'Plas Trimer'(Griffith, John, [1889]: 57-58).

The latest botanical publications, gossip, and domestic news were discussed in the letters, and Roberts relied on Wilson for information regarding botany.

> I understand that you are very busy arranging Drummond's mosses, which you mention, he gathered on the Missouri, New Orleans etc. . . are there many of these mosses similar to my N. American ones or are they all new & different ones, if they are mostly new and different to mine I should like to buy a set to make my flora more complete – i.e. if they will be sold in packets, like the others. I shall thank you much to write me a few lines to say how you are getting on – what news from the botanical world, how your mother and brother are . . . I still take the Magazine of Natl History & Hooker's Miscellany. Pray what kind of book is the new Edition of the English Flora published by Sowerby. I was at Llanbedrog in Lleyn lately seeing an old gentleman Dr Williams, and near the house on the sandy coast I could find quantity of an *'Euphorbia'* [spurge] which I was not acquainted with, it proves to be the E. *Paralia &* and I see that Davies y dail [Hugh Davies] mentions his having found it there in abundance. Did you ask Dr Hooker respecting his 'System of Plants' whether it ever was published. I shall feel very much obliged if you could at some future period lend me Arnott's botanical article in the new edition of Napier's Encyclopaedia , for I think from what they say, that the perusal of it would give me much pleasure (WWCWL, Roberts to Wilson: 15 July 1833).

Roberts' mention of 'Drummond's mosses' refers to Thomas Drummond who made plant collecting trips that were sponsored by W. J. Hooker and others in return for a share of the specimens. J. E. Bowman withdrew his support leaving the responsibility for preparing sets of American mosses for sale to William Wilson after Drummond's death. The fate of Roberts' collection of mosses is not known to the present author. The herbarium at the Department of Biodiversity and Systematic Biology, National Museum and Gallery of Wales, Cardiff contains a mere two vascular plants and one moss collected by John Roberts. The vascular plants are both mossy saxifrage *(Saxifraga hypnoides)* and the label reads 'Col. Dr

John Roberts, Twll Du 1828'. The second specimen is identical except for the addition of the month (7) to the date.

Further evidence regarding 19th century botanical practices is revealed in a letter written in 1825 by John Roberts to John Stevens Henslow (1796-1861), probably in response to a previous request by the latter for plant specimens. Roberts says he picked out a few plants from his small herbarium to send with the letter, but apologises for not being able to fulfil Henslow's desiderata. Roberts explains that he had already given a number of his dried specimens to friends and regrets that he did not keep duplicates of them. He collected plant specimens while visiting his patients and some of the specimens he had gathered had, as a result of neglect, become spoilt. In order to combat this he had decided to take a book of blotting paper out with him on his journeys and lay the plants out on the spot. The letter confirms Roberts' acquaintance with Hugh Davies and says that some of the plants listed as native in *Welsh Botanology* should not have been included:

> As to my old friend & preceptor (for I was formally acquainted with the Rev. H. Davies) I think he made many additions to the Botanical list of plants to be found on the Isle of Anglesey which he was not exactly justified, although a most excellent Botanist- I will mention a few instances as I proceed . . . (CUL MS Add 8176:33; Roberts to Henslow, 15 October, 1825).

Roberts lists about forty plants from *Welsh Botanology* with added comments to justify his criticisms. A selection from the list includes:

> *Salvia pratensis* [WB: 4] inserted upon the authority of no Botanist and probably came from a garden
> *Lysimachia thyrsiflora* [WB: 21] He says by Mr Lhwyd R. Synopsis –
> *Campanula Rapunculus* [WB: 22] probably came from Baron Hill gardens *Pyrola minor* [WB: 40] taken upon hearsay I never saw any of them in this country
> *Cucubalus baccifer* [WB: 41] a complete error see Smith's English Botany
> *Cerastium humile* [WB: 44] I believe of his own creation
> *Sisymbrium monense* [WB: 64] not to be found at present
> *Cheiranthus sinuatus* [WB: 64] in Mr D's habitats
> *Santolina maritima* [WB: 76] not now to be found

Later in the 19th century J. E. Griffith sought some of the plants listed above and his comments agree to a certain extent with those made by John Roberts. Of *Salvia pratensis* he states: 'This does not grow wild in Anglesey as recorded by H. Davies; the specimens labelled so in his

Herbarium were S. Verbenaca' (Griffith, [1895]: 108); and of *Pyrola minor* (Griffith,1895: 91): 'This is stated by Davies to be growing in Lligwy Woods; I have not searched the place myself, nor have I seen it growing in either county'. Griffith also failed to find *Cucubalus baccifer*: 'This plant is recorded by Davies, on the authority of Dillenius, to be growing in Anglesey. I have carefully searched the locality in which it was stated to be growing, for several years, but in vain' (Griffith, [1895]: 21). *Cerastium humile* is not listed by Griffith, and neither is *Sisymbrium monense* and despite searching the sites given by Samuel Brewer in his diary for *Cheirianthus sinuatus*, or sea stock *(Matthiola sinuata)*, he failed to find it (Griffith, [1895]: 9). The *Santolina maritima* Cottonweed, now *Otanthus maritimus*, was noted by Griffith as being almost extinct, but adds that a single plant was found near Llanfaelog by Mrs H. Wynn Sampson of Caernarfon in October 1894 (Griffith, [1895]: 78), but there have been no confirmed recent records.

Roberts listed the plants so that Henslow could see the difficulties of procuring some of the specimens that he had asked for, with the emphasis on those which did not grow in Anglesey at that time, despite appearing in *Welsh Botanology*. Roberts then goes on to mention the botanical books he had in his possession, namely Withering's *An Arrangement of British Plants, Flora Britannica* and *English Flora* and asks Henslow if he could recommend some good books on mosses. He concludes his letter by noting that:

> Dr Smith has omitted to notice in his English Flora the beautiful nectary at the base of each petal in the *Anthericum serotinum* & also that the whole plant is covered with a kind of white shining particles which is very evident in the fresh state – I shall take the liberty of troubling you with a list of my desiderata when I shall have another opportunity – (CUL MS Add. 8176: 33; Roberts to Henslow 15 October, 1825).

At 6 o'clock on the morning of Friday 21 July 1837 Roberts was busy writing to Wilson to congratulate him on his recent marriage. The bearer of the letter was to be Elias, Roberts' son, who was on his way by steam packet to Liverpool. The letter goes on to explain that Borrer, with his son William, had arrived in a chaise from Barmouth and stayed at the Penrhyn Arms in Bangor where Roberts had promised to breakfast with him that morning (ANYBG Roberts to Wilson, 21 July, 1837).

Three years following his wife's death John Roberts apologises for his delay in writing to Wilson explaining that he had been to London with his son Elias, and goes on to mention a microscope he was after:

> I was supposed to go up in the case of Williams of Bryn Bras Castle's

alleged forgery, but I was not called after all – I took my son Elias with me who was delighted with London – I took him to almost all the Public Institutions &c I admired the Adelaide Gallery of practical science as much as anything I saw there this time . . . I have not yet had an opportunity of going to Caebold to see Mr Valentine – I shall beg of him to procure me also a microscope like yours – (ANYBG Roberts to Wilson, 14 June 1838).

Roberts' interest in plant distribution, especially that of a rare species, was not confined to Caernarfonshire and Anglesey alone as becomes evident in another of his letters to Wilson. Roberts expresses concern at the health of Wilson's brother, referring to his drinking habits, and says: 'I recommend your brother to live chiefly on milk diet – he confessed that when he abstained almost in toto from stimulants . . . he enjoys much better health'. The letter goes on to report a visit to Bangor by Borrer on the 25th of June. Borrer's daughter was recently married, and Roberts spent an hour with him at the Penrhyn Arms during which time Borrer gave him specimens of a rare sedge whose locality caused some controversy:

He gave me specimens of *Carex tomentosa* [*C. filiformis*] which he found near a place called Cricklade in Wiltshire; as to the habitat "Merston Measey" the existence of such a place is doubtful & a Mr Alexander who is now Physician at Bath told me some time ago in a letter thus, "as to Carex tomentosa I am persuaded it is all a hoax and a humbug. No person ever heard of such a place as Merston Measey in Wiltshire and the specimens sent to different Botanists must have been foreign ones, I know that Mr Teesdale stood very high as a Botanist ... but I fear he had a joke played upon him." Those are the words of Mr Alexander who is a native of Corsham Wiltshire – but Mr Borrer says "as to the existence of such a place the Dr may be right & the map-makers wrong. I do however firmly believe that such a place exists. My previous suspicions that it did being confirmed by my enquiries at Crickdale [sic], where I was assured that it was but about 3 miles off, and it was about 2 miles from the last mentioned place in the way that I was directed to proceed, that the Carex occurred. It rained hard & my wife and daughter was waiting in the carriage, so I only saw one meadow of it. I should gladly, had circumstances admitted, have investigated the extent of the station. Is it not extremely liberal to treat the assertions of a respectable person like Mr Teesdale as a "hoax & a humbug" or do superficial enquiry as the Dr must have made ? It was just so some of our leading Botanists treated the discoveries of poor

George Don: most of which have been subsequently confirmed by other collectors." (ANYBG: Roberts to Wilson; 21 August, 1838).

A record of *Carex tomentosa* from 'Meadows near Merston Measey' appeared in *The New Botanist's Guide* by Hewitt Cottrell Watson (Watson, 1835: 46), and also in later editions of *Topographical Botany* as 'Borrer sp.' (Watson, 1874: 449) and 'Wilts north. Borrer sp.' (Watson, 1883: 468).

John Roberts' interest in botany continued to the last and during the latter part of his life he also became interested in geology. His obituary in *The Lancet* states: 'The contemplation of the works of nature was doubtless a solace to him during many a gloomy hour'; and these 'gloomy' periods may well have followed the death of his wife Jane in December 1835 which is not recorded in the *Pedigrees* (Griffith, 1914) and neither is the later marriage of John Roberts to his second wife.

The identity of his second wife remains unknown; all that is known of her background is the fact that her father lived in Liverpool. The whole matter of the second marriage would have remained unknown had it not been for a letter which Roberts had written to William Wilson of Warrington on 7 January 1844 which mentions a visit to Bangor by William Wilson and his wife earlier that year during which time Mrs Wilson was expecting a baby. John Roberts apologises for the behaviour of his wife, who by the time of writing had gone back to Liverpool: 'I was surely afraid that the disturbance which Mrs R. created that night would have had some bad effect, however I hope not'. Details of what happened on the night in question are not given, but the relationship between the botanist and his second wife had been intolerable for some time:

'. . . Mrs Jezebel is gone to Liverpool and has been there about 3 months & is likely to be there a long time as she has brought me into difficulties out of which I cannot easily extricate myself . . . for unless my wife reforms I am determined to keep her with her father until she does, for otherwise I shall never put up with her nor live with her for I would rather live like an old bachelor & keep Jane as a housekeeper, than to be in continual trouble and anxiety with a woman (when too much excited) is callous to every reason & all feelings of decency & morality (WWCWL; Roberts to Wilson, 7 January 1844).

Despite being troubled with personal and domestic problems, Roberts nevertheless found the time and the will to indulge in his hobby and carry out his duties as a doctor: 'I sent the plants to Mr Edwards. It is not improbable but I shall take a trip to see you this Spring as I expect I must go to London upon some Lunacy business' (WWCWL; Roberts to Wilson 7 January 1844).

The last of Roberts' letters to William Wilson known to the present author is dated 24 January 1844, and it again shows how his strong attachment to botany overcame his many predicaments. Wilson, who before his early retirement had been a practising solicitor had told Roberts of his intention to write a strongly worded letter to Mrs Roberts, who was still at Liverpool, regarding the incident at Bangor during which Mrs Wilson, being then pregnant, had appeared to have been upset. The letter however was not sent:

> I was glad you did not write as you once intended for it would only aggravate certain kinds of inflammatory feelings & passions without mending them & it would indeed be only throwing pearls before a swine – *hwch*. I was very glad to hear that Mrs Wilson is gradually recovering her strength & sorry to hear that the baby's strength is such a precarious state. Mrs R. is still in Liverpool but I expect she will be returning here in about a fortnight. Your Uncle's motto was a good one 'what cannot be cured must be endured'. I certainly have had that self-possession and strength of mind to bear all the evils I am beset with, with more courage & *equo animo* than I expected considering all circumstances (WWCWL; Roberts to Wilson, 24 January 1844).

Botany then takes over in the form of a discussion on a volume entitled *Flora Italicae*, which according to Roberts contained the most correct account 'as well as the most minute in Latin of not only the *Callitriches*, but of all other plants which he describes.'

Roberts also points out that Wilson's name appears in the text in connection with the taxonomy of certain mosses. Replying to a previous request from Wilson, Roberts assured the bryologist that he would gather mosses from the Bangor area for him: 'I shall gather the *Hypnum* in the Canal near the Baths – *Hypnum fluviatile* near the Cegin cataracts and also *Jugermannia viticulosa* – I shall get up an hour earlier in order to procure them'. He concludes the letter by saying: 'I hope as you say that I shall find my domestic affairs in future more comfortable and that my mind will be more at ease – however I feel very happy even now in my own mind' (WWCWL; Roberts to Wilson, 24 January 1844).

John Roberts died at his home in Bangor on 27 April 1849, the cause of death being 'Affection of the hives / not certified'. He was buried in the Cathedral graveyard; his gravestone lies by the side of the pathway which connects Glanrafon Hill with Ffordd Gwynedd.

John Williams and the *Faunula Grustensis*

'It is ridiculous in a man to travel for improvement, while he remains ignorant of those things that are about him at home.' So wrote John Williams (1801-1859) on the title page of his book *Faunula Grustensis* published in 1830. This volume, neatly printed by John Jones of Llanrwst, is unusual in that it is a catalogue listing all birds, animals and plants to be found in the parish of Llanrwst; most other such works dealt with counties. The book is dedicated to John Wynne Griffith of Garn who, Williams writes: 'in his younger days explored the productions of all the mountains and valleys in North Wales, and therefore he is acquainted with the habitats of the rare Plants' (Williams, J., 1830: 3-4).

John Williams was born in Llansantffraid Glan Conwy on 1 March 1801, the son of Cadwaladr Williams of Eidda Fawr, Ysbyty Ifan, and Jane Williams who hailed from Dolwyddelan. They lived at the mill house at Felin Ucha, Pentrefelin where Cadwaladr Williams worked as a miller, and he, being a cultured man with a keen interest in literature, ensured that his eight children were educated, initially at home, and later in the Sunday School.

Cadwaladr and Jane Williams were members at the Methodist Chapel in Llansantffraid Glan Conwy, and Cadwaladr Williams was instrumental in establishing the first Sunday School in Llandudno. In those days flour could not be bought in Llandudno, only wheat, and during the summer when the wind was not sufficiently strong to turn the windmill near Glanwydden, the wheat was carted to the water powered mills at Llansantffraid, and in dry summers over Tal-y-cafn to the mills at Tal-y-bont and Borthllwyd near Trefriw. Cadwaladr Williams, being concerned at the level of illiteracy among the young men who drove the wheat carts to his mill from Llandudno suggested to his fellow Methodists that a Sunday School should be established there. A certain James Williams and W. Davies of Llandudno then joined the Llansantffraid Methodists' initiative by procuring the use of the barn of Peter Jones, Pwll y Gwichiaid as a schoolroom. Two or three people walked the six or seven miles from Llansantffraid to teach at the school, which opened in the year 1806.

When John Williams was eleven years of age he, along with his older brother William, spent a year in Liverpool attending the Harrington Academy at Bradford Place, Toxteth Park, their ambition during this time being a career at sea. In addition to maritime lessons the brothers were also taught mathematics, account keeping and English grammar. The romance of the sea soon faded, however, and at the end of the year the brothers returned home to help their father at the mill. William was later apprenticed to a chemist and surgeon, studied at London and Dublin, and obtained a licence to operate as a chemist and surgeon at Abergele. He died aged thirty-seven on 11 June 1834, but the shop was kept by his widow Mary until her death in 1873.

According to Thomas Shankland, John Williams spent a term as an apprentice gardener on one of the large estates in the Conwy valley, but precisely which one is not known (Shankland, 1916: 41). James Britten notes that he worked as a gardener for the Countess of Bridgewater at Ashridge, Hertfordshire between 1823 and 1827 (Britten, 1910: 232). Here he was permitted the use of the library and among the collection was a copy of *Hortus Gramineus Woburnensis* by George Sinclair (1786-1834), who was at one time gardener to the Duke of Bedford. The book, published privately in 1816, contained dried specimens of grasses carefully arranged and labelled. John Williams spent a further three years at Kew Gardens and the Chelsea Physic Garden, then under the curatorship of William Anderson (1766-1846). His younger brother Moses was apprenticed to an apothecary at Abergele under the care of the eldest brother William, and after five years went up to London aged twenty-one in 1824. Moses trained for six months at St Thomas' Hospital, qualifying for his Licentiateship of the Society of Apothecaries (LSA) on 13 December 1827. Licentiateships were granted only to persons who had completed a course of training. He returned to Wales and practised at Abergele, Rhuddlan and St Asaph; he is referred to as a 'surgeon' in the trade directory of 1828 while his brother William is described as a 'druggist and grocer'.

There is no definite evidence that John Williams was granted the LSA, but Thomas Shankland is of the opinion that he was (Shankland, 1916: 42). He left London in 1827 being apprenticed to his brother William at Abergele and by 1830 he was a practising doctor at Llanrwst. An article written by Reverend John Williams, son of the John Williams in question, reveals that the physician obtained his MD at the Royal College of Surgeons, Dublin under the tuition of the doctors Robert Harrison, Arthur Jacob and Samuel Stretten (Williams, J., 1893: 225). The name John Williams appears in the *Examiners Book* 1817-1837 registered as one of Mr Harrison's pupils on 24 January 1832, but there is no record of either of the brothers in the minutes of the Court of Examiners 1817-1837. Altogether there is a good deal of uncertainty about John Williams' training.

He took a great deal of interest in agriculture as well as botany; these interests no doubt arose from the influence of his greatly admired acquaintance John Wynne Griffith of Garn, mentioned earlier. John Williams subscribed to the Royal Agricultural Society's journal and during 1842 submitted an essay entitled 'The Food of Plants' in response to a competition that the society had arranged. His entry proved unsuccessful and it was not printed in the journal, but the composition shows that he was highly talented and possessed a great deal of knowledge on plant science. The essay also points out various means by which the farmer could improve his land, a matter which John Wynne Griffith had spoken strongly in favour of during his period as an MP. John Williams urged farmers to experiment with several strips of land set aside for the purpose, leaving one strip untreated and applying various types of fertilizer to the others. They should then plant a variety of vegetables in each plot which would in due course show the farmer which fertilizer was best suited to each vegetable. He goes on to suggest that farmers would benefit from learning the principles of chemistry, zoology and botany and he was also in favour of establishing agricultural schools throughout the country, or an agricultural department in every school. This, he writes, would improve and prepare those pupils whose aim in life was to become capable and efficient farmers. He wrote several letters to the *Medical Times*; the first, which was written on 23 April 1843, appeared under the heading 'Observations on the Spleen' and was signed 'Corvenius'. The second letter dated 15 August 1843, gave his own opinions on the 'Law of Periodicity' regarding a disagreement between Doctors Laycock and Dickson. This letter was signed 'Cymro'. He wrote once more to the *Medical Times* on 3 January 1844, this time in support of comments made by a certain Mr Yeatman concerning mercury, and again on 24 September discussing dropsy. This last letter was signed in his own name, but he used the pseudonym 'Corvenius' again when discussing the professional standards of doctors. On 7 August 1844 Sir James Graham's bill entitled *Further regulation of the Profession of Physic and Surgery* underwent its first reading in the House of Commons. This bill was aimed at improving the professional standards of doctors thus controlling the numbers of unqualified 'doctors' who operated freely at that time. The bill received its second reading on 28 February 1845, but despite the fact that it was approved by the House and discussed by the Select Committee it never became law, due to the widespread disagreement and bad feeling between the various medical reformers. John Williams was of the opinion that the new measure, if it became law, would mean 'allowing every mercenary and ignorant empiric to practice'. This last sentence confirms that he himself was a licensed doctor; an unqualified 'quack' would hardly have expressed himself in such a manner to the readers of the

Medical Times. (Jones, C., 1990: 27-31).

During 1829 and 1830, while living at Llanrwst, John Williams began to study and collate his researches into the natural history of the parish, work which culminated in the publication of his book *Faunula Grustensis*. He begins the book with the following words: 'My principle motive in compiling this treatise was to give a Catalogue of the Animals, Plants, Minerals, &c. which this parish contains, so that we might have some idea of what is, and what is not to be found in it: but as this itself would have been dry and uninteresting to many, I have endeavoured to collect as many facts relating to its general history, commerce, agriculture, &c. as would become the limits allotted to my little Fauna' (Williams, J., 1830: 3). He names Sir John Wynn's *History of the Gwydir Family*, and Thomas Pennant's *Tours in Wales* as being the main sources of his 'general observations'. He also pays tribute to Edward Lhuyd, Hugh Davies and John Wynne Griffith when referring to the field of natural history. He also mentions 'the Natural genius for plants of Richard Roberts of Melin y Coed' (Williams, J.,1830: 4) who will be mentioned again later.

The preface concludes with a few remarks which show his concern at the lack of similar books published in Wales on natural history. Reading, he says, was very popular among the Welsh, but the great majority of books dealt with theology and poetry. The *Faunula Grustensis* would he hoped encourage more studies in the Sciences as well as the Arts. There were at the time several Botanic Gardens, as well as Schools of Medicine in England, Scotland and Ireland, but none in Wales, and John Williams voiced his concern over this by asking: 'how can she [Wales] nurture her geniuses' (Williams, J., 1830: 4).

In describing the Nant Bwlch yr Heyrn district, John Williams names the plants for which this area is famous: the alpine penny-cress *(Thlaspi caerulescens)* on the authority of J.W. Griffith is reported as growing 'abundantly near the Cataract'; bog-myrtle *(Myrica gale)* abundant and perfumes the air with its spicy smell. In summer branches of this plant are taken and laid between the bed clothes to drive away fleas' (Williams, J., 1830: 22).

The '*Murddun*' or ruins of the house of Taliesin, the sixth century bard was, according to the *Faunula Grustensis* 'still to be seen about 300 yards this side' of Llyn Geirionydd and the surrounding district is described as being barren and 'consisting of heaths and bogs, but lately, Lord Willoughby de Eresby has planted several thousands of trees, so that in few years it will be much more valuable than it has been, since the great arboreal desolation' (Williams, J., 1830: 23).

Capel Curig is unique in that it has 'an extraordinary large Inn' and the lakes Llynnau Mymbyr were much frequented by anglers; the Welsh poppy *(Meconopsis cambrica)*, globeflower *(Trollius europaeus)*, water lobelia *(Lobelia dortmanna)*, awlwort *(Subularia aquatica)*, quillwort *(Isoetes)* and ivy-leaved bellflower *(Wahlenbergia hederacea)* are the plants noted around the Capel Curig area. The 'extraordinary large Inn' referred to was the hotel built by Lord Penrhyn shortly after 1800, now the centre for outdoor activities called Plas y Brenin.

The summit ridge of Moel Siabod, being the furthest border on the western side of the parish of Llanrwst is named as having the finest views of the Snowdon group of mountains; the work noted the following plants as growing on Moel Siabod: alpine saxifrage *(Saxifraga nivalis)*, starry saxifrage *(Saxifraga stellaris)*, mossy saxifrage *(Saxifraga hypnoides)*, and the club-mosses *Diphasiastrum alpinum, Huperzia selago* and *Selaginella selaginoides*. The ring ouzel was listed as a regular visitor.

Pennant's account of the view from the summit of Snowdon is quoted in its entirety followed by an extensive list of rare plants for which the region is noted. From Moel Siabod the parish boundaries are followed towards Betws-y-coed where Pennant is quoted as saying 'the noblest oaks in all Wales grew on this rock, within memory of man'. Williams goes on: 'I remember the stools of several which proved they were equal to any which flourish in the deepest soil; yet these rocks are totally destitute of earth for a considerable way'. Williams was always a keen advocate of the planting of trees, and adds: 'I have no doubt the Fir and other hardy trees would grow on the summit of Snowdon, for trees are found to grow in much colder countries than Snowdon is; for instance Sweden, Norway, . . .' (Williams, J., 1830: 26-27). John Wynn of Gwydir (1553-1627) writing of an earlier period states that:

> Yow are to understand that in those dayes the countrey of Nanconway was not onelie wooded, but also all Car'r , Merionythshire, and denbighe shire seemed to be but one forrest and wood, havinge few inhabitants, over that it hath this daye, thoughe of all others Nantconway had the fewest beinge the worst then, and the seate of the warres, to whom the countreys about payd contribution from the towne of Conway to Bala, and from Nantconway to denbigh (Wynn, J., 1927: 53).

The house at Maenan is mentioned as having a good greenhouse and garden; evergreen oaks *(Quercus ilex)* adorned the front of the house, and an abundance of spurge-laurel *(Daphne laureola)* grew in a wood by the road. In a nearby plantation John Williams records the deadly nightshade *(Atropa belladonna)* as growing plentifully, and goes on to note the similarities between Maenan and Ashridge in Hertfordshire where he had worked as a gardener between 1823 and 1827. Maenan, before the dissolution of the monasteries had been an abbey, having been removed there from Conwy in 1289, and Ashridge was formerly a convent. Williams recalls also having seen the deadly nightshade there. John Wynne Griffith of Garn had also observed this plant growing near three or four abbeys in north Wales and Williams suggests that the monks must have used it as a rat poison. It was used by the ordinary people of the neighbourhood to ease pain from swellings of the legs and also for rheumatism (Williams, J., 1830: 33-34).

John Williams' keen eye for plants becomes evident even when he writes about the town and castle of Conwy as he adds the odd botanical note to the text: 'Near Porth ucha' the *Rubia peregrina* [wild madder] grows so luxuriant as to be scarcely cognizable. The *Dianthus Caryophyllus* [clove pink] plentiful on the walls' (Williams, J., 1830: 35). J. E. Griffith, author of *The Flora of Anglesey and Carnarvonshire* [1895] has no record of wild madder from Conwy, and the only species of Dianthus to be recorded by him from the town walls of Conwy was the common pink *(Dianthus plumarius)*: 'On Conway Town walls, N. side !' (Griffith, J. E., [1895]: 20).

The extensive tract of salt marsh at Conwy belonged to the Corporation of the town in Williams' day, and large mounds of mussel shells, left there by the pearl gatherers, were piled at one end, Conwy pearls being considered equal to any in Britain. Plants such as the sea bindweed *(Calystegia soldanella)*, field gentian *(Gentianella campestris)*, sea rocket *(Cakile maritima)* – which J. E. Griffith also recorded in his *Flora* [1895]:16), – and bloody crane's-bill *(Geranium sanguineum)* were noted from the area.

The areas including Penygogarth or Great Orme's Head and Bodysgallen have always been a favourite hunting ground for botanists and John Williams proudly attributes the finding of the wild cotoneaster *(Cotoneaster cambricus)* to his esteemed friend John Wynne Griffith of Garn. Griffith first found the plant in 1783 but failed to communicate a specimen to Sir J. E. Smith who at the time was collating information for inclusion in his *English Botany* (Williams, J., 1830: 36). There follows on the same page a short list of plants found in the Llandudno area.

The commerce and agriculture of the parish is next dealt with; the crops which were grown during Williams' time are noted together with sound advice to farmers on how to improve the land for a better yield. 'The encouraging of Agriculture and Industry would give a new face to the country: it would ignite a more general spirit of enquiry, and make us know the great importance of diligence and exertion'. The corn-sellers who attended the weekly market at Llanrwst came from nearby Eglwysfach, Llansantffraid, Creuddyn, Llandrillo and Abergele, while the buyers came from further afield: Beddgelert, Ffestiniog, Llangwm, Cerrigydrudion and Penmachno. In the mountainous regions only oats, barley and potatoes were grown, and the farmers relied on selling cattle to the English markets for money.

John Williams was in favour of the commercialisation and expansion of the textile industry in the Conwy Valley: 'Could not the Flax be brought to a more general cultivation?' he asks. He was of the opinion that flax would grow on any kind of land and that every part of the plant would be put to some use: linseed oil could be had from the seed, and the remaining substance (the linseed cake) would provide 'a wholesome food for cattle'. The straw would then be used in the manufacturing of linen: 'could we not manufacture this as well as wool, and obtain a large quantity of good linen and flannel of our own growth and produce . . .' He foresaw the industrialisation of the Conwy Valley as being able to compete favourably with the mills of Lancashire: 'If our river, vale, and water power, had been near the active and spirited manufacturers of Manchester, it would have been universally allowed to be equal to any place in the world for conveniency, with respect to water-power for looms, and the river for exportation' (Williams, J., 1830: 41).

He recommended the planting of fruit trees and called for an increase in the number of orchards, stating that only one or two had been planted in the parish over the past fifty years. Apples and cider would help to pay the rent of a farm and he argued that much money was made in Herefordshire out of their apple trees. 'We cannot expect to ripen grapes and make wine in Wales as they do in France; . . . [but] . . . no one would deny that Cyder and Perry could be produced here as well as in any other part of the world'. Another of his proposals was the making and exporting of 'a celebrated Llanrwst Ale'. The hop, being a hardy plant which grew abundantly in the hedges of the parish, could be planted for commercial purposes in specially cultivated plots: 'Many Noblemen, &c. in England have their Hop garden on their own Farms. We can be no more justified in sending to England for Hops than we should if we were sending thither for malt' (Williams, J., 1830: 42). John Williams was a strong advocate of self sufficiency; his ideals cover almost all aspects of agriculture and industry and he was always ready to encourage improvement in the use of land and the introduction of new agrarian techniques.

The catalogue of animals and plants indigenous to the parish of

Llanrwst in the *Faunula Grustensis* was the result of a single season's field work by the author. Several additional records are inserted on the authority of John Wynne Griffith of Garn, Thomas Pennant and Richard Roberts of Melin-y-coed. The whole class of cryptogammic plants, excluding the ferns, were omitted. John Williams encouraged others to observe and record the native flora of their surrounding communities: 'Any one might with a little trouble, collect all the native plants in this neighbourhood, although, perhaps, this would not be in itself of great importance, but as a part of Science it would be very commendable. I have myself collected above 5,000 different species of plants, Indigenous and Exotic' (Williams, J., 1830: 63-64).

The botanical section of the catalogue lists 532 plants between pages 80 and 118 followed by a further twenty-two pages containing a list of garden plants. The book concludes with notes on chemistry and nosology (the classification of diseases). Some very interesting and informative notes have been appended to some plant names; they refer mainly to the localities where the plant in question grew or to its medicinal qualities. The bogbean *(Menyanthes trifoliata)*, whose infusion is recommended as a tonic, is extremely bitter, and a 'diaretic and purgative; useful in dropsy and rheumatism: sometimes used instead of hops, 2oz of these being equal to a pound of Hops'. The berries of the spindle tree *(Euonymus europaeus)*, when dried and ground were sprinkled on the hair to destroy lice. (Williams, J., 1830: 88-89). John Williams quotes Pennant regarding the lady's bedstraw *(Galium verum)*: 'Above Bwlch y Gwynt, and other places.' "The flowers will coagulate boiling milk. Boiled in alum water they tinge wool yellow. The roots dye a fine red, not inferior to madder." '(Williams, J., 1930: 86). He also, like other writers of the period who visited north Wales, notes the use of the rush light in the mountainous districts: 'In the mountains they very seldom see tallow candles'. The pith of the soft-rush *(Juncus effusus)* was used; 'They strip off the rind (leaving about one-fourth of it unstripped, to strengthen it) then they are once immersed in any melted grease and laid by for use. When they have no rushes at hand, they have another expedient; they take an old rag, which they roll and twist into a hard cord, this they dip in melted grease, which makes a lasting candle' (Williams, J., 1830: 93).

The opium poppy *(Papaver somniferum)* was noted by Williams as a frequent weed in gardens and other cultivated places. Opium was extracted by winding the green capsules until the white juice exuded, which was then dried.

The rare fern, forked spleenwort *(Asplenium septentrionale)*, is still extant in several sites about Gwydir Castle and Nant Bwlch yr Heyrn, yet

John Williams had not seen it there for himself; he writes: 'I cannot find this plant; it is inserted upon the authority Mr. Ray gives us in his Synopsis; it is something ambiguous, for we have no place near here called Llandethylae; *"In muris antiquis Llan-Dethylae uno circiter milliari a Llanrhoost aquilonem versus"'*(Williams, J., 1830: 117). The stately royal fern *(Osmunda regalis)* completes the botanical list: 'In the river that flows from Llyn Geirionydd, and above Trefriw, tho' not strictly within this parish' (Williams, J., 1830: 118).

The above mentioned record of the forked spleenwort which appeared in John Ray's *Synopsis* puzzled not only John Williams but other botanists as well (Newman, 1854: 268). The record was not in either of the first two editions of the *Synopsis* which appeared in 1690 and 1696, but appears in the 1724 edition which was revised and enlarged by Johann Jacob Dillenius: 'In muris antiquis *Lhan-Dethylae* uno circiter milliari a *Lhan-Rhoost* aquilonem versus; *D. Richards.*' [On old walls at Lhan-Dethylæ about one mile from Lhan-Rhoost towards the north] (Dillenius,1724: 120). The mystery of the 'Lhan-Dethylæ' forked spleenwort continued up until the last decade of the 19th century, when a copy of the 1696 edition of Ray's *Synopsis*, which once belonged to Richard Richardson, was bought by bryologist Daniel Angell Jones of Harlech (1861-1936) from William Pamplin, botanist, publisher and distributor of scientific books, who by then was retired and living at Llandderfel. Annotated in the bottom margin of page 47 which described the forked spleenwort were the words: 'On some dry walls at Lhan Degla nigh Lhan Rhoost Denbyshire observed Jun 29 1711'.

John Lloyd Williams (1854-1945), the botanist and a close friend of D.A. Jones, wrote an account of the discovery and this was later published in *The Western Mail* (Williams, J. L., 1937: 9). It was evident from the annotation that Richardson had found the forked spleenwort near Llanrwst in June, 1711, and had written the details in his personal copy of Ray's *Synopsis*. When it was decided to print a revised edition of Ray's book it seems probable that Richardson's new locality for the forked spleenwort was included, and the printer misread the word Llan Degla for Lhan-Dethylæ. There is no place of that name in the vicinity of Llanrwst or anywhere else in Wales, and the site where Richardson found the forked spleenwort is probably the one which is still extant, situated in the interstices of a stone wall near Llanrwst. It is not known why Richardson described Llandegla as being near Llanrwst as the two places are about twenty-five miles apart, unless he meant that he passed through the former on his way; furthermore, there have not been any records of forked spleenwort from Llandegla.

H.A. Hyde (1892-1973) later wrote to *The Western Mail* in response to J. Lloyd Williams' article confirming that Richardson's personal copy of Ray's *Synopsis* had by then been passed on to the library of the Department of Botany, National Museum of Wales, Cardiff:

> Sir, – my friend Mr. John Rees, of University College, Cardiff, has drawn my attention to and translated for me the Welsh article by Dr. J. Lloyd Williams which appeared under the title "Yr Ymchwil am Lysiau Prin" in your issue of November 29. / Your readers may be interested to know that the copy of Ray's *Synopsis Methodica Stirpium Britannicarum* (Ed. 2, 1696) to which Dr. Lloyd Williams refers is now in the library of this department of the National Museum. It contains numerous manuscript notes in the hand of its original owner, Dr. Richard Richardson, F. R. S., who, together with Edward Lhwyd, was one of the first to explore fully the botanical riches of North Wales. In particular, the marginal note on Asplenium septentrionale (page 47), to which Dr. Lloyd Williams refers reads: "On some dry walls at Llan Degla, nigh Lhan Rhoost, Denbyshire observed Jun: 29 1711 / Book Plate / The book contains also the book plate of Mathew Wilson, who married the widow of Richard Richardson's grandson Henry Richardson (1758-1784), and in addition the inscription "William & Caroline Pamplin, 1840." / William Pamplin died at Llandderfel in 1899, and, as Dr. Lloyd Williams tells us, some of his books were purchased from his widow by the late Mr. D. A. Jones, then of Harlech, by whose instrumentality the one in question came into the possession of the National Museum. The chain of ownership of this very interesting volume may therefore be traced virtually without a break from the end of the seventeenth century when, as the latest and best book on its subject, it was used as an aid to botanising in Wales down to the present time. – Yours &c., H. A. Hyde. / Keeper of the Department of Botany, National Museum of Wales, Cardiff, Dec. 6 (Hyde, 1937: 11).

In a letter to Dillenius dated 25 October 1726 Richardson mentions finding *'Adiantum acrosticum Thali' [Asplenium septentrionale]* 'upon a wall not far from LhâRoost upon the river Conway, and no where else in Wales or England;' (Druce and Vines, 1907: lxxix). Unfortunately Richardson does not give any dates for this botanical discovery, but the fact that he stated that he did not find this plant in any other place in either Wales or England will rule out Llandegla as a possible site for the forked spleenwort.

On 1 January 1838 John Williams married Emma Owen (1801-1868) at

St Hilary's Church, Denbigh; he had been living in Corwen since May 1832 having established a medical practice there. Emma was the youngest of the fourteen children of Thomas Owen (1757-1827), rector of Llangelynnin, Meirionnydd and Jane Giles (1759-1848) of Ruthin. The 1841 Census Returns show that John and Emma Williams resided at Crown Street, Corwen and had a fourteen year old girl servant called Margaret Williams. Their first child, Jane Emma was born on 17 February 1843, and on 6 December 1844 their son John was born.

In January 1848 gold was discovered in California and by the following year forty thousand emigrants had moved into San Francisco, lured there by an irresistible desire to 'get rich quick'. John Williams, seized by the 'gold fever', sold his property and practice at Corwen and emigrated with his family to America in 1850. He bought several acres of land near Norristown, Pennsylvania and built a home for his wife and family. The house was named 'Corwen Place'. Once his wife and children had settled down in their new home John Williams set out for the gold fields of California. His aim initially was to establish a medical practice among the gold miners and to venture to do a little prospecting himself whenever an opportunity presented itself. He journeyed to California via Panama, but was cheated and robbed of all his possessions before arriving at that city. The American Consul helped him continue his journey northwards to San Francisco, and following his arrival there he spent his remaining money on equipment and supplies before embarking on his gold-seeking venture. He spent five months in Chenhollow near Placerville and later bought a fifty dollar 'claim' at Ouseley's Bar near Marysville, but soon realized his mistake; despite repeated efforts he never became rich. The hard life of the gold prospector had taken its toll on John Williams during his year spent among the mountains of northern California, but he never missed an opportunity to study his favourite subject, and made several observations about the plants of the new world. Following repeated attacks of yellow fever he decided to sell his interests in California and Pennsylvania and he returned to Wales with his family in 1853. He practised medicine for a short while in Froncysyllte near Llangollen, moving soon after to Wrexham and Mold. He died on 1 November 1859 and was buried in the churchyard at Llanfair Dyffryn Clwyd. His son Reverend John Williams, who was rector of Llanwddyn near Oswestry between 1890 and 1916, presented his father's Herbarium, consisting of 5,000 plants and a copy of the *Faunula Grustensis* to the University of Wales, Bangor in 1902.

Richard Roberts of Melin-y-coed, and the 'Old Mountain Doctor'

In the preface of his *Faunula Grustensis* John Williams pays tribute to Richard Roberts of Melin-y-coed, Llanrwst and describes him as 'a natural genius for Plants . . . who, with his son, Mr. David Roberts, Surgeon, knew British Plants very well' (Williams, J., 1830: 4). Richard Roberts had noted the habitats of the plants he had observed in the parish in the margins of a copy of Withering's *An Arrangement of British Plants* and the work later came into the possession of John Williams. Richard Roberts is credited with fifteen plant records in the *Faunula Grustensis*; twelve flowering plants and three ferns. They appear as follows; modern scientific names having been used whenever practicable:

Page 90   Dodder *(Cuscuta epithymum)* 'Between Maen gwyn and Gwytherin'

Page 92   Bladdernut *(Staphylea pinnata)* 'About Melin y coed and Bryn tirion'

Page 94   Rosebay willowherb *(Chamerion angustifolium)* 'In Dol Cwm lannerch'

Page 94   Cranberry *(Vaccinium oxycoccos)* 'In Cae pella' Bryn Ifan, Capel Garmon'

Page 100   Marsh cinquefoil *(Potentilla palustris)* 'In Gwaun Ty'n twll'

Page 101   Common meadow-rue *(Thalictrum flavum)* 'In Gwydir park, above the Waterfall'

Page 105   Daisy-leaved ladies smock *(Cardamine bellidifolia)* 'By Pistyll gwyn, Nant y goron and Gallt yr efal' [This plant appears listed in Withering's *An Arrangement of British Plants* (1796, iii: 577) but J.D. Hooker however, in the *'Appendix of Excluded Species'* of his *Students Flora of the British Isles* (3ed., 1884) states that the plant was 'Confounded with a form of C. hirsuta', i.e., hairy bitter-cress].

Page 107   Dyer's greenweed *(Genista tinctoria)* 'By the Canal, under Ty'n twll'

Page 107   Petty whin *(Genista anglica)* 'At Tybrith ucha'

Page 112   Purple helleborine *(Epipactis rubra)* 'In Nant Bwlch y gwynt'. [This plant appears in Withering's *An Arrangement of British Plants* (1796, ii: 42-43) named *Serapias rubra* and the following note is appended] 'Mr Ray inserted this on the authority of Pluckenet, who says he received it from Ireland, and Mr

Hudson says it grows in thickets on the side of mountains about Clapham and Ingleton, Yorkshire, but its existence as a native of Britain or Ireland is yet very doubtful'. [This is now considered to be an error for another species of *Epipactis* or *Cephalanthera*].

Page 113   Flea sedge *(Carex pulicaris)* 'In Cae mawn y Fron'

Page 113   Bladder-sedge *(Carex vesicaria)* 'Below Ty'n twll'

Page 117   Oak fern *(Gymnocarpium dryopteris)* 'The lower side of the wooden bridge, in Nant y goron'

Page 117   Beech fern *(Phegopteris connectilis)* 'Farthest end of Carreg walch wood'

Page 117   Lemon-scented fern *(Oreopteris limbosperma)* 'In Nant Cae'r groes, pen isa' Nant y goron'

Richard Roberts was born in 1744, the son of Robert Pritchard of Ty'n y Fynwent, Llanrwst who died 9 July 1774 aged sixty-seven. His mother was Lettice Foulkes of the 'Eagles' Llanrwst who died 22 January 1790 aged seventy-nine. On 25 February 1785, when he was forty-one years of age Richard Roberts married twenty-five year old Margaret Pritchard of Llanefydd.

Richard Roberts was a farmer and a miller who owned his own farm, Tŷ Ucha, and the mill at Melin-y-coed near Llanrwst. He supported the non-conformists and was one of the two deacons serving the Methodist denomination at their meeting house in a weaver's workshop in the upper part of the town of Llanrwst in 1770. The first Sunday School was held in 1793 in a barn belonging to Richard Roberts, and four years later his name appeared in an appeal addressed to the Bishop of St Asaph for a licence to conduct religious services at Melin-y-coed.

> To the Right Revd. Father in God Lewis Lord Bishop of Saint Asaph – We whose names are hereunto signed being Protestant Dissenters of the Church of England do hereby certify to your Lordship that there is a Dwelling House and the adjoining Yard situate lying and being in the Parish of Llanrwst and County of Denbigh and diocese of St Asaph, called and known by the name of Melyn y Coed intended to be a place of Divine Worship to Almighty God and consecrated to the service of Almighty God and which we request your Lordship will cause to be duly registered in the Registry of St Asaph and a copy thereof delivered to us according to the Act of Toleration in that case made and provided as witness our hands this 24th day of April in the year of our Lord one thousand seven hundred and ninety seven – signed by us Richard Roberts, John Richard, John Hughes, Hugh Jones.

At the bottom of the document are the following words:

Entréd of Record the twenty fourth day of April 1797 in the Publick Episcopal Registry of Saint Asaph. – John Jones (Dep. Regr.) (Williams, W., 1917: 118).

Richard Roberts was described as being a man of short build, with a slow, careful and deliberate nature. When called upon to address the congregation, this being one of the duties of the head deacon, he would deliver his address slowly, deliberately, and would continue for fifteen or twenty minutes. An incident later in his life caused him to leave the Methodists and join the Independent denomination. During a dry summer, when the streams of the parish were all but dried up, an unexpected downpour happened one Sunday. Richard Roberts took advantage of the swollen stream to work his mill and was subsequently called before the small brotherhood of the chapel to answer to the serious charge made against him of breaking the Sabbath. He argued his case, stating that the prevailing circumstances justified his actions, but the church disagreed. He remained with the Independent Church for the rest of his life, passing away quietly and suddenly at the end of August 1817 while eating his lunch. He was seventy-three years of age and he lies buried close to the porch of the parish church at Llanrwst. His wife was buried in 1834 aged seventy-four. Richard Roberts' son David Roberts, a surgeon, is also named in the Preface of the *Faunula Grustensis*. He died 9 May 1815 aged twenty-six and lies buried in the same grave as 'David Roberts Mercht. And Harp Maker Who died at Liverpool June 23 1779 Aged 48 years' (Jones, T. L., 1916: 216); the latter named was a brother of Richards Roberts.

Early in the 19th century David Thomas Jones, a doctor living at Hafod yr Esgob, Mynydd Llanllyfni in the Nantlle Valley, translated the *Herbal* of Nicholas Culpeper into Welsh, and also included some of his own remedies. This volume is known locally as '*Llyfr yr hen Ddoctor Mynydd*' (the book of the old Mountain Doctor), which ran into several editions. His son, who had the same name, was also a well known herbalist and physician. Their medications, especially those related to children's ailments, were said to be well known not only throughout north Wales, but also in parts of Europe and America. The plants used, being gathered from the surrounding countryside, were transplanted with other herbs into their garden at Hafod yr Esgob. Among the tales of the district is one which tells of how a tramp during the early years of the 20th century, passed through the village of Nebo and paused to gather a cluster of leaves from the roadside close to Hafod yr Esgob. One of the villagers, on enquiring what he wanted the leaves for, was told that a concoction made from those particular leaves was the best cure for a sore throat. The plant in question was believed to have been originally planted by the Mountain Doctor in his garden (Roberts, J.D., 1985: 38-39).

High on the south western slope of Garnedd Goch above Llyn Cwm Dulyn is a spring which, according to local tradition, was frequently used by the 'old Mountain Doctor'. It was called *'Ffynnon Doctor'*, or *'Ffynnon Dŵr Oer'* (The doctor's spring or the cold water spring) and those patients who suffered from rheumatism were taken to the spring and treated with the cold water which was considered beneficial to this and other ailments of the body. These days the site of the old spring often becomes overgrown with mosses and other plants but a few local people usually remove these so that the stones which were placed to support the banks are kept visible. The grave of the two doctors stands in the farthest corner of the Scotch Baptist cemetery in the village of Llanllyfni and is marked with the following inscription on one side:

David Thomas Jones of Hafod yr Esgob
died July 13 1839 aged 60 years
Also Elizabeth, his wife
Died June 14 1849 aged 68 years

And on the opposite side:

David Thomas Jones,
Died May 18 1888 aged 64

Well known throughout North Wales as an eminent Herbalist and Physician.

The Searches of Bowman and Wilson

The New Botanist's Guide to the localities of the rarer plants of Britain by
Hewett Cottrell Watson (1804-1881) (Watson, 1835) followed the same
pattern as the first published *Botanist's Guide* of Turner and Dillwyn
(1805). Both works listed British plants on a county by county basis, and
Watson's first book *Outlines of the geographical distribution of British plants*
(1832) contained the embryonic idea for this method which later
developed into the vice-county system which is used today.

Turner and Dillwyn's records for north-west Wales owed a great deal
to those supplied by the two eminent Welsh botanists John Wynne
Griffith of Garn and Reverend Hugh Davies. The later work of Watson
however, as far as Snowdonia was concerned, relied on records published
by Turner and Dillwyn and records only available to him from the
manuscripts of Nathaniel J. Winch (1768-1838) and J.E. Bowman (1785-
1841) as he explains:

> On this account, I regret not having the means of giving a complete list
> of the rarer plants within it. Such are very little known to me from
> actual observation, not withstanding that the county has been thrice
> visited, but unluckily at very unfit periods for mountain botany. The
> lists for the adjacent counties of Anglesea and Denbigh, being pretty
> complete, will show what may be expected in the present county, and
> doubtless most of the rarest species will be named in our list. Indeed,
> I have usually found it more difficult to get the stations for plants only
> moderately scarce or of partial occurrence, than for those of decided
> rarity. The stations copied from the *Magazine of Natural History* are
> there on the authority of N. J. Winch, Esq., almost all the species
> having been gathered by himself in the places named. The *Botanist's
> Guide* has many localities for Caernarvonshire. The *British Flora* and
> *English Flora* add somewhat to them. And several more will be inserted
> on MS authority (Watson, 1835: 235-236).

John Eddowes Bowman was born on 30 October 1785 at Nantwich,
Cheshire, and following his education at the grammar school he left to
work in his father's tobacconist's business becoming manager of the
manufacturing department, and traveller. He lost his wealth in 1816 after
the failure of a banking business which he had joined as a junior partner
in 1813. His fortunes soon took a turn for the better, however, and he
became manager of the Welshpool branch of the bank of Beck and
Company of Shrewsbury. In 1824 he moved to Wrexham to manage

another bank and retired from business in 1830. He lived in Manchester from 1837 onwards, interesting himself in several different branches of science and was one of the founders of the Manchester Geological Society, and a fellow of both the Linnean and Geological Societies. His more important discoveries were in relation to the lower plants, chiefly mosses and fungi. Like William Wilson of Warrington, he was a frequent visitor to north Wales staying at the home of John Roberts (mentioned earlier), who accompanied him on many of his botanical rambles.

William Wilson (1799-1871) was a native of Warrington and the second son of Thomas Wilson, a local chemist. He attended Prestbury Grammar School and completed his education at the Dissenters' Academy in Leaf Square, Manchester. He entered the legal profession being articled as a pupil to Messrs Barratt and Wilson, solicitors at Manchester. Over-commitment to his studies led to a deterioration in his health, and in a bid to combat his illness he found it necessary to take holidays and undertake long journeys. William Wilson had a keen interest in natural history from an early age and while on these lonely rambles he began to study botany. During 1824 and 1825 his mother offered him a sum of money, the interest of which would enable him to pursue his adopted studies and resign his position with the Manchester firm of solicitors. At first he hesitated to give way, but his precarious state of health eventually persuaded him.

In 1826 Sir James Edward Smith (1759-1828) was so impressed with a parcel of plants, together with notes on the various species, that Wilson had sent him that he immediately invited him to become one of his correspondents. Smith, the country's leading botanist at the time, replied to Wilson in a letter dated 10 May of that year; this letter convinced Wilson to adopt botany not only for relaxation, but also as his life's work. 'More letters to answer', wrote Smith as he penned his thoughts upon receiving Wilson's parcel:

> The more I write the more I receive! I had not for some moments courage to open it. But when I did, how was my tone changed! Instead of idle questions, I found an assemblage of varieties and novelties and such kind offers as made me put everything else aside and resign myself to that pure pleasure which is botany . . . has so often afforded me. Be pleased, therefore, Sir, to accept in the first place my grateful thanks for your liberality and kindness to an entire stranger, but (I hope) to one who will not prove unworthy . . . Any important corrections or remarks cannot but be welcome from your pen (Cash, 1873: 153-154).

So wrote the foremost botanical authority in the land: they were words that were to encourage the modest young Wilson to pursue his favourite science to the utmost of his capabilities.

Two more distinguished botanists joined the ranks of Wilson's ever increasing band of correspondents. Sir William Jackson Hooker (1785-1865), then Professor of Botany at Glasgow, asked for Wilson's expertise in preparation for a forthcoming issue of the *Flora Londinensis*, and on 17 April 1827 introductions were made through Professor John Stevens Henslow of Cambridge, who had been acquainted with the young botanist since May 1826. A letter from Hooker to Wilson dated 16 May 1827 recommends the study of mosses as a field in need of attention; Hooker also acknowledges Wilson's valuable help and gave him an invitation to join his class on a five day botanical excursion among the Breadalbane Hills, which he accepted. Wilson prolonged his stay in the vicinity of Killin until mid September (Cash, 1873: 154). Hooker wrote to Wilson's mother on 18 September 1827 following the botanical excursion, assuring her of her son's improving health, and adding that he had sailed from Glasgow to the Isle of Man; the letter continues:

> He was so agreeable an inmate of our house that I assure you both myself and all my family are looking forward to his paying us some future visit with great pleasure. There are few persons in whom I have felt so much interest upon so short an acquaintance (Cash, 1873: 155).

Thus began the friendship and collaboration between Hooker and Wilson which lasted for the rest of their lives. Liverpool solicitor and bryologist Thomas Palgrave (1804-1891), a cousin of W.J. Hooker and another correspondent of Wilson, expressed a desire to have a field excursion with him saying:

> . . . I hope you will be free for a ramble and that I may meet you in Liverpool or elsewhere by chance, in like manner as I did my cousin Sir W. Hooker in April last year, when at 70 years of age he walked over Snowdon and through part of North Wales as well as myself 20 years his junior (LMA Palgrave to Wilson 28 July, 1856).

Wilson then spent two years in Ireland, making some of his most important discoveries. In 1830 Charles Edward Sowerby (1795-1842) and his brother James De Carle Sowerby (1787-1871) were engaged in the publication of the *Supplement to English Botany* (1831-1840); for that work Wilson illustrated and described various plants newly discovered in Britain. He gathered specimens of the rare fern oblong woodsia *(Woodsia ilvensis)* from the Devil's Kitchen above Cwm Idwal, furnishing fronds for the illustrator to copy. He also provided a specimen of Wilson's filmy-fern

(Hymenophyllum wlsonii) appending the following note after the usual descriptive comments. It should be remembered that prior to this period the British filmy-fern *(Hymenophyllum)* was considered to be only one species, *H. tunbrigense*:

> So very different in aspect is this truly distinct species from the far more elegant *H. tunbridgense* that no one who has had the good fortune to see them luxuriantly growing in company in the rocky woods that border the wild and sequestered upper lake of Killarney would hesitate to pronounce them two species. It was there that in the summer of 1829 I became first acquainted with the true *Hymenophyllum tunbridgense*, and had at once the gratification of clearing up my doubts concerning the spurious kind, with which as the common *Hymenophyllum* of North Wales, Cumberland and Perthshire, I had long been imperfectly familiar, and also of unexpectedly adding another fern to the British Flora (Cash, 1887: 181).

William Wilson's *magnum opus* appeared in 1855. *Bryologia Britannica* contained descriptions of all the known mosses of Britain and Ireland systematically arranged according to the method of Brüch and Schimper; it was a much enlarged third edition of Hooker and Taylor's standard work called *Muscologia Britannica*, including many additions and alterations. Editions with coloured illustrations were offered at 4 guineas per copy and those with black and white illustrations at 2 guineas. Professor Wilhelm Schimper of Strasbourg, although himself an eminent bryologist, was an admirer of Wilson, and during a visit to Warrington Schimper is said to have been astonished at seeing Wilson sketching with one hand while dissecting a plant with the other (Cash, 1873; 145). Schimper wrote an interesting letter to Wilson in French dated 12 November 1870 describing his experiences during the siege of Strasbourg which reveals Wilson's plans to publish a second edition of *Bryologia Britannica* and wishing him well with it. The following is a translated portion of that letter as published in James Cash's *Where there's a will there's a way*:

> I thank you much for your kind letter, in which you have kindly wished to express your sympathy with us in the sad circumstances which overwhelm us. You will understand how in the midst of the great misfortunes which have overtaken my country my mind is indisposed for scientific researches. During my absence, when the Prussians began to bombard the town, my friends had my library and my collections carried into the cellars. These now find themselves once

more in their old place, but in great disorder, nor do I know when I shall be able to find time or sufficient quietness of mind to set them to rights. I have had to give up my study to the soldiers, and it will be out of the question to attempt even the smallest microscopical work. I had hoped to finish my great work on vegetable palæontology by the end of this year, and get back to my dear mosses at the beginning of the next; but now all that is interrupted. It is a great pity that you cannot get an assistant for your second edition of 'Bryologia'. It will be a most unfortunate thing for science if the large quantity of material you have collected should be lost, but I hope that your health may be sufficiently restored to enable you to bring your second edition to a successful and happy termination (Cash, 1873: 146).

Earlier in his career Wilson had assisted Hooker as he prepared his *British Flora* (1830) and this help is frequently acknowledged by remarks such as: 'I am glad to have Mr Wilson's authority for this', and 'I am supported in this view by Mr Wilson'.

J. E. Bowman introduced himself to William Wilson by letter in May 1830 stating that he had of late added the study of mosses to his long-standing interest in vascular plants (flowering plants and ferns). Wilson's name had long been known to Bowman and when he was in Glasgow the year before he said that Hooker spoke of Wilson in glowing terms which induced him to write the letter of introduction. A letter dated 26 March 1831 from Bowman to Wilson reads:

I first began to dabble in botany in 1807. For the first ten years I knew only a few common plants, and I did not preserve a single specimen; and for twenty years it was not my fortune to come into personal contact with any one who could be called a botanist, or to whom I could apply for a solution of my difficulties or the correction of my errors (Cash, 1887: 188).

In his first letter Bowman mentions his intention of spending a week botanizing among the Snowdonian hills, adding that nothing would give him more pleasure than to have Wilson accompanying him. Wilson reciprocated these feelings and with his reply sent specimens of a rare moss he had gathered in Ireland. Bowman's reply is lengthy and in anticipation of Wilson being able to accompany him in Snowdonia writes:

I am happy to find that there is some prospect of your being able to accompany me on my projected Snowdonian ramble. From your extensive knowledge of Snowdonia I will leave you to fix the plan for that ramble, promising that my friend Salwey, of Oswestry (a learned lichenist), recommends me to examine some excellent old woods near Bettws-y-coed, where he has found some rare lichens, and to go from thence to Capel Curig. It may also be well to state, as we are not yet personally known to each other, that on these occasions I always regard conveniences and accommodation as of secondary importance, and prefer an inferior inn near a good station to a better at some distance, to save time and labour in walking to and fro. I believe I shall not be limited to time on the journey, and conceive the coaches between Holyhead and Shrewsbury will afford us all the helps we want between our pedestrian rambles (Cash, 1887: 186).

There follows a long discussion on plant taxonomy (or naming system), habitats and various potential areas for plant hunting. Bowman, despite being the elder of the two men, was at all times modest; cautious not to overstate his experiences or capabilities, he always regarded Wilson as being the master. 'Nor have I been entirely unsuccessful in the way of discovery during my short career' he writes, 'though I cannot boast, with you, of having added a new phanerogamous plant to our native flora, and, that to the confusion of Welsh botanists, upon our own hills too' (Cash, 1887: 187). Bowman evidently considered himself a 'Welsh botanist'.

Both Wilson and Bowman were regular visitors to north Wales either independently, together or as guests of Dr John Roberts at Bangor. In a letter to Hooker sent from Bangor in May, 1828, Wilson regrets having only made 'short excursions in the neighbourhood' due to the 'general badness of the weather' and proceeds to write a lengthy note on botanical matters, noting that sadly he had 'not yet penetrated far into the mountainous regions' (RBGK Director's Correspondence vol.1, letter 281).

Wilson was at Bangor again in July of that year stating that Nathaniel J. Winch, whom he had guided to the stations of some of the neighbourhood's more interesting plants, had left for home on 11 June. Wilson's letter to W. J. Hooker dated 23 July 1828 (RBGK Director's Correspondence vol. 1, letter 282) continues:

Long before your highly welcome letter reached me Mr Winch had taken his departure, & I was unable, during the very short stay that he made to do more than conduct him to some of the stations of the rarer plants which I had already gathered, and we had not time to explore the mountains in making any new discoveries nor did we even visit Snowdon so that what we did amounts to very little . . .

A very interesting passage about his recent botanical observations then follows:

> *Jungermannia Hutchinsiae* (barren) is plentiful in one station near Llanberis, & lately found *J. Lyellii* with anthers, pistilla, & calyces in Anglesea near Aberffraw not far from the sea side on a wet sandy common growing in clustered patches, male & female separate . . . *J. compressa* with anthers, & sparingly with capsules,upon Snowdon . . . *Gymnostomum Griffithianum [Oedipodium griffithianum]* is in notable plenty upon Snowdon near the summit . . . I have observed *Hookeria lucens* very near the summit of one of the peaks of Snowdon at an elevation of not less than 3000 feet. *Anthericum serotinum* [Snowdon lily; *(Lloydia serotina)*] has not flowered well this summer, & the wet weather hindered me from gathering above two or three specimens in a fit state . . .

Wilson then proceeds to discuss the many-stalked spike-rush *(Eleocharis multicaulis)* and supports Hugh Davies' description of the plant [*Scirpus multicaulis*] in *Welsh Botanology* (Davies, 1813: 6):

> 'Of *Eleocharis multicaulis* I have secured some good characteristic specimens which will I trust, leave the question no longer doubtful. It is most surprising to me that Wahlenberg should deny the presence of a creeping root in *E. pa.* [*E. palustris*] I shall send you specimens of both . . . Old Hugh Davies has well distinguished them in *Welsh Botanology E. multicaulis* having constantly six bristles at the base of the germen & *E. palustris* as constantly 4 only . . .

Wilson however disagreed with Davies concerning the recording of the field pepperwort *(Lepidium campestre)* in *Welsh Botanology (Thlaspi campestre*, Davies, 1813: 62) 'It is very little to the credit of Davies or myself as diligent botanists, that *Lepidium hirtum* should have been so long overlooked in Anglesea – it was only early in June last that I observed it for the first time. I believe it is the only *Lepidium* growing wild in Anglesea. Having never been able to find *L. campestre*, for which Davies has probably mistaken *L. hirtum* . . . *L. campestre* is very rare also in Caernarvonshire while *hirtum* is quite abundant in both counties'. In his *Flora of Anglesey and Carnarvonshire* J.E. Griffith has this to say on the matter: 'Mr William Wilson (in his MSS notes on Davies' Welsh Botanology which I now possess) remarks about this plant as follows: "must be very rare in Anglesey and probably mistaken by Davies for *Lepidium Smithii* which is very common all over Anglesey". I quite agree with Mr Wilson as I have never seen *L. campestre* growing in either of the two counties' (Griffith, [1895]: 15). Modern-day botanists know the plant in question as Smith's pepperwort or Smith's cress (*Lepidium heterophyllum*) and it has been recorded from both Anglesey and Caernarfonshire.

By 1830 Wilson's connections with north Wales had become personal as well as botanical. In a letter to W. J. Hooker written at Aberffraw in Anglesey on 15 September 1830 (RBGK Director's Correspondence vol. 2, letter 196) he begins with an apology for not having replied to a letter:

> due to a very unwelcome occupation which still detains me here & almost bans me from botanical pursuits. A sister in law whose a widow with a small precarious income has removed from Staffordshire to this neighbourhood in expectation of finding a cheap [...] residence with the advantages of sea air and bathing – the goods were prematurely brought over before the house had undergone the necessary alterations & everything has been in confusion.

On 13 August J.E. Bowman arrived and spent a week with Wilson, who was unable, owing to his predicament, to give him much of his time. During his stay Bowman made an important discovery, a new British species of waterwort (*Elatine*). Although not named by Wilson in his letter, this was most probably the eight-stamened waterwort (*Elatine hydropiper*) found at Llyn Coron, north east of Aberffraw. This was included by W.J. Hooker in his *British Flora* published in 1830. The same letter mentions 'the Snowdon sketches' which were drawn by Wilson and despatched to Hooker:

> Pray consider yourself at liberty to make any use you think of the Snowdon sketches, there is one consideration however which I would wish to make & that is whether an unfair use will not be made of them by indolent botanists or rapacious mercenary gardeners . . . I have known tourists to send up their guides for plants, while they remain below, and what they had [. . .] paid for, they would probably boast of as their own genuine acquisitions.

The 'Illustrations of Snowdon – Botanical and Graphical', are preserved at the Archives of the Royal Botanic Gardens, Kew among the correspondence of Sir W. J. Hooker (RBGK Director's Correspondence, vol. 7/102). These sketches, drawn from Treborth near Telford's bridge over the Menai Straits and by the cromlech at Plas Newydd, Anglesey, show an outline of the Snowdonian range of mountains with the names of the various peaks, ridges, lakes and *cymoedd* (corries) and some of the rare plants found there, annotated above.

During the latter half of the 18th and the early 19th century a great interest in botany developed among the working classes of Lancashire, Yorkshire and Cheshire.

One of these self taught botanists, bryologist John Nowell (1802-1867) a handloom weaver from Todmorden, Yorkshire, became a regular correspondent of William Wilson. So many people took up this interest that clubs were formed, with meetings held to exhibit plant specimens, and field excursions arranged. John Nowell's visits to north Wales are mentioned in his letters to Wilson, dated 29 July 1852 and 6 July 1853, now kept at the Natural History Museum, London. In the 1853 letter Nowell mentions travelling with a party by cheap train to Bangor and then on to Llanberis during Whitsun. Cheap railway excursions and day-return tickets provided the working-class naturalist with a wider scope for travel and Nowell made good use of this convenient public transport. He spent two days on Snowdon naming 'Crib y Ddesgil on the range of moist rocks right above the small Lake called Fynon Frech' where he found the rare moss *Hypnum hamulosum*, the record of which appears with the name of the discoverer cited in Wilson's *Bryologia Britannica* (Wilson, 1855: 397). A more recent record of this moss from Cwmglas Mawr on Snowdon, which might be where Nowell found it, was published in the *Journal of Bryology* (Hill, 1988: 488). In 1865 Nowell again travelled to north Wales, this time with J.B. Wood and Wilhelm Schimper, and he may well have visited on other occasions collecting for others. He is known to have allowed botanists like J.B. Wood to pay his travelling expenses.

The notebook of William Wilson, together with his Herbarium is kept at the Natural History Museum. A note on the cover of the notebook written when it was acquired in 1903 reads: 'This book is of value as affording a legible transcript of names of localities which are not clearly written on labels in the Herbm.' The mountain plants listed include:

Interrupted clubmoss *(Lycopodium annotinum)* from Glyder
Dwarf juniper *(Juniperis communis* subsp. *alpina)* from Glyder
Black alpine-sedge *(Carex atrata)* from Twll Du
Holly fern *(Polystichum lonchitis)* from Cwm Idwal
Forked spleenwort *(Asplenium septentrionale)* near Twll Du
Oblong woodsia *(Woodsia ilvensis)* near Llyn y Cŵn
Wilson's filmy-fern *(Hymenophyllum wilsonii)* near Llanberis
Alpine saxifrage *(Saxifraga nivalis)*, Mossy saxifrage *(Saxifraga hypnoides)*
Cerastium latifolium from Snowdon.

The latter named plant could be either *C. alpinum* or *C. arcticum* as Wilson does not specify the exact spot from which the plant was gathered. Both species have in the past been recorded from Snowdon. J.E. Griffith notes the following regarding the arctic mouse-ear *(Cerastium arcticum)*: 'I always took this to be *C. latifolium* Sm., till Rev. A. Ley, had it determined, through Mr. A. Bennett, by Dr. Lange. See J.[ournal] of B.[otany], p. 373, 1887' (Griffith, J.E., [1895]: 23).

Lesser meadow-rue *(Thalictrum minus)* Snowdon
Spring sandwort *(Minuartia verna)* Cwm Idwal
Alpine penny-cress *(Thlaspi caerulescens)* Gwydir. This plant was most probably shown to Wilson by John Roberts of Bangor whose name is appended to the entry.

The plants of Anglesey and Caernarfonshire, numbered from one to eighty-four, are listed in the notebook on five pages.

In 1836 William Wilson married Mrs Lane, a cousin of his, at St Pancras Church, London, and from then on his botanical excursions became curtailed as the modest private income, which had served him so adequately during his bachelor days, was now needed to support a family. He died on 3 April 1871 at Paddington, about two miles from Warrington.

Babington's Journal

Another eminent botanist who found himself drawn to Snowdonia and visited the district regularly throughout his long life was Charles Cardale Babington (1808-1895). He was born in Ludlow, Shropshire on 23 November 1808, the son of Reverend Joseph Babington (1768-1826), physician and rector, who studied plants; he contributed to J. Plumley's *General View of Agriculture of Shropshire* (1803), and Sowerby and Smith's *English Botany* (1790-1814). Charles Babington took his BA degree at Cambridge in January 1830 and in July of the same year embarked on his first 'Welsh Tour'. He travelled by coach entering Wales from Shrewsbury and continued along the Holyhead road through Betws-y-coed to Bangor, accompanied by three friends, Mallet, Hockin and Fleming. The next day, 7 July, the party walked a distance of ten and a half miles from their lodgings to Caernarfon, arriving at the Uxbridge Arms (now called Gwesty'r Celt / Celtic Royal Hotel) wet through, having walked the last seven miles in continuous rain.

Having found lodgings in Caernarfon, they spent a few days botanizing in the neighbourhood of the town and on 11 July, it being a Sunday, they attended service at St Mary's Church which Babington says 'is a neat one, having one of its sides formed part of the town wall, and its tower being a round stunted one belonging originally to the same'(Babington, 1897: 5). On the 12th he recorded opium poppy *(Papaver somniferum)*, rosebay willowherb *(Chamerion angustifolium)* and sweet violet *(Viola odorata)* 'with blue flowers, in a corn field near the town, but on the other side of the river, where there are no houses, or I should have thought them cultivated' (Babington, 1897: 6). The following day he and his colleagues travelled to the vale of Llanberis with the intention of finding their way to the mountains. There is no mention of a guide being sought; the weather being favourable they attempted to find their own way but soon ran into difficulties:

> by taking what we supposed to be a short cut, arrived at the river having only a foot bridge over it, with a gate in the middle well guarded with spikes. The bridge was formed of two planks parallel to each other, and bent into an elliptical arch by being fastened tight to the rock on each side without any support in the middle. Being stopped by this, we had to return nearly three quarters of a mile, and then continued the road we were in before. After having crossed the river by a stone bridge further up, we were foolish enough to take another short cut which appeared to lead to the mountains, which we

followed for about two miles, and then stopped to examine a bog in which we found nothing worth having, and then turned back, not having time to go farther (Babington, 1897: 6).

Only two plants are recorded for the day, annual knawel *(Sceleranthus annuus)* and lady's-mantle *(Alchemilla vulgaris)*.

During the days which followed the weather took a turn for the worse, the wind rose and they only ventured outside to collect a few plants and insects from localities close by. There are no entries in the journal from the 19th to the 31st of July. On the 31st with his friend Mallet, Babington again travelled to Llanberis; taking a boat from Pen-llyn at the lower end of Llyn Padarn and disembarking at a point close to Pont y bala. They then walked up to Nant Peris village, which Babington refers to in his journal as Llanberis: 'the road to which is only passable for horses; it passes under the enormous precipices of Snowdon, near a copper mine'. They stayed the night at the Dolbadarn Inn, with a view to ascending Snowdon on the following day, but the weather changed for the worse forcing them to change their plans.

Babington and his colleague went up Moel Eilio on 13 August, the view from the summit being considered adequate recompense for the uninteresting climbing; the 15th saw the two on the summit of Mynydd Mawr; he had found his first mountain saxifrage, the starry saxifrage *(Saxifraga stellaris)* whilst climbing the mountain. Also recorded were parsley fern *(Cryptogramma crispa)* and autumnal water-starwort *(Callitriche hermaphroditica)* the latter seen 'in great plenty in the river which runs out of Llyn Cwellyn'(Babington, 1897: 7). Babington returned to Mynydd Mawr on the 29th to look for insects 'but found no land ones, and only some water ones; got quite wet through by a storm on the top of the mountain'.

On 31 August Babington ascended Snowdon for the first time, taking no guide. The entry in the journal records no difficulties: 'Obtained a large number of plants in the rocks near the mouth of the copper mine', he stated, but he failed to give any indication as to the location he visited, which could be either the Clogwyn Coch mine near Clogwyn Du'r Arddu or the Snowdon mine near Llyn Glaslyn. Both these sites were much frequented by botanists during their visits to Snowdon. Babington claimed to have taken a thirty-two mile walk on 1 September. On the preceding day he had walked up Snowdon and returned to the Dolbadarn Inn where he spent the night:

Started at a quarter past eight in the morning, and after ascending part of Glydr-y-Vawr, passed through Llanberis Pass, at the head of which

159

I ascended another mountain on the left [probably Moel Berfedd]. Descended into Nant Gwynant, which I followed to Beddgelert, where I dined, and afterwards walked back to Carnarvon. Whilst my dinner was cooking, I walked to Pont Aberglasllyn, which is about a mile and a half from Beddgelert. Total distance in day about thirty-two miles (Babington,1897: 7).

On 4 September Babington, in the company of Mallet, again walked up Snowdon reaching the summit at 2.00 p.m. In this entry he again refers to 'the face of the precipice in which the copper mine is' as the site from where he gathered plant specimens, and from where 'we ascended to the top, and re-visited both the tops . . .' This suggests that Clogwyn y Garnedd was the precipice in question, but none of the plants found there are noted in the journal. The pair then descended the mountain by following the track known today as the Rhyd-ddu path, but lost all trace of it lower down. After a great deal of trouble the Beddgelert road was reached at a point about three miles outside the village.

Babington's first visit to Snowdonia ended on 11 September; he left Caernarfon on the 10th but did not arrive in Bangor in time for the Shrewsbury coach, and only left at 7.00 a.m. the following morning.

He returned in 1832, leaving Shrewsbury at 6.45 on the morning of 27 June. He notes in his journal the fine view of the Snowdonian range of mountains from the vicinity of the inn at Cernioge near Pentrefoelas. On the 28th he walked from Bangor to view the slate quarries at Dolawen:

the property of Mr Pennant, of Penrhyn Castle. They are now cut into the very heart of the mountain, and employ more than 1600 men. The slates are conveyed by a railroad to Port Penrhyn, near Bangor, from which place they are shipped, twelve shiploads having this year gone from them to America (Babington, 1897: 9).

On the 29th he went to Caernarfon by coach at 9.00 a.m. and began to walk up to Llanberis with a view to seeking accommodation for a few days. This he found at the Vaynol Arms in Nant Peris where the landlord Robert Closs, charged a shilling (5p) for a bed and a shilling for a meal. On the following day Babington, in the company of two other botanists he names as Holmes and Leighton, walked part of the way up Snowdon, finding mossy saxifrage *(Saxifraga hypnoides)*, roseroot *(Sedum rosea)*, parsley fern *(Cryptogramma crispa)* and marsh violet *(Viola palustris)*. His two colleagues during this trip were, most likely, Reverend Edward Adolphus Holmes (?-1886) and Reverend William Allport Leighton (1805-1889). After dinner on the same day they 'walked a short distance up the Llanberis Pass, or Cwmglas, as it is called in Welsh.' Leighton was the author of the *Lichen Flora of Great Britain, Ireland and the Channel Islands* (1871), with another edition published in 1879. His personal records number around 287, observed not only from the old classic botanical sites such as Snowdon, Cwm Idwal and the Glyder mountains, but from places further afield in the country such as Nefyn, Pwllheli, Cricieth, Conwy, Gwydir Woods, and Moel y Gest near Porthmadog. Holmes, the other botanist named, was rector at South Elsham, Suffolk from 1833 until his death on 3 June 1886.

On 2 July Babington again visited Snowdon, this time ascending the ridge of hills which rise steeply behind Nant Peris Church. The precise line of path is not stated. Having gained the crest of the ridge he turned left and followed the Pony track towards the summit. Ascending the steep bank called Llechwedd y Re he soon arrived at the spring near Bwlch Glas where 'the horses of those who ride are left'. In the entry for that day (Babington,1897:10) he named Clogwyn y Garnedd as the precipice from which he gathered such rare plants as alpine saxifrage *(Saxifraga nivalis)*, tufted saxifrage *(Saxifraga cespitosa)*, arctic mouse-ear *(Cerastium arcticum)* and spring sandwort *(Minuartia verna)*. On the 5th he went to Clogwyn Du'r Arddu, finding, among other things, brittle bladder-fern *(Cystopteris fragilis)*, green spleenwort *(Asplenium viride)*, alpine meadow-rue *(Thalictrum alpinum)* spring sandwort *(Minuartia verna)*, globeflower *(Trollius europaeus)*, northern rock-cress *(Arabis petraea)* and tufted saxifrage *(Saxifraga cespitosa)*.

Babington's excursion to the Glyder from Nant Peris on 10 July is worth noting as it describes a route to Llyn y Cŵn which was probably in use from the earliest times. 'We went by direction up the stream opposite the inn until we came to the place where two streams and an empty channel meet, then turned to the right up the mountain, and on our arrival at the top kept rather to the left between the one which we ascended and the next (i.e. due east), and soon arrived at Llyn y Cwm' [cŵn]. He then followed the stream from the lake to the top of the Devil's Kitchen chasm:

> We tried hard to find a place at which it would be possible to descend to the bottom of the fissure where it opens in the face of the precipice called Castell y Geifr over Llyn Idwal. After some time we found on the south side a way down a ledge of rocks (near the top of which I found *Gnaphalium dioicum* [mountain everlasting *(Antennaria dioica)*] which led us to the lower opening of the fissure. We then went along a narrow ledge on the other side of the stream, which, after leading us for some way along the face of the precipice and under a sort of showerbath, took us with some exertion to the top of the rocks

(Babington, 1897: 11).

Having arrived back on the plateau close to Llyn y Cŵn, Babington then decided to climb Glyder Fawr, and coming to at an 'eminence' he calls 'Carnedd y Gwynt' he found the wind so strong that he could hardly stand against it. He says that the summit area was 'covered with loose stones almost like the seaside' (Babington, 1897: 12). He then returned to Nant Peris by the same route that he had used for the ascent.

On 12 July after a period of heavy rain, Babington found the waterfall of Ceunant Mawr, Llanberis, in spate; he then spent the remainder of the day botanizing at the lower end of Llyn Padarn where he found pillwort *(Pilularia globulifera)*, water lobelia *(Lobelia dortmanna)* and white water-lily *(Nymphaea alba)*. On the following day he took the Capel Curig coach to Swallow Falls and near there he found Wilson's filmy-fern *(Hymenophyllum wilsonii)* and oak fern *(Gymnocarpium dryopteris)*. About a mile on the Capel Curig side of Pen-y-gwryd, he notes having found ivy-leaved bellflower *(Wahlenbergia hederacea)* in plenty. The following day Babington was again on Snowdon and counted twenty-nine lakes he had seen from the summit. Descending to Clogwyn y Garnedd to botanize, he noted the much sought after holly fern *(Polystichum lonchitis)* in his journal for the first time.

Another important discovery is noted in the journal for 16 July 1832 when Babington visited the Llyn y Cŵn area and continued on to the summit of Glyder Fawr. On the way back his friend Holmes found small quantities of the interrupted clubmoss *(Lycopodium annotinum)*. This rare clubmoss was first found on Glyder Fawr above Llyn y Cŵn by Edward Lhuyd during one of his visits to Snowdonia in the late 17th century (Camden, 1695: 701). William Wilson of Warrington noted it in his 'Illustrations of Snowdon – Botanical and Graphical' naming Glyder Fawr as the locality (RBGK, Director's Correspondence vol. 7/102). This could be the last record of the plant from this locality. *Lycopodium annotinum* is also noted from the same locality by Newman (1854: 110) and Humphreys ([1850]: 26). By the last decade of the 19th century local botanist J.E. Griffith admits to having failed to find the plant: 'I am afraid this is extinct in Carnarvonshire. It used to grow on the Glyders, but I have failed to find it for years now' (Griffith: [1895]:171).

A search in the Llanberis area resulted in their finding Wilson's filmy-fern *(Hymenophyllum wilsonii)* on the 17th and the following day Babington in the company of Holmes walked over the Llanberis Pass as far as Pen-y-gwryd; on returning they found the forked spleenwort *(Asplenium septentrionale)* in small quantities on rocks at the lower end of the pass. On the 19th Babington again climbed Snowdon, this time by an obscure route which led from behind the church at Nant Peris and on gaining the ridge descended a short distance joining the Pony track from Llanberis and followed it to Llechwedd y Re from where he descended into Cwmglas Mawr: 'We then ascended a precipice near to Crib Goch and found, after we had gone some way, that we could not return, so we were obliged to go to the top of it' (Babington, 1897: 13). The two plants noted in the journal from the day's excursion were alpine bistort *(Persicaria vivipara)* and hoary whitlowgrass *(Draba incana)*; both plants are rare, but still extant in this area. 'The place to which we came on the top of the precipice was a grassy ridge between Crib Goch and Crib-y-Distill. For some time we could not find a way from it, but at last after some hard climbing, we attained the summit of the mountain and returned home' The plant-collector's vascula (collecting flasks) must have contained considerably more specimens that day than the two above named plants, judging from the entry in the journal for the 20th: 'Did not start on account of the number of plants wanting to be looked over'. Having completed this task the botanists spent the remaining hours of the 20th gathering wetland plants from the area surrounding the shores of Llyn Padarn, Llanberis. The collecting continued on the 21st:

> Started early and went up Snowdon to examine another part of Clogwyn y Garnedd . . . We then set to work at Clogwyn y Garnedd, and I found one specimen of *Carex atrata* [black alpine sedge] and Holmes one of *Epilobium alsinifolium* [chickweed willowherb]. We found about thirty specimens of *Saxifraga nivalis* [alpine saxifrage] in Clogwyn y Garnedd, and one a short distance up the first ascent behind the church at Llanberis (Babington, 1897: 13).

The remaining days of Babington's second (1832) tour of north Wales were spent in the Dolgellau district and in exploring Cadair Idris:

> July 23. Started to walk to Dolgelly to see Cader Idris. Went by the Capel Curig coach as far as the top of the pass, and met with Mr D. Williams, agent to Sir R. Bulkeley . . . He put us into a track over the mountains to Festiniog, but the track not being at all well marked we nearly lost our way, and had it not been for the map and my compass seal, we must have turned back, but with the assistance of these we at length found our way to that part of the vale near Llyn Cwmorthin. The road, or rather way, for path there is none, was very wild and dreary, but the prospects from some parts very fine and extensive. Not knowing in what part of the vale Festiniog was situated we passed it, and walked two-and-a-half miles to Maentwrog. This was a very hard day's work (Babington, 1897: 13-14).

The remainder of the journey was completed on the 24th by following the road from Maentwrog to Trawsfynydd and on through Llanelltyd to Dolgellau. The following morning Babington employed the services of W.R. Pugh, a well-known guide, and climbed Cadair Idris. They crossed Mynydd Moel and Bwlch Coch before descending to the road and making their way to Dinas Mawddwy, arriving there in the evening. The only plant recorded during the ascent of Cadair Idris was 'a very hairy corolla'd *Festuca*' (fescue). They left Dinas Mawddwy on the 26th and followed the course of the river Dyfi to Llanymawddwy, crossed the 'very lofty pass of Bwlch-y-Groes from the top of which the prospect was most extensive'. They later arrived at Bala and stayed overnight at the Lion, 'a most excellent inn'. From Bala they walked to Ffestiniog along the 'old road' a distance of over nineteen miles continuing from there to Maentwrog where they stopped for the night. On the 28th they were on the road to Beddgelert before 6.30 a.m. and breakfasted there on arrival. Soon afterwards they struck the road again walking through Nantgwynant to Pen-y-gwryd and over into Llanberis, a total distance of twenty-two miles according to Babington. The 1832 tour came to an end on 3 August when the journal records: 'Started for Shrewsbury'. By the end of his second botanical tour of Snowdonia, Babington had a good knowledge of the plant localities of Snowdon and Glyder as well as those on Anglesey. There is no mention in the journal of a local guide being taken on any of these early excursions, apart from Pugh who led him to Cadair Idris. It must therefore be assumed that Babington, in the company of a few friends, explored the cliffs and *cymoedd* of Eryri with the aid of map and compass but without any local help.

At a later date in his journal, and also among other correspondence there is, however, evidence to suggest that Babington had at different times acquired the services of three local men to act as guides on various mountain excursions. They were John Roberts, William Williams and Hugh Lewis, who according to the 1861 census returns lived in houses known collectively as Blaen-y-ddôl in Llanberis. The two first named served as guides for the Royal Victoria Hotel, Llanberis while Hugh Lewis (in whose house William Williams was a lodger) was a quarryman who seems to have acted as guide on a casual basis.

In August, 1862 the distinguished French botanist J. Gay visited Snowdonia, primarily to study the quillwort *(Isoetes)* and Babington recorded in his journal his meeting with Gay at Bangor on the 12th. On the following day Babington, together with Gay and Reverend William Williamson Newbould, went to stay at the Padarn Villa Hotel in Llanberis. They walked around the shores of Llyn Padarn finding quillwort *(Isoetes echinospora)* 'near Ynys, on the left bank'. More specimens of quillwort was found in Llyn y Cŵn on the 15th; Babington records: 'Mr Gay was very much fatigued by his trip to Llyn y Cwm' [cŵn] (Babington, 1897: 199). There are references to John Roberts the guide in Gay's published account of his visit entitled: *Voyage botanique au Caernarvonshire, dans le North Wales fait en Aout 1862 en vue d'une etude particuliere des Isoetes de cette contrée* . . . (Carter, 1956: 47).

Another reference to John Roberts the guide is found in the entry in Babington's journal dated 24 September 1860: 'Busk, his brother Charles, and I went with John Roberts, the guide, to Cwm Glas, by ascending highly on Snowdon, and descending into it. We went as far as the saddle of turf by Crib Goch [Bwlch Coch], and descended into Llanberis pass'. The same John Roberts was also involved in the running of one of the Snowdon summit huts which provided tourists with refreshments. William Williams, the 'Botanical Guide' or 'Will boots' as he was known locally, is not mentioned anywhere in Babington's journal, but there is no doubt that Babington knew Williams and this acquaintance will be dealt with in a later chapter.

In 1835 Babington became acquainted with John Roberts the surgeon and botanist from Bangor mentioned in a previous chapter, and on 29 July of that year the journal records that both men visited the classical botanical site of Clogwyn Du'r Arddu finding the northern rock-cress *(Arabis petraea)* in fine state and on continuing to the summit of Snowdon found a few specimens the rare moss *Oedipodium griffithianum* (Babington, 1897: 42).

On the 30th Babington went to Clogwyn y Garnedd but failed in his quest to find the tiny rare fern alpine woodsia *(Woodsia alpina)*. An interesting entry in the journal dated 11 August 1847 reads: 'By coach to Capel Curig. Met Wollaston at Cerrig y drudion on his return from Wales. Examined the rounded hill opposite to the turn to Capel Curig from the main road to see if we could find *Cotoneaster*, said by Kingsley of Sidney to grow there, but we could find nothing like it except a *Salix*. Do not believe it grows there, as it is not a likely place for it' (Babington, 1897: 141). The Cotoneaster they were looking for was probably *Cotoneaster cambricus* which is only found growing wild in Britain on the Great Orme at Llandudno.

On the morning of the 13th Babington took a carriage from Capel Curig to Nant Peris with the intention of booking in at the Vaynol Arms, but on arriving there he found that the former landlord and his family had gone to America. Moving on, he found what he describes as 'excellent quarters' at the Dolbadarn Inn, Llanberis, which served ideally as a base from which to explore Snowdon. He explored the whole length of the base of Clogwyn Du'r Arddu finding the Snowdon lily *(Lloydia serotina)*; Babington was fortunate to see the plant so late in the season. The Snowdon lily flowers for only a few short weeks between late May and June, after which time only the long slender rush-like leaves remain. He was lucky again on the 18th after climbing from Nant Peris to Llyn y Cŵn, 'in a thick cloud on the mountain we saw Twll Dhû to great advantage both from above and below. I gathered one fruited plant of *Lloydia* a little before reaching the lower opening of Twll Dhû' (Babington, 1897: 141). The journal is full of similar comments which portray the strong determined character of a truly dedicated Victorian plant hunter. Babington remained a regular visitor to Snowdonia all his life; he became Professor of Botany at Cambridge in 1861, and he served as Honorary Secretary of the Ray Club for fifty-five years but he missed no opportunity to see the plants about which he taught in their natural habitats.

Having already published several books, the most popular of which was his *Manual of British Botany* (1843), Babington decided to study the two main problems of the time, the classification of the most difficult groups of plants, the brambles and the hawkweeds (Allen, 1999: 2-11). Most other botanists were very wary of taking up such a task and saw plants of these groups as being so indistinguishable from one another that they had to be grouped together and left at that. Babington however was aware of the constant disagreements which were always present between the aptly named 'splitters' and 'lumpers'. He began to collect both groups but decided to concentrate on the brambles. This was at the time when almost everyone believed that all species were created by the hand of God and remained that way for all time. It was also believed that hybrids in nature seldom occurred, and when they did their sterility exposed them. Babington, being a devout Christian, had not been inclined to accept Darwin's theory of evolution and, admitted to a colleague quite late in his life that: 'I have but little belief in evolution or hybridization, but time will shew' (Allen, 1999: 7). The different kinds of brambles growing in Europe are now thought to be several thousand microspecies and they are still regarded as an extremely complex group. Babington's first work on the brambles entitled *A Synopsis of the British Rubi* was published in 1846, followed by *The British Rubi* in 1869. In between those years he published his *Flora of Cambridgeshire* (1860).

By the time that Babington had settled in his Chair at Cambridge the old botany was gradually being replaced by the new study of plant physiology. He was being regarded by many of his colleagues as old fashioned, belonging to the outdated herbarium forming generation and on one occasion voiced his feelings during a meeting of the Cambridge Ray Club:

> It is rare now to find an Undergraduate or B.A. who knows, or cares to know, one plant from another, or distinguish insects scientifically. I am one of those who consider this to be a sad state of things. I know that much of what is called Botany is admirably taught amongst us; but it is not what is usually known as Botany outside the Universities, and does not lead to a practical knowledge of even the most common plants. It is really Vegetable Physiology, and ought to be so called. It is a very important subject, but does not convey a knowledge of plants (Allen, 1994: 166).

The new generation of botanists resented the space that was taken up by the herbarium and library when it was badly needed for a modern laboratory. Babington's health eventually began to fail, forcing him to cut down on his work load, and he finally became confined to a wheelchair following an attack of pneumonia and a rheumatic condition which prevented his visits to his herbarium. Francis Darwin was appointed as his deputy and Babington's salary was subsequently reduced, but as was the custom his tenure of the Chair could only be terminated by his death which occurred on 22 July 1895.

The Great Victorian Fern Craze

As the 19th century progressed the geographical distribution of plants developed into a major study among British botanists. Hewett Cottrell Watson (1804-1881), mentioned previously, pioneered a system which was based on dividing Britain into areas he called 'vice counties' starting with west Cornwall, vice-county number 1, and ending with the Shetland Isles, vice-county number 112. This enabled the plant distribution system to be conveniently displayed using maps. Of the thirteen Welsh vice-counties Caernarfonshire provided the longest and most interesting list of plants published by Watson in his The *New Botanist's Guide to the Localities of the Rarer Plants of Britain* (Watson, 1835).

Watson's greatest work *Topographical Botany* was first published in two volumes in 1873-1874, with a second edition appearing in 1883, two years after his death. The vice-county system had by this time been perfected and was used for the first time in this work.

Records of Snowdonian plants were frequently published during the 19th century, appearing in the printed works of visiting naturalists, local guide books and in various issues of botanical journals. These botanical records were usually supported by voucher specimens gathered from the habitats in unlimited quantities. An ever increasing number of members of the upper and middle classes adopted this pastime during the 1830s, the forming of a personal and complete *hortus siccus* (dry garden) being their ultimate target of achievement. Another major trend coinciding with this was the great Victorian fern craze. Until this time few field botanists had taken any special interest in ferns; the field offered but a limited challenge to the collectors due to the relatively small number of British species. In order to constitute a wider field of interest the fern enthusiasts began to look for varieties among each separate species and these were either dried and pressed and mounted in their albums, transplanted into their gardens, or displayed in fashionable Wardian cases at home.

The classical regions of Snowdonia, while continuing to attract visiting botanists, now began to experience, in the plant hunters, a new kind of collector. The local people soon began to realize that they could profit from the demand for plant specimens, especially ferns; unlimited supplies of the more common species were always available during the summer months by the wayside. These were gathered by the basketful and sold to visitors as rarities. For supplying genuine specimens of rarities to the specialist collector, however, a different kind of supplier was needed. 'Alpines', such as holly fern *(Polystichum lonchitis)* for instance, could be acquired through the services of the mountain guides; some of the quarrymen were also competent collectors. These men were accustomed to finding their way across the mountains in any weather, and due to their station in life they were always eager for an opportunity to supplement their family income.

An irate John Ralfs (1807-1890), writing from Penzance to William Wilson in 1855, expressed his concern about the over-collecting of the woodsia fern (probably *Woodsia alpina*) from Snowdon and mentions an incident involving a local guide:

A few weeks ago I was much annoyed by a call from a dealer in Fern-roots who brought a letter from a correspondent of mine – Dr Fox of Bristol – I got very angry with him & told that although I should certainly like to have roots of some of the Ferns for cultivation I could not encourage such disgraceful conduct.

The circumstance that particularly angered me was the following – He said that he had been recently to Snowdon & gave the guide there 5/ – [25p] to show him the habitat of the Woodsia – that the guide only showed him one plant but that after much search he found a few others & gathered all he could find so that I should not be surprised if it was now extirpated there. I wish one could punish such persons (WWC BLNHM Ralfs to Wilson, 23 June 1855. Reproduced by kind permission of the Trustees of The Natural History Museum, London).

An article published anonymously in a gardening journal by a lady plant hunter writing under the pseudonym 'Filix fœmina' (lady fern) gives a highly interesting and informative account of her fern collecting holiday in the Llanberis area during the 1860s thereby providing an insight into this fascinating chapter in the history of plant hunting in Snowdonia (Filix fœmina, 1867: 154-155). The main purpose of the holiday was the procuring of fern specimens – flowering plants are only mentioned occasionally – and on departing for her holiday she was reminded by two friends to bring them specimens of green spleenwort (*Asplenium viride*), holly fern (*Polystichum lonchitis*), oblong woodsia (*Woodsia ilvensis*) and forked spleenwort (*Asplenium septentrionale*). The following quotation shows that the mania created by the hobby of collecting ferns was well established by the time '*Filix-fœmina*' made her visit:

Years ago, and Fern-hunting about Snowdon was not only Fern-hunting, but Fern-finding. Now all is changed, *"pteridomania"* has seized upon young and old, and people who hardly know a Fern from a flowering plant, will have a fernery because it is the fashion to have one. It is true they cannot be worried to look for the Ferns, but they are quite ready to give the best price to those who will take the trouble off their hands. . . . Fern-hunting has become a trade, and little tables set out with rare and dainty Ferns stand by cottage doors, and instead of giving a nurseryman a couple of shillings for a Fern raised from seed, you give one shilling to a poor man who finds Fern-collecting more profitable than field labour, and ruthlessly seizes on all the rare Ferns he can find, drags them from their hiding places, and thanks Providence for the "fashion" that brings meat and white bread to a cottage where it has seldom been seen before (Filix-fœmina, 1867: 154).

The article goes on to disclose more interesting facts about the gathering of ferns in Snowdonia, the source of this information undoubtedly being her guide:

There is also, I fear, a darker side to the picture, for I have heard of Ferns once accessible to the botanist in a morning's ramble, being removed from his path to safer localities, so that hurried visitors may be compelled to buy if they are determined to have; but I hope this is of a very rare occurrence, and I only mention it to show how much danger an indigenous plant may stand of being exterminated from a country . . . But it is not the Ferns alone of Llanberis that are so charming; flowering plants are not outdone by their acrogenous neighbours, and each month of the sweet spring-tide ushers in the fair blossoming of many a mountain plant. Nor is it the vegetable world that constitutes the only spell that yearly attracts so many Saxons to the land of the Cymri (Filix-fœmina, 1867: 154).

The 19th century saw a significant increase in the population of the Snowdonia region as the slate and tourist industries expanded. Various accounts of field trips to collect specific plants show that both 'fashionable' and serious botanists relied heavily on local help, but they rarely reveal the importance of the role they played. Filix-fœmina respectfully notes how fortunate she was in her own botanical guide:

Here and there, amongst the very poor, you meet with a nature-formed botanist. I found such a one, and had to blush again and again at my own poor and lazily-acquired attainments, as he explained to me, in broken English, through what difficulties he had climbed the tree of knowledge, his "dim Saesneg" [no English] and dim [no] Latin standing in his way at every step (Filix-fœmina, 1867:154).

The name of this local botanical guide does not appear in the article, but a clue to his identity is given by the anonymous fern collector as she describes how she had invited her guide to dine at her lodgings, during which time she showed him her collection of dried ferns. The local man showed a keen interest in the ferns as each specimen was displayed before him; and when the landlady entered the room in order to return the favour he asked her to tell the lady collector that he would gladly take her to see the hybrid alternate-leaved spleenwort *(Asplenium x alternifolium)* where he had taken 'Mr Babington' before. An entry in Babington's journal dated 4 September 1865 reads: 'With Hugh Lewis to a spot high up on the further side of the mass of mountain which projects into the pass on the left side to see *Asplenium alternifolium*. He shewed me one small plant of it, and knows of another. Saw plenty of *A. septentrionale*.' (Babington, 1897: 205).

Arrangements were made to take the lady fern collector to see the alternate-leaved spleenwort in the Llanberis Pass and the journey vividly described:

So I went, bound to secrecy, and with my eyes metaphorically bandaged till I should arrive at a given spot; a long drive, a steep ascent, and then, "Yes indeed, we must climb up there (far away in the cloud), and we must have a rope . . ." It is a fact, that Mr. Babington, under the guidance of my friend, *did* see *Asplenium germanicum* [*A. x alternifolium*] in its mountain home; but it is, alas! also a fact that my coward heart failed me, and I did not see it, though I have two fronds gathered from it. I would not even ask for a plant, for *A. germanicum* is very rare as a British species, and I would not willingly have one habitat destroyed . . . However, I consoled myself with *A. septentrionale* (the very finest I ever saw), . . . and with a basketload of *Allosorus crispus* (Parsley fern), that grows in wondrous tufts of brilliant green amidst the slate *debris* of the grand old Glyder Fawr (Filix-fœmina, 1867: 154).

It is evident that Hugh Lewis and others like him provided an important service to visiting botanists to Snowdonia during the 19th century when times for working class families were hard. The anonymous collector commented on the local industry with compassion, revealing the difference between those days and now, when the noise of heavy industry was a constant background to the plant collecting done by visitors who ventured onto the hills:

The great drawback of Llanberis is the slate quarries, with the constant explosions that the blasting produces. Hour by hour, as the clock strikes, at the sound of a bugle, the thundering blasts bellow forth, and vast masses of slate are seen to fly up into the air amidst smoke and dust, till the huge rock appears like so many small volcanoes: and when to the noise the thought is added that each blast may be carrying death to some poor workman of the thousands congregated there, the notes of the bugle have a peculiarly touching effect, and become like a call to prayer (Filix-fœmina, 1867: 155).

She made use of her guide, and also his young daughter, to gather some of the plants she could not reach, but it was the steady hand of Hugh Lewis who 'dragged' the oblong woodsia *(Woodsia ilvensis)* 'from its fastness' while holly fern *(Polystichum lonchitis)* grew 'at such an elevation that I sat down in despair, and sent a mountain child, the pretty daughter of my botanical friend, to gather it for me' (Filix-fœmina, 1867: 155). The young girl was probably Ellen, eldest daughter of Hugh Lewis from his first marriage.

The Snowdon lily *(Lloydia serotina)* was found in fruit by the party who ventured up the Glyder to the vicinity of the Devil's Kitchen before continuing down to Cwm Idwal where green spleenwort *(Asplenium viride)* and brittle bladder-fern *(Cystopteris fragilis)* were found growing in the interstices of a stone wall by the lake although, according to the lady fern collector there were not many fronds left. When oak fern *(Gymnocarpium dryopteris)* was spotted at a new site she 'pounced upon it at once from a great distance; not that I wished to bring away the roots, only to a Fern-collector the finding fresh habitats for any Fern is an intense pleasure' (Filix-fœmina, 1867: 155). The success of her plant hunting trip as noted in her article had rested upon the effort of botanical guide Hugh Lewis and his local knowledge, not only of the various ferns but also of such flowering plants as fragrant orchid *(Gymnadenia conopsea)* and the two butterfly orchids *Platanthera bifolia* and *P. chlorantha*.

Most of the ferns I have which I have enumerated are local in their choice of habitats, and no one must expect to find them all at once. If a collector is simply wishing for species, and his time is limited, the best plan is to hire the services of a local botanist, for a stranger might hunt for weeks together without being able to "drop" upon the home of Woodsia ilvensis, Asplenium germanicum, or even Polystichum lonchitis; but for the search after varieties the collector can scarcely go amiss, and as he wanders about he will be sure to pick up many a goodly species by the way (Filix-fœmina, 1867: 155).

Apart from his interest in the localities of the rare plants of Snowdonia, Hugh Lewis (Jones, 2002: 31-50) was a poet and he also wrote papers which he presented at local literary meetings on subjects which included astronomy, sound, psychology, temperance, geology and theology. Hugh

Lewis' family had moved from Anglesey to find work at the Dinorwic Slate Quarry and his name appears in the 1861 census described as a thirty-five year old widowed quarryman and 'head' of a family of four living at Blaen-y-ddôl, Llanberis. He had a son John, entered as 'scholar' aged twelve, and a daughter Ellen, aged ten. Hugh Lewis' sister, also called Ellen, lived with them. The fifth member of the household was none other than William Williams, the famous 'Botanical Guide', recorded by the census enumerator as 'Snowdon Guide' and 'Boarder', aged fifty-two and born in Ruthin, Denbighshire. According to the 1871 census returns Hugh Lewis still worked in the quarry, was aged forty-four, but had moved into a house called Pen-y-Bryn in Llanberis, with his second wife Margaret who, like her husband, was a native of Anglesey. There were ten people listed in the household including Hugh Lewis' children from his first marriage, plus the children of Margaret from her first marriage and one thirteen year old female servant.

Hugh Lewis had been promoted to a deputy supervisor's position at the Dinorwic Slate Quarry where he worked (Parry, 1888), but was dismissed following a lock-out. Lewis is said to have become disillusioned following this industrial dispute, which occurred when the North Wales Quarrymen's Union was being formed (Jones, R.M., 1982), and had planned to move to Bangor to start a business in that city. He was promised a small pension by his former employer and a group of his close friends were arranging a testimonial collection for him. His health deteriorated before his plans could materialise and he died in 1886 being buried at Nant Peris, where his gravestone records:

Am
Hugh Lewis
Pen y Bryn Llanberis
yr hwn a hunodd yn
yr Iesu Mawrth 17eg
1886 yn 59 mlwydd oed
hefyd
Er serchog gof
am
Margaret
m Hydref 27 1911
yn 76 ml oed.

In 1888 Hugh Lewis' biography was published by Reverend G. Tecwyn Parry, the minister who officiated at Gorffwysfa Chapel, Llanberis, from 1870. For some unknown reason Parry only records Lewis' theological and literary achievements and completely ignores his botanical interests which were considerable, considering his connections with Babington and William Williams, the Botanical Guide. Parry obviously did not consider such knowledge worthy of mention despite the fact that he later published a book on the topography of the Llanberis area which included a chapter on botany (Parry, 1908: 293-299).

More evidence of the plant-locality knowledge the botanical guides of Snowdonia had appears in the pocket-book of John Hughes who, like Hugh Lewis, was successful in combining his daily work as a slate quarryman with that of a mountain guide. By the mid 19th century the Snowdonian guides were carrying pocket-books which they used as testimonials. On returning from a trip a client would be requested to enter any comments he wished to make regarding the guide's professional conduct. The entries made in these pocket books invariably begin with the time taken to the reach the summit, followed by the weather conditions with regard to the views they had, and conclude with a few favourable words on the conduct of the guide. Like Hugh Lewis, John Hughes was born in Anglesey and crossed the Menai Straits to find work in the Dinorwic Slate Quarry. Hughes' pocket-book was passed down in the family and was in the possession of his great-grandson Owen George Hughes of Llanberis, when it was borrowed by the present author in 1992.

The 1871 census returns for the parish of Llanberis registered John Hughes as a forty-seven year old 'Labourer' (the term 'Quarrier' appears in the 1881 Census and 'Slate Quarryman' in 1891) living in Goodman Street, Llanberis and married to forty-four year old Anglesey born Mary who had two sons, Owen and Henry. The inscription on the first page of John Hughes' pocket-book advertises 'John Hughes / Guide / to / Snowdon', giving 'Coed-y-Ddôl / Llanberris' as his address, with the year '1867' at the bottom of the page; noted also are the words 'Hair Dresser &c', with the original leather binding bearing the marks of razor-sharpening. Each quarry had among its workforce men who, at home after work or following the lunch break in the *caban* (canteen), ran a portable barber's shop in a suitable corner. John Hughes evidently provided such a service.

The first entry in John Hughes' pocket-book is dated 26 July 1867; the last was written on 31 August 1876. No entries appear for the years 1870, 1874, and only one for 1876. It is not possible to say whether any of the original pages have been removed. Some of the entries speak volumes about the capability of John Hughes as a guide and of his knowledge of specialist subjects:

Friday July 26th 1867

Mrs W H & Miss Maria Dale of York Mr D & the Misses Parker of Broom House nr Doncaster ascended Snowdon and on the following day crossed the Glyder Mountain to the Devil's Kitchen where they spent the day collecting ferns etc – Jno [John] Hughes acted as guide on both occasions – his kindness and attention were much appreciated, also his superior knowledge of the different specimens of ferns and of the difficult paths leading to this grand and solitary spot render his services very acceptable especially when ladies are of the party. They strongly recommend the guide and the Twl-Du [sic] excursion.

Other entries in the pocket-book speak in glowing terms of John Hughes' self-taught local knowledge:

Sep. 19 1871

I ascended Snowdon, descending via the Capel Curig route, under the guidance of John Hughes. I found him a most intelligent guide having a good knowledge of the Glacial Phenomena of the district / Frank Clarkson / F.G.S.

Sept 21 1871

I ascended Snowdon to day, returning by the Capel Curig route, under the guidance of John Hughes. I found him every way capable, and intelligent, and possessed of a good knowledge of the geological formation of the region and of its botanical products / W. H. L. Lee.

The rarest and most coveted of all the ferns of Snowdonia was and still is the Killarney fern *(Trichomanes speciosum)* which favours dark damp holes and shaded river gorges as its habitat and retains a mysterious, almost enchanting quality, due to vaguely written old records and long lost localities. The south-western counties of Ireland are in fact the stronghold of the plant. The Killarney fern was first recorded in Britain by Dr Richard Richardson at a site near Bingley in Yorkshire. The specimen he gathered was preserved among Uvedale's plants in the Sloane Herbarium housed in the British Museum. On the strength of a specimen gathered by Richardson the record was published in the third edition of Ray's *Synopsis*:

Found by *Dr. Richardson* at *Belbank*, scarce half a Mile from Bingley, at the Head of a remarkable Spring, and no where else that he knows of (Dillenius, (ed.), 1724: 128).

Information regarding the exact localities of this fern was kept secret by those who knew them for fear of the plant becoming extinct due to over collecting. This actually happened at a site in the Harlech area, and could well have been the case with the old Snowdon locality, where once the finest colony in Britain grew (Ratcliffe, Birks, Birks, 1993: 233).

The mystery and romance surrounding the rare plant localities were much coveted by the plant hunters during the great Victorian collecting era. A similar sense of achievement is experienced by present day field botanists when during the course of a day's excursion a new locality for a plant is discovered; the main difference between them and their forerunners is that the camera has replaced the vasculum as a vital part of the botanist's equipment. The feeling of satisfaction however remains the same.

The first record of a discovery of the Killarney fern in Wales was made by J. F. Rowbotham of Manchester in 1863. The exact locality is not given apart from the fact that it was found on part of the Snowdon range. The following description of the site appeared in *Journal of Botany* in a note by Thomas Moore who had been corresponding with Rowbotham regarding the discovery:

I learn further, from Mr. J. F. Rowbotham, of Manchester, that he has more recently found *Trichomanes radicans* [Killarney fern: *Trichomanes speciosum*] in North Wales, in a part of the Snowdon range. The precise locality it would be imprudent to indicate, lest the information should lead to the eradication of the plant. The fronds were, as I learn, abundant, and remarkably fine; one of them, which Mr. Rowbotham had kindly favoured me, is quite equal to the bulk of the Irish specimens in luxuriance of development, the frond having the broad or triangular-ovate outline of the more perfect examples of this fern, and measuring about seven inches across the widest part, and nearly ten inches in length, in addition to a stipe of eight inches long. This specimen is not fertile. Another frond in Mr. Rowbotham's possession is rather larger, having a total length of about twenty-two inches. . . . "I found it," he writes, "in a large hole formed by fallen rocks alongside a cascade of water; and admission to this hole, which is about five feet high by four feet wide, is obstructed after a depth of about three feet by this Fern falling from the rocks at the top, and growing out of the sides in the form of a beautiful curtain, down which the water is constantly trickling; the whole having the appearance of a crystal screen." What a treat to a Fern-seeker, to stumble on such a sight as this! So unwilling was the finder to disturb the singular and beautiful effect, that he took with him only an offshoot or two from the principal network of rhizomes, "out of which the innumerable fronds were projected." To so much, as the discoverer, he was fairly entitled, but it will be a sacrilegious hand that does aught beyond this, to destroy so unexpected a habitat for so rare a plant (Moore, 1863: 238-239).

In 1864 the Botanical Society of Edinburgh received Killarney fern specimens from nurseryman James Backhouse Jnr., which he claimed to have gathered in Caernarfonshire. No more details of the exact locality were given but it is believed that the fronds came from the same site as that described by Rowbotham. One of the Killarney fern sites of north Wales was shown by Backhouse to a local botanist, D. A. Jones of Harlech (1861-1936), who later recorded the incident in his manuscript flora of Merioneth (NMGW D.A. Jones MS.,1898: 289). There is evidence that the Killarney fern was planted in north Wales as R. H. Roberts notes:

In a tribute to the recently deceased Herbert Stansfield, E. H. Hawkins wrote: "I recall that some years ago he spent some time in North Wales, taking with him some plants of the Killarney Fern, which he planted in some wild and congenial places, with the hope that they may be found subsequently by fern hunters. This thoughtfulness was ever typical of him" (Roberts, R. H., 1979: 3).

Some scepticism was aroused concerning the authenticity of these discoveries, and William Williams (1805-1861) the 'Botanical Guide' was rumoured to have planted Irish specimens of the Killarney fern in the Snowdon district prior to the discovery made by Rowbotham in 1863, but according to Moore (1863: 239) the luxuriant state of the Rowbotham specimens disproved this, suggesting a long established colony. James Britten in his *European Ferns* (1879-1881) mentions such rumours but adds that the fern was already known in two Carnarfonshire sites thirty years prior to the 1863 discovery.

Britten who also prepared a note on the botany of north Wales published in *Jenkinson's Practical Guide to North Wales* has this to say on the Killarney fern: 'This rare and beautiful fern exists in the Snowdon district; but the exact locality is known to very few, and is wisely kept concealed' (Britten,1878: xcviii). Babington records in his journal an entry dated 17 July 1832 that he spent the day examining the rocks in the vicinity of Dolbadarn Castle, Llanberis in a vain attempt to find the Killarney fern that had been mentioned as growing there (Babington, 1897: 12).

Rowbothan's locality for the Killarney fern remains a mystery to this day. To the best of the present author's knowledge there have been no reports of the fern having been seen on the Snowdon range since Sir John Bretland Farmer, writing on the flora of the region in Carr and Lister's *The*

Mountains of Snowdonia, claimed to have known one locality in the area for more than twenty years. (Farmer, 1948: 152). The present author is of the opinion that the Killarney fern locality to which Bretland Farmer refers was probably shown to him by John Lloyd Williams who discovered it in 1887.

The autobiography of John Lloyd Williams (1854-1945), which in general deals with the ordinary aspects of the life of a 19th century country schoolmaster with varied interests in the arts, also mentions botany and some of the collectors he encountered, during the great collecting era. He remembered the women of Llanrwst, his native town, when he was a boy bringing basketsful of ferns to sell at the station on the morning of Llandudno Fair. They offered such common species as the male fern *(Dryopters filix-mas)* as rarities, claiming that it was 'very rare indeed and difficult to get – it is called "The Prince of Wales' Feathers"' and that its locality was known only to them (Williams, J.L., 1944: 156). After experiencing an incident involving a collector who had called upon his services as a botanical guide he, unlike other botanists, did not pursue to the full the fashionable trend of forming a complete herbarium. He had been approached by a clergyman, who had recently published a Flora of one of the English counties, and who wanted a specimen of a certain rare plant which grew in the vicinity of Llanrwst for his herbarium. Once the specimen had been procured Lloyd Williams mentioned to the collector that he knew of a good site for the forked spleenwort *(Asplenium septentrionale)* close by and that he would take him to see it, being that they were so close. The clergyman turned down the offer since he already had a specimen of that fern in his herbarium. Lloyd Williams realized that this collector lost all interest in a plant once he had a specimen of it in his collection, and he subsequently gave up collecting for its own sake lest he should end up with the same attitude (Williams, J.L., 1945: 66).

In 1887 Lloyd Williams published a note in the *Journal of Botany* recording his discovery of a Killarney fern colony on Moel Hebog, near Beddgelert in 1887, but refrains from even divulging the name of the mountain:

> In July last I found a very good specimen of *Trichomanes radicans* [Killarney fern; *Trichomanes speciosum*] growing in a damp hole near the top of a range of mountains. Not knowing the locality in which this fern was discovered before, I cannot guarantee but that this one is identical with it, and for the same reason as that which induced the locality reported in 1865 to be kept secret, I must take the same precaution in this case. I may state, however, that it was not found on any part of Snowdon. I took a small portion of the fern and planted it,

but left the greater part of it behind (Williams, J.L., 1887: 215).

According to the above the discovery was made in July, but on reading his autobiography the discovery was made prior to 30 May, which corresponds with an entry in his notebook for that date:

> Got up 5.30 & made preps for a picnic in Bwlch Meillionen Father, Dick, Wm Hugh, Owen . . . & I – fished part of the way but not successfully . . . After frequent stoppings we reached the camping ground abt 11 & picd on bread & butter, corned beef & hard boiled eggs with plenty of fun and laughter the whole washed down with sparkling water – as bright as Hugh's wit. After dinner we took the things into the house . . . a large boulder cave & rested on cushions of filmy fern. Then [?] Wm Dick F and I went to visit the Killarney Fern & found it all right (NLWA JLW B2/7).

Being that the above entry in the notebook says that he went to see the Killarney fern, it can only be concluded that Lloyd Williams already knew the site from a previous visit. This was two months prior to the date when the find was published, but this, however, was not the end of the story. According to his autobiography all the fronds were taken from the newly discovered site soon after, and the small cave was still barren at the time that Lloyd Williams left Garndolbenmaen in 1893 (Williams, J.L., 1945: 190). He went on to say that the fern did not reappear until twenty-four years later during the time he was Demonstrator of Botany at the University of Wales, Bangor.

R. H. Roberts has pointed out some discrepancies concerning Lloyd Williams' account of the disappearance of the Killarney fern, stating that fronds were gathered there by J. E. Griffith of Bangor during July, 1891, two years before Lloyd Williams left the area (Roberts, 1979: 2). Griffith's specimen, now kept at the National Museum and Gallery of Wales, Cardiff, has an interesting note attached to the herbarium sheet:

> Trichomanes radicans: seen on Garndolbenmaen, Moel Hebog, by A. H. Trow in the company of J. Lloyd Williams: fronds described as being two feet long. Date not stated. Recorded from conversation. 1st December 1937. H.A. Hyde (NMGW Herbarium Sheet 27.73.4).

The two-foot-long fronds mentioned above did not come from the Moel Hebog site. The fronds growing there, as Griffith's and later specimens show, are about six inches in length including the stipe, which raises the question of whether or not another site was known to J. Lloyd Williams and Trow. J.E. Griffith, during the 1890s, was still gathering plant records for his forthcoming *Flora of Anglesey and Carnarvonshire*, and in order to keep the site secret gives nothing away when recording the Killarney fern: 'I have seen this fern growing, undoubtedly wild, in one place only. This was first found by Mr. J. Lloyd Williams. I refrain from giving the locality as it is so rare' (Griffith, [1895]:165). The following passage was found by the present author in one of Lloyd Williams' notebooks describing a visit he made to the Killarney fern site in 1922 while he was head of botany at the University of Wales, Aberystwyth:

> I cut across the boggy land and made straight for the . . . [site] . . . In the old locality I found to my great joy that *Trichomanes radicans* had come up again – there was a longish rhizome with 5 or 6 fronds each nearly as big as a hand. This is very remarkable when it is remembered that for long years (the first find was 35 years ago) there was no sign of the plant after the original had been uprooted and carried away (NLWA JLW MB1/15).

According to his autobiography he had made arrangements to meet up with some other botanists on this day with a view of spending a day botanizing on the mountain, but arrived at the meeting place half an hour before the others. During that interval he walked quickly up the mountain to the old site to find the fern had reappeared. He took one frond before returning back down the mountain to meet the others. He showed the frond to his friends, but did not give away the locality despite the fact that they spent the day botanizing on the mountain (Williams, J.L., 1945: 191).

Due to failing health and memory it is evident that Lloyd Williams did not check his diaries whilst writing his account of the Killarney fern for the fourth and final part of his autobiography. He was Professor of Botany at Aberystwyth when he found that the fern had reappeared, and not at Bangor as he says in his autobiography.

In 1921 Thomas Pritchard Edwards, under his bardic name 'Caerwyson', published an article on ferns in the journal *Cymru* (Caerwyson, 1921: 206-208), in which he claimed to have found the Killarney fern on Moel Hebog; the description of the locality being similar to the one given by Lloyd Williams in the fourth volume of his autobiography. There is no mention of Edwards in the autobiography, but he claimed in his article that he had discussed the Killarney fern with Lloyd Williams at an Eisteddfod shortly after J. E. Griffith's *Flora of Anglesey and Carnarvonshire* had been published. Edwards had asked whether or not Griffith had seen the Killarney fern for himself, to which Lloyd Williams replied that he had told him where some used to grow. Edwards had decided to keep quiet about his discovery and did not visit the site again for two years. So concerned was he over the safety of the rare fern during his second visit that he took an indirect route to the site with an occasional glance over his shoulder to make sure he was not being followed. On arrival he found the recess stripped completely bare.

Edwards' claim to be the first to discover the Killarney fern on Moel Hebog was justified by the fact that he published details of the locality, plus the ensuing fate of the fern, in 1921, twenty-four years before Lloyd Williams' account in his autobiography. Both botanists give a similar description of the site; a small damp rocky recess above which grew some harts-tongue *(Phyllitis scolopendrium)* which first aroused their curiosity and induced closer inspection. Thomas Pritchard Edwards was a native of Caerwys in Flintshire as his literary pseudonym 'Caerwyson' suggests. He served as an Independent minister at Llanrwst and later with the Wesleyans at Blaenau Ffestiniog where he was the editor of the local newspaper *Rhedegydd* from 1899 until 1906, and edited a guide book for the area in 1911 in which he included a note on the botany of the district. In his article on ferns which appeared in *Cymru* he claimed to have been a Fellow of the Linnean Society, but on enquiring further the present author found no evidence to substantiate this. Edwards spent the last part of his life at Arenig near Bala where he died on 4 March 1922 being buried at Capel Celyn in the cemetery which now lies beneath the waters of the Llyn Celyn reservoir.

Despite continued efforts by botanists during the first half of the 20th century the secret locality of the Moel Hebog Killarney fern remained unknown until 1967, when G. M. Hughes found it whilst looking for mosses (Hyde and Wade, 1978: 85). The previous year W. M. Condry (1966: 153) in his book on the Snowdonia National Park had mentioned the fern:

I unrolled my sleeping-bag by a murmuring stream and went to sleep . . . thinking of the botanist J. Lloyd Williams who, when a young schoolmaster here years ago, found the Killarney fern, Snowdonia's rarest species . . . It has not been seen since because the precise locality was never recorded . . .

When the fourth and last volume of J. Lloyd Williams' autobiography appeared shortly after his death in 1945, it was avidly read by botanists as it included the name Cwm Llefrith, the actual locality in which the fern grew, for the first time. The only clue prior to this was that it grew on Moel Hebog as stated in an early edition of *Welsh Ferns* (Hyde and Wade, 1940: 54), which was correct, as Cwm Llefrith lies at the base of Moel Hebog, but most botanists conducted their searches from the opposite side of the mountain to that where the fern grew. Despite the depredation it suffered during the Victorian era it is encouraging to know that this rare and beautiful fern remains extant at the site where it was first discovered in 1887. Recent studies undertaken by Dr F. Rumsey of the Natural History Museum resulted in the finding of an abundance of the gametophytes of this plant in north Wales, and the introduction of the Wildlife and Countryside Act and other associated legislation has helped safeguard the future of this and other rare ferns.

The fern craze *(pteridomania)* has been extensively discussed in an informative book and a later article by D. E. Allen (1969, 1993) and these are without doubt the definitive works on the subject. The craze was an interest which appealed to both sexes and to varying social classes in Britain during the Victorian period from the humble but proud quarrymen of north Wales to the middle classes. David Lloyd George, who later became Prime Minister, was proud of a royal fern *(Osmunda regalis)* he had gathered from among the rocks overlooking the river Dwyfor near his home, which he transplanted into his uncle's garden at Highgate, Llanystumdwy. When the family moved to Morvin House, Cricieth, the fern went too, and from there it went with the family to Garthcelyn in 1892. When Bryn Awelon was built an attempt was made to divide the royal fern and transplant the other half there. Unfortunately both halves withered causing considerable grief to both Lloyd George and his brother; the royal fern had been a symbol of their boyhood in Llanystumdwy (George, 1976: 97).

The fern collecting mania lasted throughout the Victorian age, reaching its peak during the 1860s, but the gathering of plant specimens in general continued beyond that era, and, as many will testify, well into the 20th century.

John Lloyd Williams

John Williams – he adopted the middle name of 'Lloyd' later in life on the advice of one of the Bangor Normal College lecturers – was one of eight children of a local lead miner who later worked in the Ffestiniog slate quarries. He was born at Plas Isa, Llanrwst, which was once the home of the celebrated William Salesbury, mentioned earlier. Lloyd Williams once referred to this historic connection saying that the walls of Plas Isa did not transfer to him a particle of that scholar's talent (Williams, J.L., 1941: 7). These were modest words from a man who, among his varied achievements, had been a Professor of Botany, and an avid collector of traditional Welsh folk-songs and editor of the music journal *Y Cerddor* for many years.

He was educated at the British School, Llanrwst and later entered Bangor Normal College as the holder of a Queen's Scholarship where he spent two years studying for a teaching career. Despite the death of his mother during his term at Bangor, Lloyd Williams successfully completed his teacher's training course, and in 1875 was appointed first headmaster of the newly built school at Garndolbenmaen. Due to the death of the mother the family home at Llanrwst was by then being cared for by one of the grandmothers, and when the time came for Lloyd Williams to take up his teaching post at Garndolbenmaen his thirteen year old sister Elizabeth moved there with him. She was later appointed pupil teacher, while also undertaking the duties of looking after their new home. Following eighteen years as a schoolteacher, Lloyd Williams studied the cytology of marine algae at the Royal College of Science, South Kensington for four years before spending seventeen years in Bangor as Assistant Lecturer in Botany. For a brief period before leaving Bangor he moved to the newly established post of advisor in Agricultural Botany there. He was appointed Professor of Botany at the University of Wales, Aberystwyth in 1915 and remained in this post until his retirement in 1926.

Lloyd Williams' interest in natural history began when he was a boy. In his autobiography he recalls how he used to be more inclined to study the behaviour of birds rather than just collect eggs. He also collected insects, noting the different species and studying their habits with the aid of a crudely fashioned pocket lens of his own design. This he would make using a piece of glass onto which a drop of glue was dropped and it served as a lens as long as the glue remained in a convex form. Another device he used to study small creatures was simply a glass tumbler filled with water. The insects were placed inside the receptacle and examined as they swam close to the swollen parts of the glass. He collected all manner of natural curiosities, this collection being known in the family as 'John's Museum', described below and translated from one of his sister Elizabeth's memoirs:

> A length of wood hung from one of the rafters in the back kitchen and on each branch a nest was placed with a stuffed bird sitting on each one. The taxidermy being the work of John himself. He also kept water beetles in bottles. I remember one item of the museum which was more precious than the others; a box with a glass lid which was full of birds eggs, each one different with the name of the bird attached. I never used to tire looking at them. But if mother was around we weren't allowed to touch any of them, such was her deep interest in 'John's Museum' as she called it . . . Strangely enough John lost all interest in birds, nests and beetles after he went to college. He turned all his attention to botany (Williams, E., 1951: 26).

Lloyd Williams as a boy also collected mosses and ferns which he dried and pressed and pasted on sheets of paper, but not having any books to help him with the naming of the different species he gave them names which he himself had coined. Years later he was to introduce the teaching of natural history through the 'Museum' method at his new school in Garndolbenmaen.

The information which Lloyd Williams sought during his boyhood years was to be had in journals like *Good Words* and *Leisure Hour*, which he borrowed from the Chapel library at Llanrwst; he mentions an excellent series on the sea shore which was published in *Good Words* and later appeared as a book entitled *A Year at the Shore* (Gosse, 1865). When the railway from Llandudno Junction to Llanrwst opened in 1863 he went with his family on one of the cheap day excursions to Bangor, and took advantage of the trip to visit the shores of the Menai Straits so that he could look out for the various natural wonders he had read about in *Good Words*. As the tide was out he began filling his pockets with seaweed and after returning home that evening proceeded to dry and place them on sheets of paper. Little did the nine year old realize at the time that this was his first collection of an order of plants in which he was later to achieve distinction, gaining a D.Sc. from the University of Wales in 1908.

Apart from the many botanical rambles in the vicinity of Llanrwst that he undertook as a boy, Lloyd Williams also recorded journeys which took him further afield. He once ascended Carnedd Llywelyn starting from Trefriw, climbing over Cefn Cyfarwydd into Cwm Cowlyd towards Afon

Ddu. After crossing the hills between Pen Llithrig and Moel Eilio he descended into Cwm Eigiau where he saw an abundance of trout in the Porthllwyd river. On reaching Cedryn farmhouse he was invited in and given a drink of buttermilk before starting on the final stage of the walk to the summit. He names the various plants seen on the way among which were heath rush *(Juncus squarrosus)* and the different species of heather which had sheets of a white flowered variety. The woolly-haired moss *(Racomitrium lanuginosum)* which grows in luxuriant carpets among the rocks and heather also caught the keen eye of the young botanist, and there follows a short but interesting note on the ecology of the plant. Lloyd Williams returned home from Carnedd Llywelyn by descending into Cwm Dulyn from where he made his way down to Llanbedr-y-cennin before continuing on his way home to Llanrwst through Talybont and Trefriw.

He climbed Tryfan for the first time when he was twelve years old. Lloyd Williams had been sent with his cousin whom he calls by his nickname 'Wil Sarnau', to Bethesda to represent the family at a funeral there. While walking along the Holyhead road west from Capel Curig (now A5) opposite Tryfan an argument developed between the two boys concerning the two columnar boulders which stand on the summit. In order to settle the argument they decided to climb the mountain on the way back from Bethesda to find out whether the two figures on the summit were indeed two carved statues as Wil Sarnau had claimed. They climbed Tryfan from the western side passing Llyn Bochlwyd and, on gaining the summit, Lloyd Williams scrambled to the top of one of the two monoliths, known as 'Adam and Eve', and leapt from one to the other, a custom still practised by present day climbers and hill-walkers. On the summit he saw the beautiful hawkweed *(Hieracium holosericeum)*, a plant that was new to him; he later learned that it was very rare in Wales (Williams, J.L., 1944: 95). The Capel Curig road was regained most probably by scrambling down to Bwlch Tryfan before continuing down through Cwm Tryfan to the road.

During his period as a schoolteacher at Garndolbenmaen, Lloyd Williams studied the flora of north-west Wales, becoming an authority on the Arctic-Alpine flora of Snowdonia. His botanical excursions, duly noted in his diaries, are a vivid example of the way in which the plant-hunters of the period worked; his remarks are in many ways similar to the comments of Babington and Wilson mentioned earlier. Over the years Lloyd Williams botanized both by himself and also in the company of others. Three of his most regular companions were D. A. (Dan) Jones (1861-1936) of Harlech, a famous bryologist and author of a manuscript flora of Merioneth which won a prize at the National Eisteddfod held at Blaenau Ffestiniog in 1898, John Griffith (1863-1933) of Rhiw, Lleyn, schoolmaster and musician and R. W. Phillips (1854-1926), Professor of Botany at the University of Wales, Bangor. He was also occasionally accompanied by A. H. Trow (1863-1939), who held the Chair of Botany at the University of Wales, Cardiff, and J. E. Griffith (1843-1933) of Bangor, author of *The Flora of Anglesey and Carnarvonshire.*

John Edwards Griffith, the son of Griffith Griffith, Taldrwst, Llangristiolus, Anglesey, was apprenticed at his uncle's chemist shop in High Street, Bangor, taking over the business in 1864 when his uncle died. Griffith was married to Ann, the daughter of Rowland Parry, Fron Heulog, Bangor, who died in 1888. He was shortly to re-marry Ellen Augusta, the only daughter of Reverend John Williams Ellis of Glasfryn, Llangybi and Plas Lodwig, Bangor. He gave up the chemist business shortly after re-marrying, spending the remainder of his life as a gentleman of private means. In addition to his botanical work he also wrote the *Portfolio of Photographs of Cromlechs* (1900) and *Pedigrees of Anglesey and Carnarvonshire Families* (1914).

Griffith studied the plants of Anglesey and Caernarfonshire for twenty years prior to the publication of his *Flora* of the two counties circa 1895. He had already published a shorter version of this fifteen years previously by instalments which appeared in the *Naturalist*, (Griffith, 1879) the journal of the Yorkshire Naturalists Society; this formed the basis of his major work. Griffith's personal copy of the *Flora* is kept at the Bangor City Library (Ref. 581.9 429). The volume has been rebound and interleaved with blank pages and was used by the author to note additional records which he had amassed over a thirty year period following the publication of the original work (Roberts, R.H., 1984). The *Flora* included 1119 species of flowering plants and 219 varieties of which nine species and varieties were, at the time, new to science, and seventeen species and varieties, new to the British flora. J.E. Griffith is remembered mainly for his *Pedigrees of Anglesey and Carnarvonshire Families* (1914) but among his many interests were archaeology, antiquities and photography as well as botany. He was also a J.P. and a director of the Bangor Market Company. He died at Bryn Dinas, Bangor in July 1933, aged ninety, and was buried at Glanadda Cemetary. Lloyd Williams was the chief contributor to Griffith's *Flora*, supplying records of 81 flowering plants and 14 ferns.

1887 had been a successful year for Lloyd Williams as a field botanist; his discovery of a new site for the Killarney fern (mentioned in last chapter) in his own back yard encouraged him to conduct his searches further afield. On the morning of 11 June 1887 he walked from Bethesda up Nant Ffrancon, to Cwm Idwal, before continuing up to Cwm Clyd recording starry saxifrage *(Saxifraga stellaris)*, tormentil *(Potentilla erecta)*, common butterwort *(Pinguicula vulgaris)* and common dog-violet *(Viola riviniana)*. The path follows the stream up to Cwm Clyd and in the gorge he saw mountain sorrel *(Oxyria digyna)*, wood-sorrel *(Oxalis acetosella)*, alpine meadow-rue *(Thalictrum alpinum)* and roseroot *(Sedum rosea)*. As he climbed higher he noted mossy saxifrage *(Saxifraga hypnoides)*, common scurvygrass *(Cochlearia officinalis agg)*, parsley fern *(Cryptogramma crispa)* and beech fern *(Phegopteris connectilis)* and he was astonished to find lesser celandine *(Ranunculus ficaria)* in flower. Having reached the base of the cliff he paused for lunch and noticed a cushion of pink coloured plants on a ledge nearby. He scrambled towards it and found a patch of moss campion *(Silene acaulis)* and on venturing further he reached a point where he saw the Snowdon lily for the first time:

> From this point I had a terrible scramble. First of all I had to go down for I had managed to get into an awkward place then I had to climb up a very steep slope with loose stones to try and reach a steep cliff in the face of which I could see a likely cavity for plants. With great pains and some danger I managed to reach within abt 50 yds to the ft of the precipice & began to climb gingerly over an uninteresting patch of steep slippery rock when my opera glass fell out of my pocket and began jumping from point to point down the slope in the most daring and reckless manner. To swear wd have been a comfort – as it was, there was nothing to be done but to retrace my steps all the way down the slope. After this to reascend with a heavy knapsack on my back and under a broiling sun was no joke. Perhaps though it was quite as well – for the way I tried was a very dangerous one. Taking another path I managed to reach the foot of the cliff. The cleft I had seen from below was high & deep, the bottom being full of Woodrush. I managed by its aid to hoist myself into the cavity, but found nothing except Woodrush and Woodsorrel. Feeling disappointed at the result of so much toil & exertion I went on, when I could see in a crevice above me a little white flower. I at once threw down my knapsack, and began climbing up the face but I soon came to a full stop when a little more than an arm's length from the plant. Taking my trowel I managed to flake off a large flat cake of rock which formed the side of the crevice which the plant grew, exposing bulbs and fibrous roots flattened against the rock. I was now able to scrape off the plant & recognize it at once as the very rare spiderwort [Snowdon lily] . . . so that my climb was not fruitless after all (NLW JLW B2/7).

Following his adventure that day Lloyd Williams climbed over the ridge of Y Garn and made his way to the base of the Devil's Kitchen chasm and followed Llwybr y Carw (the Deer Path) to Llyn y Cŵn and down to catch the train home from Llanberis. Further searches on the eastern side of Cwm Idwal on 4 July 1889 are recorded in his diary:

> The steep slope of stony debris soon came to an end & I came to the bare rock. From below these looked unclimbable but I determined to have a try at them. The cliffs seemed to be built of huge blocks laid on end with vertical grooves & occasional short ledges . . . Before long the rock became so steep & smoother that I had to take off my heavy boots & tie the laces together so as to throw my boots over my shoulder & climb by means of the tennis shoes which gripped the rock much better. Still it was tough work; tougher on account of the bag, the shoes & the stick I had to carry (NLWA JLW B2/8).

'Botany is perhaps the least sensational of sciences', or so wrote John Gilmour in his fascinating book *British Botanists* (1944: 7). Snowdonian botanists like Lloyd Williams who ventured onto the cliffs in search of plants might have argued with this. Accompanied by D. A. Jones they climbed the severe cliff face of Clogwyn Du'r Arddu on 24 June 1893 in search of plants:

> Jones went up the main gully while I took a side one. When I finished my own Jones had disappeared in the mist. On trying to follow him a lot of stones came pelting down and I had great difficulty in dodging them. Later on I tried again the chimney as I could hear nothing of my companion. I had climbed about 30 feet when I could hear an avalanche coming. There was no possibility of dodging now as the place was too narrow and all the stones would have to come through the groove in which I was. I rushed upwards and flattened myself against a slightly rising crag, the next instant the stones began to pelt around, one hitting the edge of the rock just above my head, others just clearing my feet. As soon as a lull occurred I rushed headlong down without any care as to footing to get out of the way of the cannonade. When Jones came down he reported a great wealth of plants and particularly a hollow containing 7 holly ferns, Meconopsis [Welsh poppy], filmy fern etc. He had been to some dangerous places but had come off with only the tail of his Ulster torn by stones dislodged (NLWA JLW B2/9).

A similar adventure occurred during a day on the cliffs above Cwm Clogwyn on the western side of Snowdon when Lloyd Williams and Dan

Jones spent a week searching the rocks of the area. They each chose a separate gully to explore just as they had during their visit to Clogwyn Du'r Arddu. After about an hour's climbing Lloyd Williams reached the top expecting to find his friend waiting there for him, but found instead two visitors busy trundling boulders over the edge of the gully in which Dan Jones was climbing. With the thought of his friend lying dead or injured from the falling boulders Lloyd Williams lost all control and began shouting at the two fleeing visitors, calling them murderers and worse, before going to the top of the other gully calling out to try and find out whether his friend was still alive. To his great relief he heard the voice of Dan Jones hailing his reply in the distance – but from a different gully to that in which he had begun to climb. Dan Jones had found the first gully so poor in vegetation that he switched to another, thereby dodging the falling boulders. On the following day the two offending visitors, undoubtedly feeling guilty, were rumoured to be making discreet enquiries around Llanberis to find out if there had been any fatalities on Snowdon on the previous day (Williams, J.L., 1936: 11).

Years later, while he was an Assistant Lecturer in Botany at the University of Wales, Bangor Lloyd Williams was able to spend more time botanizing in the Ogwen district. During this period he received a letter dated 25 May 1898 signed 'W. West jnr' asking whether he would take an acquaintance of his to see the Snowdon lily *(Lloydia serotina)*:

> I am writing to ask you to do me a favour, on behalf of a friend of mine. . . . The gentleman in question is Franklin T. Richards, MA. He was for about 20 years tutor at Trinity College, Oxford, & now lives at Dorking. He is an excellent field-botanist who does not collect at all; he has been the constant companion of G. C. Druce in numberless rambles in Oxford & Berks. In addition, however, he has visited most parts of these islands & seen the greater number of our species in situ. The point is, he would very much like to see *Lloydia* growing. Last September, when out with him near Box Hill, he & I discussed a scheme of going there this next June; I said I had no doubt that you could show us the plant, as you know of it in several places . . . Time has gone on &, as usual I find myself unable to go . . . Mr Richards however, is examining in Durham University . . . and proposes to go to N. Wales, simply to see *Lloydia*, on his way back. . . . He will leave Durham at about 4 on Friday afternoon June 17. That night he can get to Chester by 11, or even to Bangor by the boat train. In any case, I should say he would be able to visit Twll Dû or Clogwyn Du'r Arddu (isn't that right?) on either Sat. or Sun. June 18 or 19. ... Do you think you could manage to accompany him on either of these dates? If so, it

would afford us great satisfaction. I think you would find him a very agreeable companion (NLWA JLW B1/2/89).

Although no names are mentioned it was probably this meeting that was described by Lloyd Williams in an article which later appeared in a Welsh language periodical (Williams, J. L., 1933: 221-222). Lloyd Williams cycled from Bangor to Ogwen to meet an Oxford Professor whose main ambition was to see as many rare plants as he could growing in their natural habitats. The visitor, on stepping out of his carriage, promptly inquired as to the site of the Snowdon lily to which the local man replied by pointing to the Glyder cliffs which were at the time partly obscured by clouds. One look at the dark glowering cliffs caused the visiting botanist to change his mind, and he quickly stepped back into his carriage, promising to return the following June. The don, true to his word returned the following year and, with Lloyd Williams leading the way, they set off for the mountains on a clear sunny morning. The visitor wore smooth soled leather boots which presented problems whilst climbing steep grassy slopes, but otherwise all went well until they arrived at the last stage of the journey, just below the *Lloydia* site. This final pitch consisted of a steep slope of short grass, loose stones and exposed soil. Here the don stopped and nervously announced that he could go no further. As they were only a few feet from the Snowdon lily Lloyd Williams tried to persuade his companion to carry on, and, after several minutes of discussion, the don reluctantly agreed. The locality was finally reached after Lloyd Williams had helped the terrified visitor along, creeping on all fours and clinging to anything that he could grasp, but he refused to open his eyes when he arrived at the base of the cliffs. This meant that he did not see the *Lloydia* and Lloyd Williams removed one plant out of the dozen or so that were within easy reach, and placed it in his pocket. The pair then made their way slowly and carefully down from the base of the cliffs, the don gradually regaining his composure once an easier path was reached. Within days the story was spreading around Oxford of a mad Welshman who had led an eminent Professor on a perilous expedition among the mountains to see a rare flower. The Snowdon lily however was one rare plant that the Professor did not actually see growing in its natural habitat.

During the 19th century botany remained mainly outdoor work, noting the distribution of plants, and collecting, drying and pressing them; there had not been any great changes since the days of Edward Lhuyd, but towards the end of the Victorian era, with an increase in the number of Universities, some botanists were turning their attention to other aspects of botany as one advocate of the 'new science' noted:

Thus during the major part of the 19th century classification was pursued with an enthusiasm which almost excluded other aspects of botany, little attention being paid to the modern developments in comparative anatomy and physiology which had made such strides in German laboratories (Blackman, 1945-1948: 17).

Having obtained a Free Studentship Lloyd Williams left Garndolbenmaen for a three year course to study the cytology of marine algae at the Royal College of Science, South Kensington under John Bretland Farmer (1865-1944) beginning on 8 October 1893. He was led to work on certain species of the *Phaeophyceae* (brown) group of seaweeds and won the Marshall Scholarship in 1896-1897, and then allowed to stay on for a further year to complete his studies in his chosen field. Lloyd Williams had become familiar with the Royal College of Science during his period at Garndolbenmaen by attending the summer courses held for the benefit of teachers and which were organized under the auspices of the Science and Art Department. These three week courses were given annually in different branches of science for the benefit of teachers; 250 applicants would be accepted and they received 3rd class railway fare to and from South Kensington and a £3 bonus towards their incidental expenses (PRCS, 1892-1893: 19).

Sometime between the summer of 1893 and December 1894 Lloyd Williams married Elizabeth, the daughter of Emmanuel Jones, a fishmonger living at Tŷ Mawr, Cricieth. Their son Idwal was born on 11 December 1894, and Geraint on 9 December 1897. The name of another son, Gwynedd Robert, appears on J. Lloyd Williams' gravestone at Cricieth. He died on 15 March 1894 aged four months.

Lloyd Williams corresponded regularly with his wife during his stay at South Kensington; some of the surviving letters were written during 1895 and 1896, addressed from 12, Goldney Road and signed 'Jack' instead of 'John', a signature used only when writing to his wife. His concern at being a man with family responsibilities but without a regular salary living on the allowance provided by the college continued to worry him. He always asked after his son Idwal, and spoke of his studies at the college:

> 25 October, 1895. The work is still obstinate. Tuesday Mr. Farmer tried to persuade me to give it up as it was too difficult. Yesterday & today however he had changed his tone. "By jo" said he "You'll do it yet". Lets hope I will (NLWA JLW MP1/1).

H. G. Wells, who studied biology and zoology at South Kensington during the years 1884-1885, recalls his own struggle to make ends meet on his meagre weekly allowance:

> The "Teachers in Training" ... were paid a maintenance allowance of a guinea weekly, which even in those days was rather insufficient. After I had paid for my lodgings, breakfasts and so forth, I was left with only a shilling or two for a week of midday meals. Pay day was Wednesday and not infrequently my money had run out before Monday or Tuesday and then I ate nothing in the nine hour interval between the breakfast and the high tea I had at my lodgings (Wells, 1966: 199-206).

As a husband with a young family, Lloyd Williams was always on the lookout for some part-time employment to help his family at home in Cricieth but such openings were not easy to find:

> [23 November,1895] . . . I had a small disappointment this week. I got to hear . . . that some people were looking for a Teacher of Botany for an evening Class. As soon as I heard I applied and after some time I got a reply which I enclose. You will see from it that another fellow had been there before me. The class met once a week for an hour and a half. Pay 5/– [25p] an hour. This would mean 7/6 [37.5p] a week. I am much afraid that there will be no chance again for such a thing, the teachers having been all secured during the Summer. It would have been funny my going to a Convent to teach Botany wouldn't it (NLWA JLW MP1/1).

During January 1896 Lloyd Williams was busy with his studies on the seaweed *Fucus* when he was interrupted by Bretland Farmer who told him the news that a leading botanist was working on the same species. He wrote to his wife on 9 January, 1896:

> Farmer gave me such a fright yesterday. He burst into the room crying "Williams, I have bad news for you." I turned round to see if he was joking. But no – he looked disturbed . . . Said Farmer "Strasburger is working at Fucus." This is the common seaweed which I began when at home and Strasburger is one of the best botanists in Europe. So now I have to run a race with this man. I know it is quite useless and I am quite surprised at Farmer wanting me to do it for it is sheer waste of time and nothing else. The idea of my getting this out before old Strasburger is perfectly ridiculous. However, I had to telegraph for gwmon [seaweed] from Bangor and to order a small cask of sea water from the east coast – both arrived today. I have more work than ever on my hands now (NLWA JLW MP1/1).

The paper on *Fucus* prepared by Lloyd Williams under the supervision of Farmer was presented before the Royal Society by D. H. Scott and was later published in the *Proceedings of the Royal Society* (Farmer and Williams, 1896a: 188-195) and later during the same year in *Annals of Botany* (Farmer and Williams, 1896b: 479-487). The paper published the results of an 'investigation into the processes connected with the formation and fertilisation of the oospheres and the germination of the spore in *Ascophyllum nodosum, Fucus vesiculosus*, and *F. platycarpus*' (Farmer and Williams, 1896a: 188). It notes that the work was an addition to the studies of other experts like Thuret and Oltmanns, but further explains that these had paid but little attention to the behaviour of the cell-nuclei, and that they had not succeeded in observing the actual process of fertilization. Specimens for the experiments were gathered at Bangor, Plymouth and Jersey and compared with others from Bangor, Weymouth and Cricieth, collected between the tides and fixed immediately while others were preserved in salt water:

> the best results, however, were obtained from plants collected in a boat about two or three hours after the tide had reached the plant, and also from other plants taken a short time before they were left exposed by the ebb tide (Farmer and Williams, 1896a: 188).

In a letter to his wife dated 19 May 1896 Lloyd Williams reveals that the paper was but a 'mere skeleton of a bigger work to come out later on. . . . At first it was to be sent to the Journal of Botany then to Annals – but at last it got to the Royal Soc. – the most honourable place for a paper to be read in this country' (NLWA JLW MP1/1). The main reason for publishing the paper may have been so that the results of the study would have been in print before those of Strasburger, who did not get his paper out until the following year.

In the 45th Report of the Department of Science and Art, Royal College of Science (1898), it is noted that Lloyd Williams was appointed Demonstrator in Botany to the Pharmaceutical Society of Great Britain, but had resigned on gaining a post as Demonstrator and Lecturer in Botany at the University College of North Wales, Bangor.

In 1897 Lloyd Williams published a paper describing his discovery of motile antherozoids of *Dictyota dichotoma* and *Taonia atomaria* (Williams, J.L., 1897) and was awarded grants by the British Association for the Advancement of Science to continue his researches. This discovery was a major breakthrough as previous authors like Thuret, Crouan and Reinke had described the liberated antherozoids as being non-motile.

On 16 June, 1898, D.H. Scott presented Farmer and Lloyd Williams' advanced paper on *Fucus* before the Royal Society and this was later published in the *Philosophic Transactions* (Farmer and Williams, 1898: 623-645). These papers later came to be regarded as classics. Whilst at Bangor Lloyd Williams took advantage of the close proximity of the surrounding habitats and led his students to explore the Arctic-Alpine flora of Snowdonia, and the marine algae of the nearby Menai Straits. He always believed in letting his students see the various plants in their natural habitats and was critical of lecturers who kept their students in the classroom learning from text books. Making use of the double tides of the Menai Straits that conveniently occurred during morning and evening he discovered how the tides influenced the liberating of the spores of *Dictyota*:

> A closer study enabled one to see that each crop was initiated, matured and discharged all within a fortnight, and that a general liberation of the oospheres and antherozoids of this locality took place on a certain day, or sometimes two or three days, immediately after the highest spring tide (Williams, J.L., 1905: 531).

He also claimed the startling result of producing a hybrid between *Fucus* and *Ascophyllum*. It is now known that different species of *Fucus* hybridise but Lloyd Williams' result was, as far as is known, never followed up (Williams, J.L., 1899: 187-188).

By this time Lloyd Williams was based at Bangor and despite winning the Marshall Scholarship and receiving a Certificate of Associateship of the Royal College of Science, he still did not have a University degree and this went against him when he applied for the Chair of Botany at Aberystwyth when it became vacant in 1903. The successful applicant was Richard Henry Yapp (1871-1929) who remained in the post until 1914. In 1904 Lloyd Williams received a grant from the council of the Royal Society to proceed further with his work on the seaweed *Dictyotacea* at the Marine Laboratory, Plymouth. He wrote to his wife after arriving there:

> [29 August, 1904] . . . I had a pleasant journey yesterday from Chester to Bristol although the train was very full – it was a quarter of an hour late starting from Shrewsbury but it made up time on the way . . . arrived in Plymouth very late and found that neither Bike nor Portmanteau had come . . . The guard said that only a third of the Bristol luggage had come . . . when the next train came I thought there was nothing for me but after a lot of trouble I found my Bike, . . . I have not seen my Portmanteau yet. I had to walk through the rain through the back streets to discover the business parts. It was useless looking for lodgings so I went to a Temperance. I'll tell you more of my

adventure again – but I'm not going to take a long journey Bank Holiday time again. Saturday morning. Another day of pouring rain – I went to find the Lab. It is a fine building on the seafront, my table overlooks the bay and there is a big Torpedo boat Destroyer right in front . . . After seeing the place I went to secure lodgings . . . there was a gentleman working here during the week – he is leaving today so for the next week I have taken his room at the Waverley Temperance, Plymouth. I have a beautiful room . . . big and well furnished and I get Breakfast and tea, and sandwiches to take with me to the Lab. – the charge will be 5/– [25p] a day. In the meantime I shall be able to look about me and try and discover a cheaper place. I am going now to the other station to see if my bag has arrived . . . North Road 12 o clock Bag alright – it had been to Truro and back . . . the boat is already out dredging stuff for me. I have a key which will enable me to get into the Lab at any hour day or night – Sunday or Bank Holiday – have to post before 3 . . . Your loving –Jack – (NLWA JLW MP1/1).

Lloyd Williams' major work on the *Dictyotaceae* was published in *Annals of Botany* during 1904 and 1905 (Williams, J.L., 1904, 1905) in which he expresses his debt to the Royal Society and the Marine Laboratory at Plymouth:

I gratefully beg to express my obligation to the Council of the Royal Society for giving me a grant of money to enable me to carry on my study of the Dictyotaceae on the South Coast, and also to the Royal Microscopical Society for nominating me to their table in the Marine Biological Laboratory at Plymouth. To Dr. Allen, the Director of the latter institution, and his assistant, Mr. Smith, I also wish to express my deep obligation for their unfailing courtesy and their readiness to place the resources of the establishment at my disposal. It is a matter of surprise that so few algologists take advantage of such a well-equipped and admirably conducted station (Williams, J.L., 1905: 557).

Lloyd Williams' name became familiar to botanists not only in Britain but also in Europe and America. W. D. Hoyt communicated with him from the John Hopkins University, Baltimore, stating that he had read Lloyd Williams' papers on *Dictyota dichotoma* having used it in comparison with the plants of North Carolina which he had studied:

I expect to present a preliminary paper on this subject before the A.A.A.S. at Christmas in the hope of inducing other American Botanists to commence observations on this form. It seems that only by a number of observations at different places for long periods of time and a careful comparison of conditions can we hope to understand this remarkable behaviour. Should you care to try to exchange living sexual plants with me next summer? It may be that we can devise some way of shipping them alive, and in view of the differences exhibited by your plants and mine, I should greatly like to try the effect of a change of conditions. I expect to continue this study next summer and shall be greatly obliged if you can spare some reprints of your papers. I shall also greatly appreciate any suggestions that you may care to give. I hope to return to Beaufort next summer and to continue observations on Dictyota along the lines suggested in your article in the last number of Annals of Botany. If you can give any further suggestions to my guidance, I shall be greatly obliged to you. I shall be glad to have your articles before me and I shall appreciate it if you can send me reprints of them (NLWA JLW B1/2/8-9).

Lloyd Williams was frequently cited by Oltmanns in his *Morphologie und Biologie der Algen* (Oltmanns, 1904-1905) and was highly respected by other German scientists. Amy Graves, the daughter of Heinrich Ritter von Ranke, Professor of Medicine at Munich University, in a letter to Lloyd Williams dated 11 January 1907, passed on a message from her father which read:

Only a short time ago I was able to speak with Professor Go'bel about the pamphlets of Mr. Lloyd Williams. It appears (or shows itself) that the works of Mr. Lloyd Williams are well valued in Germany. Mr. Williams is counted an authority on his subject. Prof Go'bel showed me the newest great German work on the Algae: "Morphology & Biology of the Algae" by Oltmanns, . . . in which the name of Mr. W. is frequently cited. This you can communicate to Mr. Lloyd Williams. Please ask him the same time if he is a member of the Linnean Society? Should this not be the case, Prof Go'bel would propose him as such, if he wishes it (NLWA JLW B1/2/2).

Lloyd Williams was elected a Fellow of the Linnean Society in 1916, his Certificate of Election being supported by the signatures of Reginald W. Phillips, F.W. Oliver and A.H. Trow. He withdrew from Fellowship in 1927.

Having completed his work at Plymouth he returned to his post as Demonstrator and Assistant Lecturer in Botany at Bangor and in 1908 was awarded a D. Sc. for his work on marine algae. In 1912 he moved to a new position at Bangor when a Government grant enabled the Agricultural Department to establish two new advisory posts, but the Reports of the Heads of Departments for Session 1914-1915 stated:

During the year the valuable services of Dr. J. Lloyd Williams were lost to the department, on account of his appointment to the Professorship of Botany at Aberystwyth. Mr T. J. Jenkins, B. Sc. an Aberystwyth student . . . was appointed to fill the vacancy. He commenced work in March, 1915 (UWB, RHD: 4 October 1915).

Lloyd Williams began his term as Professor of Botany at Aberystwyth at the beginning of the Great War of 1914-1918 which greatly reduced the number of students attending the lectures, and this situation continued until after the end of the conflict. The ex-servicemen returning to college after the war earned the praise of Lloyd Williams:

> I wish to bear testimony to the whole-hearted way the ex-servicemen threw themselves into the work in spite of the difficulty they must have felt in adapting to conditions so different from those they had experienced during the preceding years of stress. Their success in the examinations showed that the responsibilities they had borne, and their novel experiences, had given them a wider outlook and a more mature judgement, which in a very striking degree reflected themselves in their academic work (UWA, RCG: 17 October 1919).

The botany department at Aberystwyth continued to grow during 1920 despite some delay in obtaining apparatus such as new microscopes. Lloyd Williams continued with his work on marine algae preparing an abstract of it to read at a meeting of the British Association to be held in Cardiff. During that year Dr Charles Joseph Chamberlain (1863-1943) of the University of Chicago, being familiar with the work of Lloyd Williams, wrote him on 26 October 1920 (NLWA JLW B1/1/9) urging him to publish a paper on his work with the seaweeds *Laminaria* and *Chorda*. He had previously presented papers on *Laminaria* before the British Association at Bradford in 1900 and at Dundee in 1912, and Chamberlain was anxious for him to claim credit for his work by being first in print. Claiming authenticity by publishing without delay was regarded as vital before someone else could benefit from the preliminary work. This prompted Lloyd Williams' last published paper on marine algae, which explained the actual fertilisation process of *Laminaria* and *Chorda* (Williams, J.L., 1921: 603-607). In this paper Lloyd Williams confirms C. F. Sauvageau's theory concerning a different species:

> Until recently all attempts at verifying this conjecture by observing the liberation of the contents and the process of fertilization failed. To Sauvaugeau [sic] belongs the credit of finding the first piece of evidence in favour of the correctness of the above suggestion.

Although he, also, failed to find actual liberation of male gametes and fertilization, he was lucky enough to find in *Saccorhiza* abnormal cases of germination of zoospores within liberated but unripe sporangia (Williams, J.L., 1921: 603).

Despite the title noting that the paper was a 'preliminary account' and that a series of reports of a more detailed nature would be forthcoming, this was Lloyd Williams' last published treatise on marine algae. He was however successful in encouraging some of his students to carry on the work. One student P. W. Carter, who was later to publish a series of highly informative papers on the history of botanical exploration in Wales, published his work on the structure and cytology of the seaweed *Padina pavonia* (Carter, 1927).

Lloyd Williams' popular book *Byd y Blodau* (The World of Flowers) was published in 1924, and in 1927 an English translation entitled *Flowers of the Wayside and Meadow* appeared. The idea of producing the book was first thought of by Mrs Silyn Roberts and Dr Thomas Jones of the Cabinet Office who saw a book being used in the schools of Denmark which comprised of descriptions and illustrations of plants that were indigenous to both Denmark and Wales; the book was illustrated with lithographs which was not then generally available in colour. Professor Lange gave permission for his illustrations to be reproduced and Morris and Jones, a grocery wholesale company of Liverpool, agreed to publish both the Welsh and English versions. The services of John Lloyd Williams were called upon by the universities after his retirement in 1926, and in a letter dated 14 May 1928 from the University College of North Wales, Bangor, as it was known then, he was invited to give extension courses in biology at classes held in Trawsfynydd, while extra-mural work in places like Bala, Llangefni and Llanrwst was also mentioned. Manuscript notes of other lectures given in various towns and villages around Wales with fascinating titles like 'Darwinism and Germany', 'Gerddi gwyllt y Wyddfa' ('The wild gardens of Snowdon'), 'The social characteristics of plants', 'Light and life', 'Welsh agriculture' and 'Fy nghredo' (My belief), are held at the National Library of Wales, Aberystwyth.

He continued to develop his musical talents. He became a prominent figure at concerts and in eisteddfodic circles as a conductor and adjudicator, composed operettas and was prominent in laying the foundations for the forming of the Welsh Folk Song Society. For these services he was conferred an Honorary Doctor of Music by the University of Wales in 1936.

When Lloyd Williams was ninety years old the villagers of

Garndolbenmaen decided to honour the occasion by presenting him with a walking stick. With complete disregard for his years he thanked the audience, saying that he might find the stick useful when he grew old. In his obituary published in the *Proceedings of the Linnean Society of London* Margery Knight said:

> The contribution which a professor of Botany makes to his day and generation is only partially assessed on the criteria of his published works. There is the other side of professorial responsibility, concerned with the education of the student; the inculcation of scientific accuracy, and above all, the stimulation and transfer of enthusiasm; the spark of spirit which lights the torch in the minds of colleagues and students alike. In these qualities Lloyd Williams was markedly rich. He was a first class teacher and an excellent field botanist. Snowdonia was his happy hunting ground . . . He was a remarkable personality. Spare in figure; possessed of immense vigour; a mobile face expressing freely the Celtic fervour of his feelings; choleric, whole-heartedly amused, frankly incredulous, or kindly considerate, he was forthright in all his dealings. As one of his old students said of him 'one knew where one was with him, but woe betide any one who let him down' (Knight, 1947: 73).

Following the death of his wife Lloyd Williams spent his remaining years with his son Dr Idwal Williams and his family at Peasedown St John, near Bath, Somerset, and he died there aged ninety-one on 15 November, 1945. He lies buried at Cricieth.

William Williams, the 'Botanical Guide'

William Williams was born in 1805 in the parish of Llanfwrog, Denbighshire, and entered service at the age of thirteen being engaged mainly as a sub-groom. He stayed with Mr M. Turner of Abbot's Bromley, Staffordshire, for four years working as a groom. He subsequently worked at various hotels and inns, namely the White Lion, Ruthin, Black Lion, Mold and the Penrhyn Arms and Liverpool Arms, Bangor as a general driver. During his stay in Bangor he attended school for about six months, the fees being paid by himself; this was the only period of official education he ever received (Anon., 1861a: 308). He came to Llanberis in 1832 to work at the Royal Victoria Hotel, and also maintained connections with the Dolbadarn Hotel. His early period working as a boot-boy earned him the nick-name 'Will boots'. He was in Snowdonia during the heyday of the great Victorian collecting era, and when he first began to operate as a mountain guide he was a keen collector of crystals and insects. When the first huts were built on the summit of Snowdon in 1837 or 1838 Williams went into partnership with Morris Williams of Amlwch, a copper miner who first had the idea of providing refreshments on the summit, and in an attempt to add to the attraction of Snowdon 'dressed himself in a suit of goat-skin, consisting of cap, coat and trousers, which made him appear like a savage from the land of perpetual snow . . . the flocking visitors soon made the humble summit a paying concern' (Jenkins, 1899: 183). William Williams presumably left the business soon afterwards and Morris Williams sold his share to his brother Phillip who subsequently formed a partnership with another guide, John Roberts. In due course there were two separately run huts providing refreshments for tourists on the summit. John Roberts managed the hut belonging to the Royal Victoria Hotel while William Roberts managed the hut belonging to the Dolbadarn Hotel.

William Williams was familiar with the localities of the rarer plants of Snowdonia, and came to be known as 'the Botanical Guide', with a special interest in the rarer ferns. Edward Newman (1801-1876), an authority on ferns knew Williams and describes him as:

> an active and intelligent Snowdon guide . . . well acquainted with the Snowdonian stations of both the Woodsias: [*Woodsia alpina* and *W. ilvensis*] I don't think he would willingly exterminate them, but he is subject to constant solicitations from botanical tourists to be conducted to the localities, that the utter extermination of these ferns from all accessible places is not only certain, but also imminent (Newman, 1854: 77).

He occasionally ascended Snowdon three times in one day, including a night ascent; the custom of going up to watch the sunrise was popular then, especially so during the 'Harvest moon' and 'Hunter's moon' seasons of September and October. Williams became well known among the leading botanists of the day and benefited from his specialist knowledge when the collecting of ferns developed into a craze. This reputation would sometimes lead into an unpleasant confrontation with visiting plant collectors. John Barton of Cambridge (Allen, 1980: 157-158), following an ascent of Snowdon with an accomplice, approached William Williams at the foot of Clogwyn y Garnedd where he had been gathering holly fern *(Polystichum lonchitis)*, hoping to be led to the locality of the rare alpine woodsia *(Woodsia alpina)*. Williams did show Barton the fern but there followed a disagreement regarding its identity, and Barton, infuriated by not having seen more *Woodsia*, subsequently published his account of the incident in the popular botanical journal *The Phytologist* (Barton, 1857) in an attempt to discredit Williams' reputation, a reputation on which his livelihood to a great extent depended:

> . . . he showed us a very small plant of which he declared to be *Woodsia hyperborea* [*Woodsia alpina*] but for the genuineness of which I could not venture to vouch, as all the mature fronds had been stripped off for the gratification of some greedy fern-hunters. The plant itself was completely hidden under a piece of rock, so that we had before walked almost over it; and Williams informed us, with a grin that it was his usual practice either thus to hide all the plants of *Woodsia* he could find, or to transplant them when growing in too exposed a situation, so as to prevent all possibility of their being detected. Another piece of information which he volunteered with equal satisfaction to himself was, that he was accustomed to give wrong habitats when applied to by Newman and other writers on Ferns for the localities of rare species . . . In fact it was very evident that he delighted in 'taking in' each successive visitor who trusted himself to his tender mercies, and then amused himself by chuckling over it to the next comer, who of course received the unpleasant impression that he was being treated in a very similar way at that very moment . . . I have little doubt in my own mind that the *Woodsia* was to be found there as elsewhere. But Williams's intention evidently was to lure us from the spot. He declared it grew below Crib Goch, about a mile or more nearer the Pass, in the direction of Gorphwysfa, said he would take us to see it; but as he wanted to go back to the inn, and we preferred to descend to the Pass, we agreed to meet him halfway up after we had breakfasted, and then go with him to the spot. Of course he did not appear; and on

meeting him a few hours later at the Victoria Hotel he tried to shuffle out of it, but only succeeded so far as to convince us that he had been intentionally misleading us (Barton,1857: 147; 149).

Williams, following the disagreement over the identity of the species in question, seems to have lost patience with Barton and led the party down the mountain to the Llanberis Pass by way of Crib y Ddysgl and Cwmglas Mawr, showing them some very special plants *en route*.

Barton's article prompted Charles Cardale Babington to write to William Pamplin, the publisher of *The Phytologist*, defending William Williams' character:

> [I] am rather angry with a Cambridge correspondent of yours unknown to me except for his letter for the mode in which he [Williams] is treated in the Phytologist. I believe the man to be honest and well intending. The Editor might use his knife a little more actively in such and few other cases with much advantage (UWB Pamplin Papers, Babington to Pamplin 7 August, 1857).

Babington's opinion was highly regarded and must have carried some weight in this matter. Pamplin, as if to redeem the reputation of William Williams and to make up for what Babington considered an injustice, published an account of a botanical ramble in Snowdonia which was led by the 'Botanical Guide'. Great emphasis is given to the trustworthiness and willingness of the guide to show visitors, in a single day's walk, a good number of plants for which Snowdonia is famous:

> On Saturday morning, at nine o'clock, William Williams, the botanical guide, true to an appointment previously made, joined us at the Rectory, and we sallied forth for a regular field day. He showed everything he had promised me, and more (Pamplin, 1858: 312).

The botanical ramble lasted all day, from 9 o'clock in the morning until 9 o'clock in the evening, returning down the lower slopes by moonlight. The plants noted included some of Snowdonia's treasures. This, together with the comments on Williams' willingness to show the localities, must have caused a great deal of mouth-watering among those eager Victorian botanists and plant-collectors who were readers of *The Phytologist* and went a long way to reinstate the good name of William Williams as an honest and reliable botanical guide. Reverend W. Lloyd Williams also speaks highly of Williams:

> I always found him straight-forward, truth-telling, and honest. A different impression of his character from this might be left on the

minds of some, who may have read a communication from Mr. John Barton, in the 'Phytologist' of January, 1857 [the correct month was July and not January]. But this may easily be explained. Mr. Williams was jealous about the rarer Ferns: not from any mercenary motive; he was jealous for the character of the locality, and did not like it to be robbed of what proved a great attraction to many visitors. To persons whom he knew, he never hesitated to show the habitats of the rarer plants (Anon., [Williams, W.L], 1861a: 309).

John Barton the Cambridge botanist was the subject of a biographical supplement by D. E. Allen: selected portions are quoted as follows:

Descended on his father's side from Quaker manufacturers in Cumberland, Barton was born in 1836 at East Leigh, near Havant (not, as the DNB has it Eastleigh, which was not then yet named), the sixth child of John Barton (1798-1852) and Frances, daughter of James Rickman . . . His mother died when he was four, the children were brought up by her only sister, Josephina Christiana Rickman (1808-1892). Both she and her father were keen botanists, . . . On moving to Stoughton, near Chichester the family had for a neighbour the Rev Gerard Edwards Smith (1804-1881), one of the ablest field botanists of the day, who became a particularly close and valued friend. . . With such a set of mentors it is no surprise that the younger Barton's interest in botany ripened early. The letters from Smith suggest that this was well developed by the time he went up to Cambridge at nineteen, and by twenty-one his herbarium had been extended to nearly 1000 species ... though what ultimately became of it is, alas, unknown . . . In June 1858 he joined the Thirsk Botanical Exchange Club, which was carrying on the annual distributions of the lately ill-fated Botanical Society of London, and the pages of Irvine's *Phytologist* bear copious witness to his intense activity at this period. So intense was this by then, indeed, that after taking his degree in January 1859 he was allowed to return to Cambridge to sit for the Natural Sciences Tripos. There is a letter from him in the Babington correspondence at the Botany School, Cambridge, written from Torquay on 26 January 1860, in which he intimates that he hopes 'to be able to do something in geology and botany, with a little chemistry' and seeks Babington's advice on the books to read on these subjects. September of that year, however, saw him ordained and a month after that he set sail for India. . . . How far his interests in botany (and geology) stayed with him in later years – he lived till 1908 – is not known (Allen, 1980: 157).

It seems likely that William Williams was the first to be credited with the discovery of the mountain avens *(Dryas octopetala)* in Snowdonia, and although the name of the plant does appear in *Welsh Botanology* (Davies, 1813: 134), there is no evidence to suggest that the author ever found it growing in the mountains of Caernarfonshire. The discovery is first revealed by William Pamplin in his account of the botanical ramble over the Glyder led by Williams, mentioned earlier: 'Please remember the entire credit of the discovery of the *Dryas* [mountain avens; *Dryas octopetala*], is entirely due to him, William Williams' (Pamplin, 1858: 315). Babington, in correspondence with Pamplin accepted that Williams made this discovery, stating: 'Williams need not to have been so anxious about the Dryas as I fully believed him. I hope that you will be careful not to publish the exact stations of it & the rare ferns – for extirpation is the rule in Wales with tourists & collectors who call themselves botanists' (UWB Pamplin Papers, Babington to Pamplin 7 August, 1857).

Rumours soon began to spread that the mountain avens was planted on the Glyder site, and in one instance published in a popular guide-book: 'This grows in great abundance between Twll Du and Glyder Fawr, but there seems a probability of its having been planted there' (Britten, 1878: lxxxix). This was the only known locality for the plant in Snowdonia until Evan Roberts (1906-1991) of Capel Curig found another on the Carneddau range in 1946 (Farmer, 1948: 150n), and this tends to strengthen the case for Williams who claimed the mountain avens to be a true native of Snowdonia. The plant is still found in both localities.

Evidence that William Williams owned a pocket-book appeared in Humphreys' *Guide to the summit of Snowdon*, a local guide-book printed and published in Caernarfon, probably in 1850. A list of plant names was included, together with the following acknowledgement: 'We are favoured with the above List from the Visitor's Book of Mr. William Williams, Guide to Snowdon from Llanberis' (Humphreys, [1850]: 25-26). Fifty-six plants were listed including two additional varieties of the spring sandwort *(Minuartia verna)* and one of alpine saw-wort *(Saussurea alpina)* which are not currently recognized. The plants appear in alphabetical order with no localities appended. The mountain avens is not listed; its discovery only occurred eight years after the publication of Humphreys' guide-book. Nothing further is known about the pocket-book of William Williams.

Williams' chief botanical mentors were Reverend Thomas Butler (1806-1886) and Charles Babington. The fact that Babington commented favourably on Williams' character is conclusive proof that they knew one another; further proof appears in a letter from Reverend W. Lloyd Williams of Llanberis: 'I have not been able to learn when he turned his attention to botany; but I have been informed that he received great help from Mr Babington and the Rev. Mr. Butler in acquiring a knowledge of the rarer plants of this neighbourhood' (Anon., [Williams, W.L.],1861a: 308).

Thomas Butler was introduced to botany by none other than Charles Darwin, having got to know him slightly during their schooldays. During the summer of 1828 both were at Barmouth, Merioneth, as members of an undergraduate reading-party where, during long mountain rambles, Butler was 'inoculated ... with a taste for botany' by Darwin, an interest which never left him (Allen, 1979). A clue to a possible professional relationship between Butler and Williams appear in Samuel Butler's note-books in a note entitled 'My father and his Woodsias': 'When I was a boy we used to get woodsias on Snowdon and Glyder Fawr. There were four plants left on Glyder Fawr when I was young and William Williams swore that there were none others' (Breuer, 1984: 212).

According to Breuer (1984: 345) William Williams was the family butler, but there is little doubt, bearing in mind the testimony of Reverend W. Lloyd Williams (1861a) quoted previously, that this William Williams was indeed the famous Llanberis guide who was leader of many a botanical excursion among the mountains of Snowdonia during the period under discussion. What better mentors could Williams have had than Butler and Babington and this teamwork worked both ways. The visitors learned from the topographical knowledge of Williams and others like him who spent most of their working days among their native mountains and valleys.

William Williams was an original character with a flair for gaining publicity and he wore a fur cap bearing the words 'Botanist Guide' in bold letters. A brief note, plus the following lines of verse were sent for publication in *The North Wales Chronicle* a short time after his death: 'The following has been forwarded to us for publication by a gentleman who has had the same in his possession for above 15 years, from which it will be seen that the poor guide who lost his life on Snowdon a few days ago, attempted poetry as well as botany. The exact time when the lines were written is not known' (Anon., 1861b).

> William Williams, guide to Snowdon,
> Anxious that all those who 'bode in
> England, Scotland, or old Ireland,
> Should place their feet upon much higher land
> Than ever was in those parts seen
> By young or old that e're have been,
> Gives notice, that if here they'll ride,

He, with much pleasure as their guide,
Will show them quarries, lakes, and mines,
Snowdon, and the place he finds,
Plants that nowhere else abound,
And which by him alone are found:-
Waterfalls with various actions,
Minerals, ores, and petrifactions;
The house where Margaret Evan died,
St Perry's well and all beside:
Anglers too, who with a boat
Can be supplied and when afloat,
Will find at once by asking him,
The places where the best trout swim;
In fact to him, no place is new,
Within the range of Snowdon view
Excepting one, which he declares
To bring folks to he never dares,
Not being on the best of terms
With him who owns these hot concerns,
'The Devil's Kitchen', it is named,
And by some tourists is much famed;
'Tis here we're told, the king satanic
Allures his own by means botanic,
But there are guides who know it true,
Its inmost parts and master too,
And folks who wish to go with these,
Can walk the road with greatest ease;
To guide elsewhere, 'midst many millions,
There's none so good as William Williams.

He became a legend in Snowdonia and 'Llyn Wil boots' (Will boots' lake) used to be a well known landmark in Llanberis, now vanished under the village by-pass. Williams was beginning to realize that the plants were being gathered to the point of near extinction, and that he would be as guilty as anyone if they disappeared. John Henry Cliffe heard about the ravages of the plant collectors from a guide at Penygwryd, and although not named, it was probably William Williams:

Bingley, who was an excellent botanist, gives a list of a number of rare alpine Plants which he discovered amongst the wilds and precipices of Snowdon and Llanberis. Since his time, however, many of the plants he mentions are entirely extinct, or become exceedingly scarce. One of the guides at the Victoria Hotel, who is a very civil intelligent man, is in great request during the summer by the numerous botanists who frequent the locality, as he knows 'the habitat of every plant in the surrounding mountains.' The last time we saw him was at Penygwryd, and he then gave us some valuable information on several particulars of which we were previously ignorant. He told us that some of the rarer species of plants, were, in consequence of the incessant researches of botanists, yearly becoming more scarce, and that in winter, when the snow was on the ground, and deep in some parts of the mountains, he had several times risked his life amongst the precipices and hollows of Snowdon, in pursuit of some rare plant which he had been commissioned to procure for some botanical enthusiast (Cliffe, 1860: 166).

Babington, Pamplin and other prominent botanists were also aware of what was happening, but the collecting went on. Williams began to construct a small lake at a site below what used to be the old Goodmans Quarry near Llanberis. In this lake he planned to build small islands where he could transplant the rarities, out of reach of greedy plant collectors. This place came to be known locally as 'Llyn Wil boots'. Had the dream of establishing a haven for the rare plants of Eryri been realized, it would have been the first nature reserve of its kind in Snowdonia, and perhaps in Wales. Despite his concern and conservationist ideals which he practiced at Llanberis, it was all very inconsistent with what he got up to on the cliffs of Snowdon.

William Bennett (1804-1873), a London botanist, visited the Snowdon district in 1849 and hired one of the younger guides to take him to Clogwyn Du'r Arddu, and after collecting several specimens of the more common ferns they continued on towards the summit of Snowdon. They met William Williams a short distance below the summit:

When on the last shoulder, in full sight of the summit, we met one of the older guides coming down, well known for his botanical lore, and especially for his knowledge, said to be exclusive, of the habitat of Woodsia in Clogwyn-y-Garnedd. After some chaffering to obtain information, and not without the aid of a little bribery, – for which, however, he promised to transmit us a plant if we did not succeed in finding it, – he brought us back a little to the edge of the ridge, and professed to point out the exact spot where the Woodsia grew, far down amid a world of rocks and precipices. All the time we did not think he meant us to find it. The absurdity of identifying by description from above one particular wet rock, when down amongst such a chaos of rocks and precipices, was apparent enough. We were determined, however, not to fail for want of trying; . . . So down the Capel Curig track we went, and then deviated to the right, to get under the precipice constituting Clogwyn-y-Garnedd. It is almost needless to say, that after a tremendous scramble we had to give up the Woodsia; but were sufficiently rewarded by capturing several plants of Polystichum Lonchitis [holly fern], and saw some still finer ones in places inaccessible. . . . After rounding the little Llyn Glas [Glaslyn] below, we had to ascend the tremendous Bwlch-y-Laethan [Saethau], to the summit, just before sunset. Here we found that the guides who are stationary at the top, having erected booths, ... had Lonchitis for sale at sixpence a root; a practice which, if encouraged, must soon annihilate this fine and sparingly scattered fern from all accessible habitats. They knew nothing of Woodsia. Since returning home, the guide, faithful to his promise has sent by post a small root, and some fronds of a true Woodsia, but unfortunately so mutilated that we cannot satisfactorily determine the species (Bennett, 1849: 713-714).

At the Natural History Museum, London, there is an envelope bearing the inscription 'Snowdon W. Williams', together with the following, preserved with the Herbarium of W. C. Barton, presented 1934: 'Woodsia alpina Gray Clogwyn y Garnedd / Snowdon N. Wales / W. Williams, Llanberris./ A [?] Bennett'

Edwin Lees (1800-1887) was informed by a guide at the Dolbadarn Hotel (then known as the Dolbadarn Castle) in Llanberis, during his visit to Snowdonia in 1838 that it would not be a profitable proposition for him to go to the plant localities of Snowdon as that would take a whole day, during which time he could lead three parties to the summit. Arrangements were subsequently made for Lees to meet a guide who specialised in that line of work:

> Next morning a brisk little Welchman, active as the goat of his native mountains, with a tin box on his back, on which was painted "William Williams," presented himself to my inspection, and said that he was so fond of plants, that he would go with me any where, as long as I pleased. My arrangements were at once made, and we started (Lees, 1851: 446).

Williams led Lees up the Llanberis path to Snowdon, pointing out to him a large cairn of stones surmounted by a tall wooden pole that had been erected by a team of surveyors. The pole bore the inscriptions of countless visitors who had climbed to the summit and while he stood there he paid his respects to the young Queen Victoria who was crowned in June of that year by drinking a toast from his 'pocket pistol', a small flask containing spirits. During the ascent Williams told Lees of how, on a previous excursion, he had been involved in the rescue of a visitor that had left a party which he was leading to the summit. Having arrived at the summit, one man decided to leave the party to find his own way down, and back to Caernarfon, instead of returning to Llanberis with the others. As the Caernarfon road could be seen from the point at which they stood, the visitor had no doubt that he would find his way down safely, and left. Williams was leading another party to the summit of Snowdon at 4 o'clock on the following morning to see the sunrise, when calls for help were heard coming from far below the southern ridge of the mountain. Williams scrambled down the slope in the direction from which the cries were heard to come and eventually found the man who had left his party the day before in a distressed state and suffering from exposure. The man later explained that during his descent from the summit the day before he had mistaken the road for a distant stream, and had become disorientated when failing to find a safe way down amid the bewildering array of crags and short precipices in the gathering dusk. The unfortunate visitor subsequently spent two weeks recovering in his room in Llanberis.

The least willow *(Salix herbacea)* which according to Lees (1851: 449) 'might be concealed within the leaves of a thumb almanack', was seen near the summit before they left to explore the steep face of the Clogwyn y Garnedd cliffs where: 'the little Welchman, with his tin box on his back, actually bounded like a roe' (Lees, 1851: 450). Among the plants gathered by Williams on this cliff were alpine saw-wort *(Saussurea alpina)*, mountain sorrel *(Oxyria digyna)*, scurvygrass *(Cochlearia)*, viviparous fescue *(Festuca viviparum)*, alpine mouse-ear *(Cerastium alpinum)*, alpine meadow-rue *(Thalictrum alpinum)*, parsley fern *(Cryptogramma crispa)*, brittle bladder-fern *(Cystopteris fragilis)*, green spleenwort *(Asplenium viride)*, alpine clubmoss *(Diphasiastrum alpinum)* and lesser clubmoss *(Selaginella selaginoides)*. The spring sandwort *(Minuartia verna)*, alpine bistort *(Persicaria vivipara)* and Wilson's filmy-fern *(Hymenophyllum wilsonii)* are also mentioned. The wet flushes among the numerous base-rich crags are rich in bryophyte species but only two are named, the apple moss *(Bartramia pomiformis)* and *Polytrichum urnigerum.*

Later that day Williams led Lees to Clogwyn Du'r Arddu which was reached by climbing the zig-zagging path from above Llyn Glaslyn to Bwlch Glas, then turning off along the upper section of the Snowdon Ranger path. They reached the top of Clogwyn Du'r Arddu, finding the head of the eastern terrace which they climbed down to the base of the cliff.

The plant rich cliffs in the vicinity of the Devil's Kitchen (Twll Du) were visited on the following day. The Afon Las flows from the plateau near Llyn y Cŵn down the south-western slopes of Y Garn before joining the Nant Peris river at the lower end of the Pass. Williams lead his party upstream from Nant Peris, passing by a deep ravine rich in plants, gathering Welsh poppy *(Meconopsis cambrica)* and grass-of-Parnassus *(Parnassia palustris)*. They saw the melancholy thistle *(Cirsium heterophyllum)* before continuing up the western slopes of Glyder Fawr, noting the alpine juniper *(Juniperus communis* subsp *nana)* which grows on the rocky flank of this mountain. After gaining the summit of Glyder Fawr they then descended to the sheltered hollow where the quiet enclosed pool of Llyn y Cŵn is to be found; Williams pausing there to gather water lobelia *(Lobelia dortmanna)*, awlwort *(Subularia aquatica)* and quillwort *(Isoetes lacustris)* for Lees. The party was then suddenly engulfed in a thick white mist near the top of the Devil's Kitchen chasm:

> This, for a season, obliged us to call a halt, and bivouac in the Satanic territory. Accordingly we sat down upon the loose blocks of stone that lay near the chasm before us, and while waiting for the dispersion of the clouds about us, with appetites whetted by the mountain air, gladly called in requisition the not forgotten sandwiches and brandy-bottle, to reanimate our half exhausted limbs stiff with climbing. My little Welchman, however, kept jumping about among the crags, with his tin box strapped to his back, to my admiration and almost terror, and soon exhibited to me the delicate Spider-wort *(Anthericum serotinum)* [Snowdon lily], while I myself had plucked the Sea Pink *(Statice armeria)* [thrift], the soft-flowered Mountain Cat's-foot *(Antennaria dioica)* [mountain everlasting], and the alpine Hawkweed *(Hieracium alpinum)* [beautiful hawkweed: *Hieracium holosericeum*] (Lees, 1851: 460).

On reaching the base of the rock syncline below the Devil's Kitchen chasm they crossed the stream and arrived at the narrow ledge at the start of Llwybr y geifr (path of the goats). This path curves across the foot of a large protruding crag, and continues under a waterfall before climbing diagonally up the opposite side of the cliff face to emerge at the foot of Y Garn, the mountain on the opposite side of the Llyn y Cŵn plateau to Glyder Fawr:

> In this favourite spot, called the Botanic Garden of Snowdonia, some of the rarest Ferns reward the enterprise of the "Botanical Explorator," as *Asplenium septentrionale* [forked spleenwort], and *Hymenophyllum*

Wilsoni [Wilson's filmy-fern]. To find the very local *Polystichum Lonchitis* [holly fern], as well as the almost eradicated *Woodsia* [oblong or alpine woodsia: *W. ilvensis* or *W. alpina*], I ventured up the front of the mural rock. Midway up, one spot made us pause. It was a part where a huge intervening mass blockaded the way, with no possible advance but by a narrow gutter on its face fit only for a chamois. One slip from that narrow gutter would have been worse than a tumble from the Tarpeian rock, for it was a perpendicular plunge of 250 feet, without a break. At this point my nerves actually quailed at the prospect, and I could move no farther. But my little guide soon gave me a recipe for my nervousness, occasioned by my looking *down* into the cloudy gulph beneath. "Look up", said he, creep close to the rock, and there is no danger." I still hesitated, till measuring the distance with my eye, and at last forming my resolve, I *closed* my eyes on the fearful view, *felt* my way with cautious steps, crossed the dreaded ledge in safety, and gathered my plant! After that all was lightsome to the summit of the cliff, and thence over the flank of the Glyder by Llyn y Cŵn, and down into the vale of Llanberis, to a glorious regale at the Dolbadarn Castle (Lees, 1851: 461-462).

Lees was keen to recommend to his readers the high standard of service provided by the welcoming widowed landlady of the Dolbadarn Castle where the contact with William Williams was made. This hostelry, formerly known as The New Inn, had a long tradition with the Snowdon guides and although Williams' name is chiefly associated with the Royal Victoria Hotel he also maintained strong connections with the Dolbadarn Castle.

Lees' book *The Botanical Looker-out*, was first published in 1842 with a revised and enlarged edition appearing in 1851. Lees testifies to the over-collecting of ferns, referring to the *Woodsia* in his first edition as being 'almost eradicated' (Lees, 1842: 288), but he was relieved to be able to incorporate the good news about the plight of this fern into the second edition of his book:

> I am glad to understand that Woodsia Ilvensis has lately re-appeared in unusual abundance at its old station, a rock above Llyn-y-Cŵn. About a hundred plants were said to be visible in 1849, but inaccessible, and not to be gathered without the aid of a ladder (Lees, 1851: 461n).

Quoting from *The Phytologist* Newman described this *Woodsia* site in almost identical wording and this could well be the source of Lees' information:

211

I am also informed by another botanist that he has found it "above" Llyn-y-cwn [sic]. My correspondent says that "as many as a hundred plants are visible, fortunately, however, nearly the whole of them are inaccessible, and cannot possibly be obtained without the assistance of a ladder." – Phytol. iii, 739 (Newman, 1854: 77).

William Williams' local knowledge also included geology and entomology, thus increasing the demand for his services as guide. W.S. Symonds, who visited Snowdonia in the company of Professor James Buckman and Reverend R. Hill, recorded an important note on this aspect of the guide's interests:

We procured the services of William Williams the well-known botanist, and Llanberis guide. I could not ascertain from him whether there was any section of the Llandeilo beds where fossils could be obtained, although he took me to several localities where Caradoc fossils might be found, and in search of them, ventured to one of the most dangerous spots on the crags of Moel-y-Wyddfa. Williams was a most daring cragsman, and my companions will not easily forget him on the precipitous escarpment of Moel Siabod, searching for the Saussurea alpina, and the Woodsia fern (Woodsia ilvensis). The purple Saxifraga oppositifolia was found by William Williams on Glyder-Fawr. It grows on the Pyrenees, and on the Matterhorn above the Smutz Glacier. Williams was afterwards killed by falling down the precipice of Moel-y-Wyddfa, when searching for the Woodsia. I do not know whether Williams left behind him any account of the localities where he obtained his specimens of the rarer plants of Snowdonia, for he owned to us that several of the old stations were completely destroyed. The spiderwort (Anthericum serotinum) grew no longer among the crags above the Devil's Kitchen, though there was a station on Carnedd Dafydd where he obtained specimens worth half a guinea each. The Woodsia ilvensis grew in 1861 on a rock above Llyn Cwm, but in a locality only practicable for goats. Williams was an ardent lover of nature, and thoroughly appreciated a day's ramble with a botanist or geologist. It may be well to mention here for the information of entomologists, that on questioning him as to the habitat of the rare beetle, Miscodera arctica, he informed me that the most probable locality for finding it, was on the Beddgelert flanks of Snowdon, and that it was never far below the summit (Symonds, 1872: 112).

It is ironic that William Williams met his death on his favourite fern-hunting cliff. He attended the service at Jerusalem, the Independent

Chapel at Llanberis, on the Sunday before his fatal accident where a collection was made to help a poor widow. Williams donated a half-crown (12½p) and one penny. The collector, thinking that a mistake had been made, called Williams' attention to the money on the plate, but the guide said it was all right. It appeared afterwards that he had given all the money he had. At 10.30 on the morning of 13 June 1861, Williams set out from Llanberis to conduct a lady and a gentleman to the summit of Snowdon, and down to Beddgelert. During the course of the ascent Williams left the couple to go and collect plants, and rejoined them later on. After reaching the summit he left them again, this time to collect specimens of alpine ferns (probably alpine woodsia) for his clients. On this occasion he failed to return. Meanwhile his clients, who were waiting for him in one of the summit huts decided to continue their journey without a guide to Beddgelert. Word soon got around about Williams' disappearance and subsequently a search party was organised. His body was later found at the foot of a gully on Clogwyn y Garnedd. This gully came to be known as 'Will Boots' gully' and a small white rock was placed at the point from which he fell (Smith, 1986: 72). He was in the habit of leaving his rope hidden beneath rocks near the cliff-top ready to be used whenever needed, but the rope having been left out in all weathers for too long, had lost its strength, and broke under his weight on that day. The fine epitaph inscribed on Williams' tombstone in the old churchyard at Nant Peris is unique in having a mention of the man and his profession, together with a brief account of how he met his end.

UNDERNEATH
LIE THE REMAINS OF
WILLIAM WILLIAMS
UPWARDS OF TWENTY FIVE
YEARS BOTANICAL GUIDE AT
THE ROYAL VICTORIA HOTEL
WHO WAS KILLED BY A FALL
FROM CLOGWYN Y GARNEDD
JUNE 13 1861 WHILST PURSUING
HIS FAVOURITE VOCATION
*This Tomb Stone was erected to
his memory by a few friends.*

The Golden Age of the Mountain Guide

During the early period of the mountain guides, the service was provided on a part time basis. By the end of the 18th century, however, the demand had increased to such an extent that Edmund Hyde Hall, writing between 1809 and 1811 describes Snowdon thus: 'This mountain is throughout the summer a source of considerable revenue to the adjacent villages, where reside the guides to whose care strangers commit themselves in order to visit the peak' (Hyde Hall, 1952: 183). A hill farmer who also conducted parties up Snowdon was Pierce Morgan of Ffridd Uchaf near Beddgelert who 'not only speaks good English, but is extremely intelligent, active and obliging' (Hyde Hall, 1952: 203n). Morgan died on 23 December, 1864 aged eighty-four and lies buried in the churchyard at Beddgelert.

As the copper and slate industries developed, more families began to move into the area and among them were men who were willing to act as guides to parties of visitors who wanted to ascend Snowdon. Unfortunately, only a small minority, it would seem took the trouble to get to know more than simply the way up Snowdon from Llanberis. In his book on the topography of the Llanberis area William Williams, Tregof, quotes from an earlier article which he says was published in an issue of the Welsh language periodical Y Gwyliedydd. Translated, it reads:

> The guide should be fluent in both English and Welsh and also be a reliable antiquarian. Many learned gentlemen ascended Snowdon accompanied by a guide and writing down the names of lakes, mountains and valleys according to what was said by their guide, but on comparing their books these gentlemen found that one noted that Moel Eilio stood to the south, and Carnedd Llywelyn to the west of Snowdon; while another book noted them in their true positions, so that it was not known which to believe . . . There are scores who know the way up Snowdon but no more than that, so that they only defraud gentlemen of their money and toil (Williams, W., 1892: 61).

There were however, certain guides who specialized in such subjects as botany, geology, and local history; their services were much sought after by visitors. The 19th century saw the opening of more, and more modern, hotels in Capel Curig, Llanberis and Beddgelert, and the services of mountain guides could be hired in all of them. Evan Jones of the Capel Curig Inn, whose name appears often in that inn's visitors' book, was a harpist as well as a guide, he also undertook the duties of barber and waiter, and – like most of the guides of the time – he had an interest in

214

botany and mineralogy. An anonymous tourist who visited Snowdonia in 1804 gave an interesting account of his visit to the Capel Curig area and although he omitted to mention the Christian name of the guide it may well have been Evan Jones who attended this party:

Capel Curig – 26th July, 1804. During breakfast a guide of Snowdonia esteemed an excellent harper, introduced himself to us with all the insinuating liveliness of a Welsh air. So engaging an address was too powerful to be resisted and we could not but comply with his wishes to be our conductor up one of the mountains. We accordingly prepared to ascend Moel Siabod, finding on inquiry Snowdon to be a too great a distance having 8 miles of difficult road to it and back and four in the ascend. It required no little exertion of patience as well as of body to gain the summit, sinking every step ankle-deep in moss which greatly retarded our progress together with the numerous bogs to avoid about a mile further crossing a field where a farmer was mowing a scanty corn of herbage his awkward exertion gave rise to some animated version on his apparent want of skill, which our guide overhearing, he reproved our hasty judgement by stating that the extreme coarseness of the grass in this county would resist a single semi-circular sweep of the English mowers and that it required not only muscular strength but great skill to cut it. We observed the scythe was considerably longer in the handle and wider in the blade than that of general use in the English counties. We could but lament that laborious industry should be so ill-repaid but rejoiced to find that he was cheerful and satisfied with what nature had given him without expectation of reaping largely the fruits of cultivation which the soil and climate would deny.

Betws y Coed. – The drought at this season having sunk the surface of the river considerably below the level of its bank, we had seated ourselves under it as being the best position from which the bridge would be seen and were absorbed in the alliteration when a rumbling noise overheard abruptly disturbed our musing and the astonishment exerted on looking up might be better imagined than expressed, when we saw the wheels of the gig suspended over the edge of the bank, our annihilation or escape being at that moment a doubtful issue! Jones, our guide, who on hearing the horses move, was no less alarmed than ourselves, forgetting his disability he ran from an adjoining field whither necessity had called him and was just in time to prevent a most fatal calamity. The horses had been tied together and the carriage supported as a declivation of stones placed under the wheels which it may be presumed had dislodged by playful restlessness and the

215

hackney feeling a weight behind him had yielded to his old propensity. Hastening from a spot where danger have frowned so terrifying a form and reflecting on this providential escape, we resumed our journey and having gained the summit of a long hill came to an extensive morass where nothing resembling cultivation was seen nor even a solitary tree to relieve a weary eye whilst the only living intelligants of this dreary waste was a few poor people gaining a scanty subsistence from the turbaries. To relieve the tediousness of such a track, Jones related to us some interesting circumstances of his early days. At the age of 23 he became the servant of an Officer under orders for foreign service and destined for the North American colonies. When they had nearly completed their voyage, a violent hurricane arose in which under all the pains of apprehension the ship becoming unmanageable and at no great distance from land they were tossed about for several days without a knowledge of their position and with a vessel much strained and leaking. At length they were wrecked on a reef of rock on the coast of Labrador and only 14 escaped a watery grave, these having been seized by the natives were stripped of their remaining apparel and taken up the country to the temporary residence of the tribe, where they were for some time confined close prisoners, and afterwards distributed as slaves among several families. Thus situated they were for a long time supposed to have no communication with each other but as forming respectively one of the family, habited in skins, were regularly led to the chase for a precarious subsistence.

After months of residence and uniform good conduct, the vigilance of the natives having been relaxed, a vessel was discovered in the offing and a plan of escape concerted. A place of rendezvous was appointed for the next night when separated from their masters and supposed to be in pursuit of game, from whence shouts immediately descended to the shore, seized a canoe and endeavoured to gain the ships. This scheme was discovered but fortunately too late to prevent 10 of the 14 effecting their escape amid showers of arrows and the active pursuits of many canoes but the occasion was sufficient to cause an exertion of strength adequate to overpower the most inveterate pursuers. After 16 hours of hard rowing without sustenance they successfully hailed the vessel and were received with great humanity. What was the fate of those left behind he has never been able to learn, but supposes them to have fallen victims to the vengeance of the savages. They were landed at Newfoundland and Jones and some others worked their passage over in a vessel homeward bound. When once secure on English soil he determined no longer to hazard his safety on foreign expeditions and proceeded immediately to his native place, where by some years service as head waiter at the Hand Inn, Llangollen and prudence management he acquired sufficient to purchase a farm.

But here he was not perfectly satisfied, for, like Adam, he wanted a companion to share his happiness and accordingly resolved to seek one. Formerly when his circumstances were no recommendation, he had seen a girl of the town of Bala, in whose society he had received much pleasure and thought if she still remained single it might be a eligible matter and in this hope he set off to for the spot . . . he found the object of his enterprise in all her virgin charms and in the course of a short time, his passion had made such pathetick and successful progress, that he was admitted to the last stage of courtship, a most strange ceremony practised universally in this country and in some parts of South Wales, in order perhaps irresistibly to attached a man to his engagements, or to show that no deformity is concealed. A few days previous to the nuptials, the elect is admitted into a female's apartment and they are placed in bed together, with a part of their dress on, where indelicacies are freely committed but however inflamed their passion, purity being the watchword, no actual criminality takes place. This singular custom in a country so thinly inhabited seems modelled upon the same principle as the institution of Lycursus and by carrying the means of more critical extremities seems better calculated to insure its end. Soon after this ordeal, Jones was married, and the fruits of his connection were very abundant in male issue, which are all distributed in service of their country. (Anon., 1804: NLW MS 1084A).

One later tourist (Freeman, 1826: 153) quoted a suitable verse to describe the Capel Curig guide:

> old age and wandering long,
> Had done his hand and harp some wrong.

Evan Jones' grave in the churchyard of St Julitta's at Capel Curig bears the following inscription:

> Beneath
> Lyeth the Remains of EVAN JONES,
> Who was Harper at CAPEL CURIG
> INN, for 28 YEARS, who died 13th,
> of SEPTEMBER 1832, AGED 62 years.

The most famous of the Capel Curig guides was Robin Hughes, also known as Robert or Bob. According to the 1861 census returns he was sixty-two years of age, married with two sons and living at number 5 Yard Newydd, Capel Curig. It is interesting to note that the entry under the occupation column describes him as a 'Guide to the Snowdonian Hills', which suggests that by the mid 19th century the once part-time occupation of guiding had developed into a vocation that provided a living wage.

Robin Hughes was over sixty when he guided John Tyndall, alpine mountaineer and scientist, and Thomas Henry Huxley (known as Darwin's Bulldog), Professor of Natural History, Royal School of Mines, up Snowdon from Pen y Pass in 1860 (Tyndall, 1899: 421-428). Tyndall, despite his Alpine experience, had arrived in the area on a snowy December day rather ill prepared for a winter assault on Snowdon, but they managed to gain the summit despite having to wade through drifts of soft snow. Neither visitor had ice axes nor had they brought gaiters. As they walked the Holyhead Road on their way from Bangor to Capel Curig they stopped at a shop in Bethesda and bought two rake handles at fourpence each and had the local blacksmith fit them with rings and iron spikes. During the ascent Tyndall complained of numbness in the feet as the result of his boots becoming filled with snow, due no doubt to the absence of gaiters.

The pace set by the local man as they set off from Pen y Pass seems to have been too fast for the visitors according to Tyndall's account of the journey: 'The guide, though he acquitted himself admirably during the day, had at first no notion that we should reach the summit; and this made him careless of preserving himself at the outset. Toning him down a little, we went forward at a calmer pace' (Tyndall, 1899: 424).

Robin Hughes was also known to that renowned angler, hill walker and author John Henry Cliffe who called upon his services on more than one occasion. Hughes took great delight in relating to his clients the legends and folklore of Snowdonia as well as accounts of his own experiences among the hills. Cliffe and Hughes were once caught in a storm whilst traversing the Glyder from Cwm Idwal to Llanberis and the author gives the following account of their time spent sheltering in the inn at Nant Peris:

On arriving at Llanberis, we were glad to seek the nearest shelter and speedily found ourselves before a roaring peat fire discussing the merits of a jug of excellent cwrw, and such rude entertainment as the "public" afforded. Here we were detained several hours; our guide in the meanwhile amusing us with a detail of sundry adventures he had met with in the mountains. Our host was a Yorkshire miner; he had migrated hither forty years before, married a Welsh girl, and in short had become so completely forgetful of "fatherland" as to speak his own native language very imperfectly. He had, in fact, been completely transformed into a Welshman in everything except his appearance, which retained unmistakeable evidence of his Saxon or Danish origin. Our homeward journey to Capel Curig was performed in the dark, and with plenty of wind and rain to add to our discomfort; we afterwards regretted that we did not remain at our humble quarters and "rough" it through the night (Cliffe, 1860: 193-194).

Robin Hughes held the greatest respect for Richard Edwards, the Beddgelert man who was known as 'the father of guides'. Richard Edwards was older than Robin Hughes, and the hard life of the mountain guide was beginning to take its toll on the veteran by the time that Thomas Roscoe visited north Wales. Roscoe climbed Snowdon under the guidance of Robin Hughes and they met Richard Edwards near the summit. The old guide shook Robin Hughes heartily by the hand and regretted that he now saw him so seldom:

'I am breaking fast, Robin,' he said, 'and you will see less of me soon.' / 'Now, you don't look so,' replied Robert, 'it's perhaps fancy; but these hard up-and-down trips are enough to break any body, let alone one of your years. It is time for you to turn gardener, like my father, and leave this work to the ponies and the easy-chairs – all the fashion now!' / 'Nay, I was a sound man,' quoth the old Guide of Beddgelert, 'till we had that unlucky long search after the poor gentleman.' 'And so was I,' retorted Robert, 'sound in wind and limb, till I made a dray-horse of myself, and carried huge, heavy parcels on my back over the hills.' (Roscoe, 1836: 123-124).

This conversation suggests that a guide not only led tourists on the mountains, but was also expected to carry any excess items they had brought along. Richard Edwards lived at a place called Pen Bont Fach (UWB MS 15723: 4), which used to stand close to the present Prince Llewelyn Hotel. He was nicknamed 'the father of guides' due to his vast experience and extensive knowledge of the Snowdon area and Cliffe (1860: 92) noted his care in not allowing his party to start from Beddgelert to Snowdon on one day in June, 1840, until the morning mists had cleared from the summit of Moel Hebog. This mountain was the Beddgelert guide's barometer. He also officiated as parish clerk for a time and was instrumental in placing the memorial slab supposedly marking the grave of Gelert, Prince Llewelyn's legendary hound (Jenkins, 1899: 69). He died 19 March 1845 aged seventy-four.

During the conversation between the two guides, Roscoe, upon enquiring, was told by Hughes of how a young visitor called Philip Homer lost his life on Moel Siabod in 1832. According to Roscoe (1836: 133-137) both Hughes and Edwards were part of the initial search party but a much clearer account of the events leading to this tragic death is revealed in the manuscript notes of another tourist, Reverend John Parker (1833).

> Friday 21 June. Heard this evening the account of Mr Homer's death near Capel Curig last November. Mr Homer was considered as partially deranged, and set out from this Hotel (the Inn at Capel Curig) with a Lieutenant whom he quitted very shortly, saying that he should go to the summit of Moel Siabod. He borrowed a pair of gloves which were afterwards found on top of that mountain. As night came on, Mr Homer's absence caused some alarm at the Inn, and on the following days much anxiety was felt as to the cause of it. In the course of about a fortnight, however, his corpse was discovered under a shelving rock that is in sight of Llyn Gwynant, on the rugged slope above the lake. The weather had been foggy with snow, and his path was traced for some distance on Moel Siabod but his body was only found by accident. The poor fellow did not seem to have received any outward injury but his death seemed rather to have arisen from cold and hunger. He could hardly have lost his way for the road was in sight and houses were I believe in view, but he had collected from distance places heaps of rushes and fern with some stones and of these materials he had made a rude shelter in addition to the natural rock which overhung them. The body had not begun to decay, his feet were without his stockings and placed in his hat round which he had also bound a part of his coat, and every circumstance appeared unaccountably perplexing. Mr Homer had received a classical education and was the son of a Tutor at Rugby. His death I imagine to have been caused by eccentric and imprudent exposure to cold accompanied by a sudden and fatal exhaustion (NLW MS 18256C).

Philip Homer was buried close to the gate to St Julitta's churchyard at Capel Curig:

To the memory of Philip;
Eldest son of Philiph and Caroline Homer;
Who died much to be lamented
On the 8th November 1832
Aged 21 years and 3 months.

Robin Hughes lies buried a few yards from this spot under an old yew tree:

ER COF AM
MARY PRIOD ROBERT HUGHES
Guide, Capel Curig,
Yr hon fu farw Ionawr 7, 1871
Yn 75 Mlwydd OED
HEFYD
Y dywededig Robert Hughes
Yr hwn a fu farw Mehefin 9, 1874
Yn 76 Mlwydd OED.

Another well known Beddgelert character who operated as a Snowdon guide was Evan Thomas. He lived in a cottage near Cae'r Gors two miles from the village along the Caernarfon road. He also worked at the Bryn y felin copper mine, Aberglaslyn, and was a typical example of the part time Snowdonian guide of the period. The following passage gives a vivid interpretation of the guide's personality plus an interesting description of his home:

We engaged the miner as our conductor over the mountain, who entertained us much with displaying, in strong colours, the tricks and impositions of his brother guides, and more particularly of the methodistical landlord of our inn, who is generally employed on these occasions. His pride, too, is not a little elevated, by having conducted the Great Doctor to its highest summit; this seeming ridiculous phrase for some time puzzled us; but we have since found out, that our guide was talking of no less a man, then the present respectable and learned Dean of Christchurch, who ascended the mountain last year. Though our guide was pompous, and rather too partial to the marvellous, yet I strenuously recommend him to all Tourists. At half past twelve, we started from our inn, determined to see the sun rise from its highest summit. The night was now very dark, and we could just discover, that the top of Snowdon was entirely enveloped in a thick impenetrable mist: this unpropitious omen staggered our resolutions; and we for some time hesitated respecting our farther progress; but

our guide assuring us that his comfortable cottage was not far distant, we again plucked up resolution; and, quitting the high way about two miles on the Caernarvon road, we turned to the right, through a boggy, unpleasant land, and in danger of losing our shoes every step we took. This soon brought us to the comfortable cot, the filth and dirtiness of which can better be imagined than described; a worm-eaten bed, two small stools, and a table fixed to the wall, composed the whole of his furniture; two fighting cocks were perched on a beam, which Thomas seemed to pride himself in the possession of: the smoke of the fire ascended through a small hole in the roof of this comfortable mansion, the door of which did not appear proof against the 'churlish chiding of the winter blast'. Such, indeed, was the situation of this Cambrian mountaineer: and, though, in our own opinion, misery, poverty, and dirt personified, seemed to be the real inhabitants of this cottage, yet there was something prepossessing in his character; for frequently, with the greatest vehemence imaginable, and in the true style of an anchorite, he declared, that, 'though he boasted not riches, yet he boasted of independence; and though he possessed not wealth, yet he possessed the home of happiness, an honest breast.'
(Whittaker, 1825: 234-237).

Evan Thomas led his party up Snowdon by joining the present Rhyd-ddu path higher up from the guide's cottage and after crossing Bwlch Main followed the southern flank of Snowdon to the summit. The guide took great delight in exhibiting daring feats of agility among the rocks and precipices. As the air grew colder hardly any persuasion was needed for Thomas to produce his pistol of rum diluted with milk to keep the body warm. Their toil was greatly rewarded as, having reached the summit, they experienced a rare occurrence of a perfect sunrise as the early mists evaporated.

Thomas Jones hailed from the parish of Penmorfa and he most probably moved to Beddgelert soon after he got married. The 1861 census returns show that he was a widower living with his daughter in Church Street. His personal pocket book which is kept at University of Wales, Bangor (UWB MSS 5406), measures 6 inches by 4 and is dated 1845 to 1849. It is evident from the entries in the pocket book that Thomas Jones conducted some very important people to the summit during his career. One entry from July 1846 states: 'Lord Lewisham has known Thomas Jones for some time and has great pleasure in recommending him as an excellent guide in every respect. He is always cheerful and extremely civil besides knowing the neighbourhood thoroughly.' R.W. Long, writing of his tour through north Wales in 1847 had this to say:

Our Guide was Thomas Jones, a man of Swiss-like appearance who might have been a Mt. Blanc Guide from his looks. He told us that an old gentleman whom from his description I recognised to be Sir Henry de la Beche (having seen his name in the Hotel Book at Llanberis) had been in the neighbourhood several days persuing [sic] his geological researches. He said he had been a Guide to a Grand Duke and the King of Saxony (NLW MS 5912B).

Sir Henry de la Beche (1796-1855), one of the foremost geologists of the time, was Founder and Director of the Museum of Geology. Thomas Jones, being a Beddgelert based guide, would use the same route to Snowdon as Evan Thomas, following the Caernarfon road before turning off near Ffridd Uchaf farm, continuing past the farmhouse, then climbing over Llechog to Clawdd Coch, Bwlch Main, and on towards the summit. The return journey would depend mainly on the client; some would ask to be led down by a different route, like the Pony track to Llanberis, or through the copper mines past Llyn Glaslyn to Pen y Pass, while others preferred to retrace their steps. Ponies were available for an extra charge, and some tourists would ride part of the way, dismount at the difficult sections of the path and walk, leaving the guide to attend to the ponies. The charges varied from village to village. The Beddgelert guides charged seven shillings to the summit and ten shillings if they wished to continue to Llanberis or Capel Curig. A night ascent from Beddgelert would cost ten shillings. The daytime charge from Penygwryd was five shillings; Snowdon Ranger, seven shillings; Capel Curig, ten shillings; and Llanberis seven shillings. There was an additional charge of five shillings for hiring a pony and this was the same in all the villages.

According to the dates of the entries in the pocket book the tourist season extended from March until November, and even snow did not put off some visitors from reaching the summit. In March 1848 a certain J. P. Easton from London ascended Snowdon under the guidance of Thomas Jones while the upper part of the mountain was covered in snow. The next entry in the pocket book records the ascent of a couple from London in similar conditions: '...but by perseverance and the great care and attention of Thomas Jones their Guide (of whom they cannot speak too highly) they arrived at the summit after wading through from five to six feet of snow in depth the greatest ever known by the Guide'. Sketches in the summit huts' visitors books show that such adventures were made by most of the Victorian tourists wearing ordinary town clothes like topcoats and top hats while the ladies wore voluminous dresses and carried umbrellas.

Years of regular exercise working in the fresh air of Snowdonia benefited Thomas Jones who lived to good age – considering the life expectancy of most men of the period – as his gravestone in the Beddgelert churchyard testifies:

Bedd
JANE
Gwraig Thomas Jones Guide
Beddgelert
Fu farw Tach 28 1857
Yn 79 ml. oed.
Hefyd
THOMAS JONES
Ei phriod a fu farw
Mai 22 1877
Yn 89 oed.

The equipment and clothing of the mid 19th century hill walker was not of the high standard familiar today, but nevertheless there are only a few reports of fatal accidents in Snowdonia subsequent to the death of Philip Homer on Moel Siabod in 1832. One incident however, still shrouded in mystery, remains unsolved to this day.

At the end of Thomas Jones' pocket book several notes have been written in Welsh explaining the procedure followed during an inquest, and this sudden interest was no doubt sparked off by the disappearance of Reverend Henry Wellington Starr of Northampton while attempting to climb Snowdon alone on a misty day in September 1846. Starr's body was not found until the following June and the circumstances which surrounded his death aroused suspicions of foul play. This unfortunately created an atmosphere of suspicion and rumour among the local inhabitants and the guides suffered more than anyone. Starr arrived at Caernarfon on the afternoon of Monday 14 September and, after finding a room at a lodging house in Pool Street, had retired early to bed. The next morning he informed his landlady that he was setting out for Llanberis, Snowdon and Beddgelert and would return later for his luggage and letters. He took with him a small oilskin knapsack containing a change of linen, but never returned.

Meanwhile his mother and sister were daily expecting a reply to their letters, and on receiving none, made enquiries of Mr Pritchard the Postmaster at Caernarfon. All the letters they had sent were still at the Post Office waiting to be collected. Mrs Starr and her daughter Emily immediately started out for north Wales and after arriving at Caernarfon went straight to the lodging house in Pool Street where Reverend Starr had been staying. After gleaning from the landlady what information she had, they took a post-chaise to Llanberis and began their inquiries at the Dolbadarn Inn. Mrs Evans the landlady there remembered a gentleman of Starr's description who had slept there on the Tuesday night, but left the next morning in the direction of the Llanberis Pass, apparently to ascend Snowdon. On the assumption that he had reached the summit and had signed the visitor's book kept there, a guide was immediately dispatched to fetch it down, but on inspection Starr's name was not there.

The next morning a guide called John Hughes stated that he had met with a gentleman answering Starr's description on the Glyder mountain on Wednesday, 16 September between 5 and 6 o'clock in the evening. The guide described in detail the man's height, and manner of attire, and said that he wore only one glove. He went on to say that the gentleman had told him that he was a clergyman and had come from Llanberis, over Snowdon, past the copper mines and then continued on up the Glyder. He added that he had accompanied the gentleman some distance down the Glyder to make sure that he avoided a dangerous precipice, and had then returned to his young son who he had left in charge of some crystals they had collected on the mountain that day. Later, while examining the contents of Starr's carpet bag and great coat at Caernarfon an odd glove was found which substantiated the relevance of the guide Hughes' account of the gentleman he had met with on the Glyder.

Another guide then claimed to have seen Starr, this time on the opposite side of Snowdon. Robert Owen, guide and landlord of the Snowdon Inn, near Llyn Cwellyn claimed to have seen Starr sitting and smoking his pipe on the bridge at the upper end of the lake between 4 and 5 o'clock on the afternoon of Tuesday 15 September. When Starr asked Robert Owen about the route to Snowdon he was advised by the guide not to go, on account of the mist that hung over the mountain at that time. Starr, however, insisted on going and was later said to have been seen by two farm hands who were working near Llyn Ffynnon y Gwas.

As the mystery surrounding Starr's disappearance continued several unsuccessful searches were made. Posters, giving a description of him, were distributed and a £50 reward was offered to anyone who could find him. A letter dated 8 November 1846 from Thomas Assheton-Smith of the Vaynol Estate to Lord Newborough shows the concern of the local gentry at the time:

As you are one of "The Magistrates" who proposed a suggestion to offer a Reward for the lost man at Llanberris I write you this time to give you my Reasons for not joining in that Subscription. If a Reward had at first been offered, it wd have been well, but I think it would but be the means of Perpetuating the mother and daughter's misery, – & the sooner they leave the scene of their woes, the better, – & as means of promoting this request, I have . . . Mrs Turner to supply them with Funds to cover their Expences down – their Cost whilst they stay – & for a few days only after she delivers it to them – & for their return to Northampton – where no doubt they will be taken care of (GAS XD2/21779 Assheton-Smith to Lord Newborough, 8 November 1846).

At one stage over 900 men from the Dinorwig Slate Quarries combed the slopes of Glyder and Snowdon in a vain attempt to solve the mystery.

On Monday 1 June 1847 William Hughes, a huntsman, was descending the Cwmbrwynog valley when he picked up a red shawl at the foot of the precipice of Moel Cynghorion and took it immediately to the Dolbadarn Inn where Mrs Evans identified it as Reverend Starr's. It was then also revealed that the oilskin knapsack of Starr had been found a month previously. On the Tuesday Williams Hughes, together with Edward Humphreys of the Dolbadarn (Mrs Evans' son in law) returned to Moel Cynghorion and searched the area around the spot where the shawl had been found. They later found the remains of the unfortunate tourist and various articles which were afterwards identified as belonging to him. The remains were conveyed to the Dolbadarn Inn and on Monday 7 June an inquest was held before the Coroner, E. G. Powell. Emily, Starr's sister, attended the hearing in order to identify the property found and John Evans, who found the oilskin knapsack, and William Hughes the huntsman were also questioned. When John Evans was asked why he waited a month before reporting finding the knapsack he replied that he had heard that the missing Starr had been seen in Ireland. The Coroner did not think that the testimony of the guides John Hughes and Robert Owen worth hearing, and they were not called upon to give evidence.

One guide was, however, called upon to give evidence and he was William Williams, then of the Royal Victoria Hotel, Llanberis. At the time of the disappearance of Starr William Williams had been assisting a certain Mr Johnstone of the Royal Victoria to move from Llanberis to Chester, and the guide did not return to Llanberis until the day after the body was found. Williams told the jury at the inquest about how he was informed by Mrs Evans of the Dolbadarn Inn of William Hughes' discovery, and how, on the following morning he had walked over to the Snowdon Inn near Llyn Cwellyn at Betws Garmon to pay ten shillings, part of a twenty-two shilling debt that he had owed there since the previous year. Williams continued: 'On my return I took the direction of the mountain where the remains were discovered, and found a piece of linen near the place; I saw a string hanging to it, and placing my foot upon the linen, I drew the string out. It had the appearance of a watchguard; and on opening the folds of the linen I found the watch' (Anon., 1847: 5). Williams kept the watch, and did not hand it over to the authorities until later; for this he was reprimanded by the Coroner for 'conducting himself as to create a suspicion on his integrity' (Anon., 1847: 5). The jury returned after a few minutes' consultation and announced:

> That the Rev. Henry Wellington Starr, in the month of September last, was ascending a certain mountain in the said country, and died on the same, without any hurt or injury having been done to or committed upon him by any person or persons whatsoever; but the said jurors are unable to state whether his death was occasioned by a fall, by cold, or how otherwise in particular, although they incline to the belief that it was caused by his accidentally falling over a precipice, during the hours of darkness (Starr, 1847: 302).

The death of Starr was still shrouded in mystery and certain suspicions pointed to the finder of the watch, William Williams. The watch, upon examination was found to be quite free of rust or moisture and in perfect working order, despite the fact that, if Williams' story is to be believed, it had been out on the mountain from September until June. It could therefore be assumed that Williams had found Starr's body soon after he died and had taken the watch. It should also be noted that when Williams, several years later, related the story of how he found the watch to a visitor he said that he had spent a week on the mountain searching before he found it (Wynter, 1861: 371-372).

Emily Starr, who later published an account of the events leading up to the tragic death of her brother, has this to say in conclusion:

> That the Welsh be jealous for the honour of their country, and greatly attached to their mountainous principality, is both natural and just; and it must be evident to all who have read the account of the inquest, that the chief endeavour was to do away with any stigma attaching to their character, from the mysterious disappearance of a traveller among them (Starr, 1847: 305).

All this happened at a time when the tourist industry was expanding rapidly in Snowdonia, businessmen were investing heavily in expanding the railways and in building larger hotels from which the mountain guides mainly operated, and therefore any suspicions as to the safety of the tourist had to be permanently removed.

*   *   *

William Williams fell to his death on Clogwyn y Garnedd, Snowdon, in 1861 while collecting ferns for a client. William E. Powell was the first person to reach his body on Clogwyn y Garnedd in June 1861. Powell, otherwise known by his bardic name of 'Gwilym Eryri', was at the time working in the nearby Snowdon copper mine, but he had also been a guide, at which time he was responsible for one of the summit huts on Snowdon. He was born at Cae'r Bompren, Beddgelert on 20 February 1841, the son of Evan and Sian. He was also employed for a time at the Bryn y felin copper mine near Aberglaslyn, where he was promoted to steward and addressed as 'Captain Powell' as was the custom in the industry. In 1865 he married Jane, the daughter of Rhys and Margaret Roberts, Bwlch Mwrchan, Nantgwynant, and in the following year they emigrated to the United States of America, settling in Milwaukee, Wisconsin. Powell found employment with the Chicago and St Paul's Railroad Company, being appointed general emigration officer in 1878. He was to lead many a family overland to settle in the rich lands of Dakota and other parts of north America, the town of 'Powell' being reputedly named in his honour. He had a likeable and helpful personality and he soon became a prominent figure among the Welsh community of the United States. He was a poet and musician and contributed a number of articles to the journals *Y Drych* and *Columbia*. He died 1 December 1910 aged sixty-nine and was buried at Forest Home, Milwaukee (Carneddog, 1927: 21).

William Roberts operated as a guide from the Dolbadarn Hotel at Llanberis. According to the 1861 census returns he was a thirty-nine year old married man with four children. During the 1850s a traveller by the name of William F. Peacock visited north Wales and later published details of his tour in a book called *The Welsh Mountains* from which the following portrait of William Roberts is quoted:

The guide Roberts' costume is rather picturesque and very characteristic, slightly savouring of Switzerland; that is to say, made up of light trousers, ditto vest (both fawn colour), no coat; the vest having long arms, and fitting to the person. A brigandish hat on his head, a knapsack or large wallet on his shoulders (well strapped over the chest), and a stout stick in his hand, which is (to crib a bit of our allies' tongue) literally his *baton* of office. Such is honest William Roberts; a civil, quiet, well informed fellow, who respects an agreement, and can be thankful for favours conferred on him; who rejoices to be guide when anybody wants to be guided, and (in a time of dearth) pursues cheerfully his work as a labourer. I have real respect for Dolbadarn Roberts and Dolgelly Pugh (of whom anon, when we ascend Cader Idris). William's memory holds many a curious legend, and he loves to satisfy your questions, though he rarely speaks unless spoken to. Like most other guides, he carries the bottles of the party; ensconces them in the capacious stomach of his wallet. Let the tourist who thinks to ascend Snowdon engage Roberts, honest Roberts; I say this with ingenuousness, for it's not a matter of *commission!* The best recommendation is, that he has gone up and over above 2,000 times in the twenty-five years of his professional life (Peacock, 1855: 8-9).

> TO THE MEMORY OF
> HARRY OWEN
> FOR 44 YEARS LANDLORD
> OF THE INN AT
> PENYGWRYD,
> AND GUIDE TO SNOWDON.
> IN BUSINESS UPRIGHT AND COURTEOUS
> IN SERVICE STRONG AND PATIENT
> IN FRIENDSHIP SIMPLE AND SINCERE.
> THIS TRIBUTE IS ERECTED
> BY OLD FRIENDS
> WHO KNEW AND HONOURED HIM.
> BORN APRIL 2 1822
> DIED MAY 5 1891.

The above inscription is quoted from the memorial slab on the wall inside the church at Beddgelert to the most successful of all the Snowdon guides. Harry Owen was born at Castell, a farm on the slopes above Llyn Dinas near Beddgelert. On 8 May 1847, when twenty-five years of age he married Ann Pritchard, who was at the time in service at nearby Plas Gwynant. Owen had already purchased the inn at Penygwryd together with some adjoining land before his marriage, and the couple ran the business for a period of over forty years. They had ten children, but two of these died in infancy. There were five sons, namely Harry, John, Owen, Griffith and Hugh, and three daughters, Catherine, Jane and Annie. Under the care of Harry Owen, Penygwryd Inn was established as a centre for mountaineering activities in Snowdonia. As the fame of the inn and its keeper spread, so did the demand for his services to guide parties to the mountains or to hire one of the rowing boats which he kept for the use of visiting anglers (Mathews, 1901).

Harry Owen shared the same ideals as Robin Hughes of Capel Curig in encouraging and developing new routes up the mountains. The following is quoted from an old Capel Curig Inn visitor's book; a rare mention of the innkeeper in action as a guide: '28 June 1865. Ascended from Penygwryd by an unusual track under the summit of Clogwyn y Garnedd – thick mist – no view . . . Henry Owen, Guide' (NLW 1608 C). Penygwryd Inn was ideally situated as a base for climbing, walking, botanizing and fishing among the mountains of Snowdonia. Horse drawn carriages were also available to convey visitors further afield to such attractions as the Swallow Falls or Betws-y-coed. The house of Harry Owen became increasingly popular with mountaineers, details of their adventures being duly recorded in the famous 'locked book' which was later to be reflected in the numerous published guide books to every crag in Snowdonia and beyond.

On 8 January 1803 a piece of land called Weirglodd Goch near Betws Garmon was leased to John Morton of Caernarfon by the landowner Sir Robert Williams of Plas y Nant (NLWA SHRWDD) and soon after the Snowdon Inn (also referred to as Glanllyn, Snowdon Guide and Snowdon Ranger) was built. John Morton had, however, adopted the name 'Snowdon Ranger' and he had begun to guide visitors up Snowdon from his house. The term 'Snowdon Ranger' however dates from an earlier period: during the 16th century Snowdon was part of the Royal Forest of Snowdon, and the Earl of Leicester held the office of chief ranger of Snowdon Forest during this period. The lease was transferred on 12 December 1812 to John Morgan, Cae Darby, Caernarfon and Ellis Roberts of Beddgelert for a further period of twenty-one years.

Evidence that Robert Owen was the landlord of the Snowdon Inn appears in the Quarter Sessions Records for 1815 which state: 'Recognizance document, . . . Henry Williams of Drws y Coed went surety for £5:0:0 for Robert Owen Glanllyn Cwellyn to appear at the next Quarter Sessions'. The nature of Robert Owen's offence is not mentioned apart from the fact that it was committed against an Elizabeth Williams. A year later a similar document dated 16 December records: 'Mem. Of Recognizance of Robert Owen of the Snowdon Ranger, pa Betws Garmon, victualler, for £10, Thomas Hughes of Glanrafon, farmer for £5 and Henry Williams of Drws y Coed, farmer, for £5 for the appearance of R.O. at the next Quarter Sessions and to keep the peace, esp. towards John Morgan of Waunfawr'. Again, details of the offence are not given (GAS XQS/1816).

It will be remembered also that Robert Owen claimed to have seen Reverend Henry Wellington Starr on the bridge near Llyn Cwellyn on the day he disappeared in September 1846. When George Borrow visited north Wales in 1854, it was probably Robert Owen who introduced himself to him as the 'Snowdon Ranger', during the course of their conversation outside the Snowdon Inn. Borrow describes him as 'an elderly man dressed in a smock frock with a hairy cap on his head' (Borrow, [n.d.]: 259), and notes how the guide gave advice on the best route up Snowdon:

People in general prefer ascending Snowdon from that trumpery place Beth Gelert; but those who do are fools – begging your honour's pardon. The place to ascend Snowdon from is my house. The way from my house up Snowdon is wonderful for the romantic scenery which it affords; that from Beth Gelert can't be named in the same day with it for scenery; moreover, from my house you may have the best guide in Wales; whereas the guides of Beth Gelert – but I say nothing (Borrow, [n.d.]: 261).

Another traveller, who was looking for a guide to conduct him up Snowdon saw Owen on the shores of Llyn Cwellyn hobbling about with the aid of two sticks:

. . . and in appearance as unlikely to mount up Snowdon as a man without legs would be; however, the prospect of seven shillings and sixpence, which he charged for his guidance, made a wonderful change in him: he walked to the house, to make some preparation, with the alacrity of youth. When we arrived at the Inn the old man was ready, and his first demand was for a pint of whiskey and some tobacco – he recommended us to stock ourselves with provisions and alcoholic spirits, which we declined doing, preferring the comfort of a regular collation – which we ordered – after our descent. The guide took the usual post of leader, and walked firmer and faster than any of us (Humphreys, [1850]:17).

Robert Owen led the party up the Snowdon Ranger path and after negotiating 'a steep ascent by a zigzag made by the miners among rocks' he paused to take a dram of whiskey and to light his pipe pointing out the precipice where Wellington Starr had fallen in 1846. About a mile below the summit of Snowdon the guide showed the party the 'Snowdon Well, a beautiful clear cold crystal spring, which is never dry', and higher still they saw the view down towards the Glaslyn and Llydaw lakes. The group of huts on the summit soon came into view, being described as:

. . . the little *town of Snowdonia*, as the guides called it, which had been apprized of our approach and prepared for our reception, by two young men, who warmly welcomed us. This town consists of four huts made of wood. One of which is called Saxony, because the King of Saxony dined in it – or sat in it, or possibly dosed in it,- perhaps all three. The men were singing and working like industrious and happy fellows . . . Supper, a bed, and breakfast, are procurable there for five shillings; and during the summer seasons vast number of tourists avail themselves of the wretched accommodation afforded there, for the sake of seeing the sun set and rise – a truly glorious sight! Those huts are to be immediately papered, and to be provided with good fires, and they say, good beds too, and, strange enough, views – guide-books – stationery, &c., are to be bought there. . . . What a change from the majesty of scenery where we had been standing a short time before! We step from the sublime (if not to the ridiculous) to a vulgar , and very dingy hut, about 12 feet long and 9 feet wide, a rusty stove in one corner, and a black coffee-pot keeping itself warm upon it! The wooden floor damp and wet as that of a vault, the paper black and falling off, the windows about 18 inches square, frames inclusive. My friend W. was seated on a three-legged stool, I was perched on one end of a bench, and the guide on the other, with a clunch of bread in his hand of at least half a-pound weight, indicating that the whiskey had not taken away his appetite. In the course of conversation with the guide (on W.'s recommending him to plant flowers about the huts) it was replied, that they would not grow there, and that potatoes, which he had planted about 100 yards below the peak, did not produce tubers (Humphreys [1850]:19-21).

Later Robert Owen and his party left the summit to the sound of a duet performed by the waiter and his companion, a guide, singing 'Hail, smiling morn'. Robert Owen, having operated as a Snowdon guide for over thirty years, died in 1855 and was buried at Beddgelert.

> Here lieth the Body of
> Owen Owens CLOGWYN Y GWIN
> who died July the 16th 1765
> AGED 49
> Also Catherine his Wife died Feb.ry
> 22nd 1811 AGED 85
> Here also lieth the Body of
> ROBERT OWEN of the Snowdon Inn,
> (Grandson of the above named)
> who died on the 6th day of January 1855
> Aged 71 years.

His son Evan Roberts then took over the business and built a new hotel close to the site of the old one calling it 'The Snowdon Ranger'; this soon became an ideal angling station according to Cliffe (1860: 110) who wrote:

'We can affirm, with perfect truth, that we know of very few places in the Principality better adapted to supply the wants of the angler or artist than the "Snowdon Ranger" Hotel.'

The summit huts of Snowdon were usually open to the public at Easter time, the guides being mainly responsible for transporting the supplies up from the hotels at Llanberis a week or two before. Griffith John Pritchard of Llanberis, known locally as 'Guto Satan', one of the guides who undertook this task, went missing after delivering a load of supplies to the summit huts late on 26 March, 1891. The upper part of Snowdon was deep in snow and this, blown by strong winds, soon caused the line of path to be obscured. Despite being advised by the guides who lived in the hut not to start back down in the growing dusk in such adverse weather conditions he set off but lost the path by veering too far left. He lost his footing and fell down the cliff into Cwm Clogwyn. Pritchard's body remained undiscovered despite early searches which were impeded by the snowdrifts and soon after these searches became less frequent. A letter which appeared in a local newspaper on 2 June written by William Williams, Tregof, Llanberis (Williams, 1891: 5) called for the search for Pritchard's body to be resumed, and this prompted a meeting to be held at the Concert Hall, Llanberis, to organise further searches. On the morning of the 12 June several hundred met at Llanberis before continuing up the Llanberis path to Snowdon, stopping at the Halfway House to organize the group into smaller search-parties, consisting of about thirty to forty people, which were later to meet at a prearranged point. William Williams, Tregof took charge naming the leaders as follows: Henry Williams, Helfa Fawr; William Jones, Nant Ddu; William J. Davies, Ty'n yr Aelgerth; William and Ellis Owen, Hafodty; John J. Roberts, Blaenyddol and William Rowlands, Pentrecastell. All but one of the search-parties returned without finding anything, but soon a messenger arrived bearing the news that Pritchard's body had been found at the bottom of a gully called Cwter Llyn Glas in Cwm Clogwyn. The body was first noticed by John T. Jones, Upper Snowdon Terrace, Llanberis, but it was Thomas J. Roberts, Pen y Wyddfa who was the first to reach the spot. Two men were immediately sent down to Llanberis to arrange for a coffin to be transported to a convenient spot on the lower mountain track, while further arrangements were made to bring the body down on a makeshift stretcher. It was carried over Bwlch Cwmbrwynog and transferred onto a horse-drawn conveyance which was waiting on the track at the top of the hill overlooking the village (Williams, 1907: 5).

Early in 1993 Gwynedd Archives Service purchased one of the visitors' books which were kept in the Snowdon summit huts during the middle years of the 19th century (GAS XM/9254). On the pages of this most important manuscript are names, descriptions, drawings, poems and all manner of personal remarks which portray the everyday life on Victorian Snowdon. Also recorded are the names of the guides who operated on Snowdon during the years 1847-1848. Robin Hughes of Capel Curig and Thomas Jones of Beddgelert feature prominently in the book; the Capel Curig guide was renowned for pioneering new routes and for criticising those who rode up Snowdon on the easier paths. He once prophesied to Roscoe that 'a long winded pony-road, winding miles round, and as smooth as a railway' would someday be built from Capel Curig to the summit of Snowdon, 'and we might then go up Snowdon in an easy-chair after dinner!' (Roscoe, 1836: 119).

Another of the guides whose name is mentioned in this visitors' book is Elias Roberts, who served the Royal Victoria Hotel at Llanberis. Elias Roberts was born in Amlwch, Anglesey in 1807 and was known locally as 'Lias bach'. In 1869 a bonfire was lit on the summit of Snowdon to celebrate the coming of age of the heir of the Vaynol Estate and it was Elias Roberts who drove a horse and cart carrying a barrel of pitch to the summit for the bonfire; this is the first record of a horse and cart getting to the top of the mountain (Anon., 1888: 8). He married Catherine from Betws-y-coed in October 1835, and all their children were born in Llanberis. When their first child John was born in January 1836 they were residing at the 'Victoria Hotel', Llanberis, and his occupation noted as 'miner and guide'. The copper mines at Nant Peris and Clogwyn Coch, Snowdon were both working at this time. By 1837 Elias Roberts and his family had moved to Tan y Dderwen, Llanberis, and in 1843 according to the birth register entry for another of his children he was described as a 'labourer'. He remained at Tan y Dderwen according to the 1851 and 1861 census returns, working as a 'Snowdon Guide'. He was quite a character, treating the ponies he kept for carrying visitors up Snowdon with special care, and speaking to them as if they were his children. He is favourably mentioned in the Snowdon summit visitors' books (UWB MSS 4150, 4151, 4152) and was a talented singer who frequently entertained those who visited the mountain. Elias Roberts was nearly 80 years of age when he died suddenly outside the post office at Llanberis; he was buried on 20 July, 1886. Owen Humphrey Davies (Eos Llechid, 1828-1898) the curate, officiated. (GAS XPE/27/10).

Other guides noted in the visitors book are David Jones, host of the Prince Llewelyn Hotel, Beddgelert, Richard Owen of the Royal Victoria, Llanberis, Evan Watkins of Capel Curig and Thomas Roberts of Beddgelert; the latter tragically lost his life as the result of an accident which occurred as he returned to Beddgelert from Snowdon. The conduct of all these guides is mentioned in glowing terms, but there is one who failed to meet the standards set by the others. An entry for 11 June 1847 states as follows:

J.W. Williams, Robert Marshall of Sheffield & Pryse Claridge of Aberystwyth ascended Snowdon one Sunday with Guide from Carnarvon and found him a dam' lazy fellow I could not get him along at all after the first mile. Mr J. Browne accompanied the lazy guide & thought himself a b'y fool for taking such trouble J. P. Hamer of Caernarvon says Jer. Bower of Liverpool (GAS XM/9254).

J.P. Hamer of Liverpool moved to Caernarfon during the 1840s and operated a guiding service to Snowdon from his office in Segontium Terrace. He advertised his service in a booklet of truly Victorian flavour that he published (Hamer, [1857]). In it he claims that the 'Hamer's Route' to the summit was shorter and easier than any other. Hamer's excursions to Snowdon started at 10:20 a.m. from Segontium Terrace and the parties were conveyed by carriage to the Snowdon Ranger Inn. 'Hamer's Route' followed for the most part the Snowdon Ranger path and the party stopped for a minute's rest out of each ten minutes of walking. Hamer assured his clients that the summit would be reached after two and a half hours walking and that a clear view was 'all but certain'. After reaching the summit the party would sign the Hamer's Log before returning to the Snowdon Ranger for a 'substantial tea' before returning to Caernarfon. The trip cost ten shillings, but the business did not prosper. There is no other mention of Hamer in this, or any of the other visitors' books, and there is no trace of the 'Hamer's Log'.

Those who visited the Snowdon district regularly during the final decades of the 19th century would have been acquainted with the old guide Tom Ward. His passing would have gone unrecorded, however, had it not been for an accident he suffered when over seventy years of age; this was not an accident which occurred during a mountain walk, but rather as a result of tripping over the shafts of a cart closer to home. He was admitted to the hospital connected with the workhouse at Caernarfon, later known as the Eryri Hospital, where a local newspaper reporter found him and published some of his recollections (Anon., 1911: 8).

Ward had moved from his native Headon, Nottingham to Llanberis at an early age. He was employed as a messenger boy at the local post office in addition to being a guide and led several prominent people to the summit of Snowdon during his career. Among those which he named were Tennyson and John Ruskin, the latter's philosophy often quoted by Ward to visitors who complained of the weather, namely that there was never any bad weather on Snowdon, only different varieties of fair weather. The injured guide claimed to have ascended Snowdon over 4,000 times using different routes and covering a distance of 30,000 miles; he longed to recover sufficiently so that he could return to his beloved mountain once more. Ward's dislike of trains is made clear as he told the reporter that he had only twice made any rail journeys, and the farthest that he had travelled was from Llanberis to Caernarfon. That had prompted many people who had never before seen him in any conveyance to come and ask him what was wrong.

His interests, apart from walking included geology and botany, and when asked about the dangers of mountaineering he replied by saying that it was no more dangerous than playing soccer providing that the necessary care and precaution was applied. He concluded that mountain walking provided the best course of exercise that the human body could have, and that many still preferred to walk up Snowdon rather than use the train, a development that had greatly affected his business and no doubt re-kindled his intense dislike of trains.

It is not known whether Ward ever got fit enough again to continue his chosen profession; the coming of the train caused a severe decline in the numbers of the Llanberis guides, but at least one of them is known to have successfully moved with the times by being employed as a conductor and porter by the 'Snowdon Tramroad and Hotels Company Limited'. 'Owen Glas', as he was known, continued to pass on to his passengers in the confines of the carriages the local knowledge that he had previously related to his clients during his guiding days (Palmer, 1937: 86-88).

Tourism increased in Snowdonia with the expansion of the railway system. The line between Caernarfon and Llanberis was opened in 1869, and visitors arriving at Llanberis Station would see there a row of sturdy mountain ponies and a guide ready to convey them up Snowdon. The following years saw an increase in the number of young men and boys willing to act as guides and there were instances of touting for business among them. Over the years the paths had become easier to follow, better maps and guide books were published and it became less 'fashionable' to procure the services of a local guide. Palmer, whose popular book was first published in 1937, asked whether there were any mountain guides left in Snowdonia: 'The routes are so well marked and cairned that there is no doubt about presence and direction, and it is rare that you come across a party with a mountain pony ridden by a lady' (Palmer, 1948: 86). The age of the traditional Snowdon Guide was over.

Bibliography of works consulted

Aikin, Arthur, 1797. *Journal of a Tour through North Wales and part of Shropshire*. London: printed for J. Johnson.

Allen, David Elliston, 1969. *The Victorian Fern Craze A History of Pteridomania*. London: Hutchinson.

Allen, D.E., 1979. 'The botanical family of Samuel Butler'. *Journal of the Society for the Bibliography of Natural History* 9 (2): 133-136.

Allen, D.E., 1980. 'John Barton: a biographical supplement' *Naturalist* 105:157-158.

Allen, David E., 1993. 'The Victorian Fern Craze: Pteridomania Revisited'. *Fern Horticulture: past, present and future perspectives*. (Edited by J.M. Ide, A.C. Jermy and A.M. Paul) Intercept, Andover: 9-19.

Allen, David Elliston, 1994. *The Naturalist in Britain a Social History*. Princeton, New Jersey: Princeton University Press.

Allen, D.E., 1999. 'C.C. Babington, Cambridge botany and the taxonomy of British flowering plants' *Nature in Cambridgeshire* 41: 2-11.

Ambrose, W. R., 1872. *Hynafiaethau, Cofiannau, a Hanes Presennol Nant Nantlle* Pen-y-groes: Griffith Lewis.

Anonymous, 1845. *The Medical Directory* p. 335. Copy at the Library, Royal College of Surgeons of England.

Anonymous, 1847. 'Discovery of the Remains of the Rev. H.W. Starr on Snowdon'. *Caernarvon and Denbigh Herald* 12 June: 5.

Anonymous, 1849. 'Botanical Memoir of the late John Roberts, Surgeon, of Bangor' *The Lancet* 1: 657.

Anonymous, 1861a. 'A brief Notice of William Williams, Botanical Guide to Llanberis, Snowdon,Twll Ddu, etc.' *The Phytologist* 5, October: 307-309.

Anonymous, 1861b. 'Snowdon'. *The North Wales Chronicle*. 29 June: 6.

Anonymous, 1888. 'Sian Closs, Gellihirbant' *Yr Herald Cymraeg*. 3 Gorffennaf: 8.

Anonymous, 1911.'I ben y Wyddfa 4 mil o weithiau' *Yr Herald Cymraeg* 28 Chwefror: 8.

Babington, Charles Cardale, 1897. *Memorials Journal and Botanical*

Correspondence of Charles Cardale Babington. Cambridge: Macmillan and Bowes.

Barton, John, 1857. 'Plants of Snowdon. A few observations on the character of the Snowdonian flora'. *The Phytologist* 2: 145-149.

Bennett, William, 1849. 'Notes on the rarer Ferns observed in a fortnight's Pedestrian Tour in North Wales; with several new Localities for Asplenium lanceolatum'. *The Phytologist* 3: 709-715.

Bingley, Rev. W., 1804. *North Wales; including its Scenery, Antiquities, Customs, and some sketches of its Natural History*. London: Printed for T.N. Longman and O. Rees.

Blackman, V. H., 1945-1948. *Obituary Notices of Fellows of the Royal Society* vol 5. London.

Borrow, George n.d., *Wild Wales*. London and Glasgow: Collins.

Bowden, Jean K., 1989. *John Lightfoot His Work and Travels*. Kew and Pittsburgh.

Breuer, Hans-Peter (editor), 1984. *The note-books of Smuel Butler*. Volume 1, (1874-1883). Lanham, New York & London: University Press of America.

Britten, James, 1878. 'Botany' in *Jenkinson's Practical Guide to North Wales*. London: Edward Stanford: lxxxii-xcix.

Britten, James, (editor) 1910. 'John Williams (1801-1859). In review of: 'Bibliographical Index of British Botanists'. *Journal of Botany* 48: 232.

Britten, James, 1923. 'Lloydia serotina' *Journal of Botany* 61: 225-229.

'Caerwyson', 1921. 'Hamddenau ym myd Adar a Rhedyn' iii (a). *Cymru* 60: 206-08.

Camden, W., 1695. *Britannia*. London: Edmund Gibson.

Camden, W., 1722. *Britannia*. London: Edmund Gibson. *Camden's Wales*, 1984 (reprint of Welsh chapters from original work) Carmarthen: Rampart Press).

Carneddog,1927. *Cerddi Eryri*. Dinbych: Argraffwyd gan Gee a'i fab.

Carter, P.W., 1927.'The structure and cytology of Padina pavonia'. *Annals of Botany* 41: 139-159.

Carter, P.W., 1955 (16): 52-59, 1956 (17): 45-61. 'Some account of the botanical exploration of Caernarfonshire' *Transactions of the*

Caernarvonshire Historical Society.

Cash, James, 1873. *Where there's a will, there's a way! or, Science in the Cottage: an account of the labours of Naturalists in humble life*. London: Robert Hardwicke.

Cash, James, 1887. 'The early botanical work of the late William Wilson' *The Naturalist*: 181-90.

Cliffe, John Henry, 1860. *Notes and Recollections of an Angler*. London: Hamilton Adams and Co.

Condry, W. M., 1966. *The Snowdonia National Park*. London: Collins.

Craddock, Joseph, 1770. *Letters from Snowdon*. London: printed for J. Ridley and W. Harris.

Dallman, A.A., 1926. (March 31) 'A Bygone Welsh Botanist' *The North Western Naturalist*: 39.

Davies, Hugh, 1813. *Welsh Botanology*. London: printed for the author by W. Marchant.

Davies, John H., (editor) *The Letters of Lewis, Richard, William and John Morris of Anglesey*. (2 volumes). Aberystwyth: published privately by the Editor, and printed for him by Fox, Jones & Co., Kemp Hall, High Street, Oxford.

Dillenius, J.J., (editor) 1724. *Joannis Raii Synopsis Methodica Stirpium Britannicarum*. Third edition. London: G. & I. Innys. (Facsimile edition, 1973. London: The Ray Society).

Druce, G.C., Vines, S.H., 1907. *The Dillenian Herbaria an account of the Dillenian Collections in the Herbarium of the University of Oxford*. Oxford: Clarendon Press.

Edgar, Iwan Rhys (golygydd), 1997. *Llysieulyfr Salesbury*. Caerdydd: Gwasg Prifysgol Cymru.

Ellis, Gwynn. *Plant Hunting in Wales*. (reprints from *Amgueddfa*, Bulletin of the National Museum of Wales, 10-Spring 1972, 13-Spring 1973, 16-Spring 1974) Cardiff: printed by A. McLay and Co.

Emery, F.V., 1970. 'The best naturalist now in Europe: Edward Lhuyd, F.R.S. (1660-1709)' *The Transactions of the Honourable Society of Cymmrodorion*. (Session 1969, Part 1.): 54-69.

Emery, Frank V., 1985. 'Edward Lhuyd and Snowdonia' *Nature in Wales* (new series) vol. 4, parts 1 and 2: 3-11.

Evans, Rev. J., 1802. *A Tour through part of North Wales*. London: printed for J. White.

Farmer, Sir John Bretland, 1948. 'Notes on the Flora of Snowdonia' in Carr, H.R.C., and Lister, G.A., *The Mountains of Snowdonia*, London: Crosby Lockwood and Son Ltd.: 144-155.

Farmer, J.B., and Williams, J.L., 1896a. 'On fertilization, and the segmentation of the spore, in Fucus'. *Proceedings of the Royal Society* 60 (361): 188-195.

Farmer, J.B., Williams, J.L., 1896b 'On fertilisation and the segmentation of the spore in Fucus'. *Annals of Botany* 10: 479-487

Farmer, J.B., and Williams, J.L., 1898. 'Contributions to our knowledge of the Fucaceae: their life-history and cytology.' *Philosophical Transactions of the Royal Society of London* 190: 623-645.

'Filix-Fœmina', 1867. 'Llanberis and its ferns' *Journal of Horticulture and Cottage Gardener*. 13: 154-55.

Francis, G.W., 1851 (4th ed). *An Analysis of British Ferns and their allies*. London: Simpkin, Marshall.

Freeman, Rev. G.J., 1826. *Sketches in Wales; or, a Diary of Three Walking Excursions in that Principality in the Years 1823, 1824, 1825*. London: Longman, Rees, Orme, Brown, and Green.

George, W.R.P., 1976. *The Making of Lloyd George*. London: Faber and Faber.

Gilmour, John 1944. *British Botanists*. London: William Collins.

Glenn, T.A., 1934. *Family of Griffith of Garn and Plasnewydd*. London: Harrison and Sons.

Gosse, Philip Henry, 1865. *A year at the shore*. London: Alexander Strahan.

Gribble, Francis, 1899. *The Early Mountaineers*. London: T. Fisher Unwin.

Griffith, John, [1889]. *Chwarelau Dyffryn Nantlle a Chymdogaeth Moeltryfan*. Conwy: argraffwyd gan R.E. Jones a'i Frodyr.

Griffith, J.E., 1879. 'The Flora of Carnarvonshire and Anglesea' The *Naturalist 5*.

Griffith, John E., [1895]. *The Flora of Anglesey and Carnarvonshire*. Bangor: Nixon and Jarvis.

Griffith, John Edwards, 1914. *Pedigrees of Anglesey and Carnarvonshire Families*. Printed for the author by W. K. Morton and Sons, Horncastle.

Gunther, R.T., 1945. *Life and Letters of Edward Lhuyd*. Oxford: Early Science in Oxford xiv.

Hamer, J.P., [1857]. *Hamer's Practical Steamboat, Railway and Road Guide to Snowdon and around*. Caernarvon: printed for the author by H. Humphreys.

Hill, M.O., 1988. 'A Bryophyte Flora of North Wales'. *Journal of Bryology* 15: 377-491.

Hobley, W., 1913, (cyf. 2). *Hanes Methodistiaeth Arfon*. Cyfarfod Misol Arfon.

Hucks, J., (1795) 1979. *A Pedestrian Tour through North Wales, in a Series of Letters*. Edited by Alun R. Jones and William Tydeman. Cardiff: University of Wales Press.

Hughes, Hugh Derfel, 1866. *Hynafiaethau Llandegai a Llanllechid*. Bethesda: argraffwyd dros yr awdur gan R. Jones, yn Swyddfa "Yr Ardd".

Hughes, W.J., 1924. *Wales and the Welsh in English Literature*. Wrexham: Hughes and Son. London: Simkin, Marshall, Hamilton, Kent and Co. Ltd.

Humphreys, H., (pub.) [1850]. *Guide to the Summit of Snowdon*. Caernarfon: H. Humphreys.

Huws, Bleddyn Owen, 2005. " '. . . henffurf y mynyddoedd hyn': Eryri yn ein Llenyddiaeth' ". Darlith lenyddol Eisteddfod Genedlaethol Eryri a'r Cyffiniau 2005.

Hyde, H.A., 1931. *Samuel Brewer's Diary*. Reprinted from B.E.C. Report 1930.

Hyde, H. A., 1937. 'Searching for rare herbs in Wales. What old book in National Museum reveals' *The Western Mail and South Wales News*. 8 December: 11.

Hyde, H.A., and Wade, A.E., 1940. *Welsh ferns, clubmosses, quillworts and horsetails*. Cardiff: National Museum of Wales.

Hyde, H.A., Wade, A.E., 1978. *Welsh ferns, clubmosses, quillworts and horsetails*. Cardiff: National Museum of Wales.

Hyde Hall, Edmund, 1952. *A description of Caernarvonshire 1809-1811*. (Caernarvonshire Historical Society Record Series Number Two)

Caernarvon: printed by Gwenlyn Evans.

Ingman, John, 1950. 'The early days of the Caernarvonshire and Anglesey Hospital' *Transactions of the Caernarvonshire Historical Society* 11: 61-72.

Jeffers, R.H., 1951-52 'Edward Morgan and the Westminster Physic Garden' *Proceedings of the Linnean Society of London.* 164 (2) Issued 24 September 1953: 102-133.

Jenkins, D.E., 1899. *Bedd Gelert Its Facts, Fairies, and Folk-lore.* Portmadoc: Llewelyn Jenkins.

Johnson, Samuel, 1816. *A Diary of a Journey into North Wales in the year 1774.* Edited, with illustrative notes, by R. Duppa. London: printed for Robert Jennings.

Johnson, Thomas, 1633. *The Herball or Generall Historie of Plantes gathered by John Gerarde of London.* London: printed by Norton and Whitakers.

Johnson, Thomas, 1641. *Mercurii Botanici Pars Altera.* London

Jones, Dewi, 2002. ' "Nature-formed botanists": notes on some nineteenth century botanical guides of Snowdonia'. *Archives of Natural History* 29 (1): 31-50.

Jones, G. Penrhyn,1962. 'Some aspects of the Medical History of Caernarvonshire' *Transactions of the Caernarvonshire Historical Society* 23: 67-91.

Jones, Carey, 1990. *Y Llanc o Lan Conwy.* Dinbych: Argraffwyd gan Wasg Gee.

Jones, R. Merfyn, 1982. *The North Wales Quarrymen.* Cardiff: University of Wales Press.

Jones, T. Llechid, 1916. 'John Williams, Awdur y Faunula Grustensis. *Y Geninen* Rhif 3, Cyfrol 34: 216.

Knight, Margery, 1947. 'Obituary Notice of John Lloyd Williams'. *Proceedings of the Linnean Society of London* 158th session (1945-46): 72-74.

Lees, Edwin, 1842. *The Botanical Looker-out among the wild flowers of the fields, woods, and mountains, of England and Wales.* London: Tilt and Bogue. Cheltenham: H. Davies.

Lees, Edwin, 1851. *The Botanical Looker-out among the wild flowers of England and Wales, at all seasons, and in the most interesting localities.* London: Hamilton, Adams, & Co.

Lindsay, Jean, 1974. *A History of the North Wales Slate Industry*. Newton Abbot: David and Charles.

Lleyn, Gwilym, 1862-3. 'Enwogion Anghofiedig Cymru' *Y Brython* 5: 271-272.

Lyttleton, Lord George, 1781. *An Account of a Journey into Wales* (appended to Wyndham, H. P., *A gentleman's Tour through Monmouthshire and Wales in the months of June and July, 1774*). London: printed for T. Evans.

Mathews, C.E., 1901.'Reminiscences of Pen-y-gwryd'. *The Climbers' Club Journal*. Volume iv, No 14: 49-71.

Mathias, W. Alun, 1970. 'William Salesbury – ei fywyd a'i weithiau' *Y Traddodiad Rhyddiaeth* (Geraint Bowen, golygydd) Llandysul: Gwasg Gomer: 27-53.

Moore, T., 1863. 'Trichomanes radicans indigenous to Yorkshire and Wales' *Journal of Botany* 1: 238-39.

Morris, R.H., (ed) 1909-1911. 'Parochialia – being a summary of answers to "Parochial Queries in order to a Geographical Dictionary, etc., of Wales"'. Supplement to *Archaeologia Cambrensis*. London: Published for the Cambrian Archæological Association.

Newman, Edward, 1854. *A History of British Ferns*. London: John van Voorst.

Newell, R. H., 1821. *Letters on the Scenery of Wales*. London: printed for Baldwin, Cradock and Joy.

Nichols, J., 1817. *Illustrations of the Literary History of the Eighteenth Century* &c., (8 volumes 1817-58). London: Nichols, Son, and Bentley.

Nicholson, George, 1813. *The Cambrian Traveller's Guide, &c*. Stourport: Longman, Hurst, Rees, Orme & Brown; Sherwood, Neely, & Jones. London: B. & R. Crosby & Co.

Oltmanns, F., 1904-1905. *Morphologie und Biologie der Algen*. Jena: Gustav Fischer. 2 volumes.

Owen, Bob, 1943. *Diwydiannau Coll Ardal y Ddwy Afon – Dwyryd a Glaslyn*. Cyhoeddwyd ar ran Eisteddfod Genedlaethol Cymru gan Hugh Evans a'i Feibion, Cyf., Lerpwl.

Palmer, William, 1948. *Odd Corners in North Wales*. London: Skeffington & Son, Ltd.

Pamplin, W., 1858. 'Welsh Botany', *The Phytologist* 2, 312-315.

Parry, William, 1868. *Hanes Llenyddiaeth ac Enwogion Llanllechid a Llandegai*. Bangor: argraffwyd gan J. Mendus Jones.

Parry, G.T., 1888. *Hugh Lewis a'i ysgrifeniadau*. Caernarfon: Swyddfa'r Herald.

Parry, G.T., 1908. *Llanberis: ei hanes, ei phobl, a'i phethau*. Caernarfon: Cwmni y Cyhoeddwyr Cymreig.

Peacock, William F., 1855. *The Welsh Mountains, on and over them, being personal ascents of Snowdon, Cader Idris and Pymlimon*. London: Simpkin and Co. Manchester: Abel Heywood.

Pennant, Thomas, 1883. *Tours in Wales*. (edited by John Rhys) Caernarvon: H. Humphreys.

Pennant, Thomas, 1793. *The Literary Life of the Late Thomas Pennant, Esq. By Himself*. London: sold by Benjamin and John White, Fleet-Street, and Robert Faulder, New Bond Street.

Preston, C.D., Pearman, D.A., Dines, T.D., 2002. *New Atlas of the British and Irish Flora*. Oxford: University Press.

PRCS – *Prospectus of the Royal College of Science, London*. Session 1892-93.

Ratcliffe, D.A., Birks, H.J.B., Birks, H.H., 1993. 'The ecology and conservation of the Killarney Fern *Trichomanes speciosum* Willd. in Britain and Ireland' *Biological Conservation* 66: 231-247.

Raven, Charles E., 1986. *John Ray Naturalist his life and works*. Cambridge Science Classics series.

Ray, J., 1696 *Synopsis Methodica Stirpium Britannicarum*. London.

Rich, T.C.G., 1991. *Crucifers of Great Britain and Ireland*. London: BSBI.

Riddelsdell, H. J., (editor) 1905. 'Lightfoot's visit to Wales in 1773'. *Journal of Botany* 43: 290-307.

Roberts, B. 1971 'Llythyrau John Lloyd at Edward Lhuyd' *The National Library of Wales Journal* xvii No 1, Summer: 88-114.

Roberts, Brynley F., 1980. *Edward Lhuyd the making of a scientist*. Cardiff: University of Wales Press.

Roberts, E. Stanton, 1916. *Llysieulyfr Meddyginiaethol a briodolir i William Salesbury*. Liverpool: Hughes a'i Fab.

Roberts, Glyn, 1948. 'The Glynnes and the Wynns of Glynllifon' *Transactions of the Caernarvonshire Historical Society* 9: 25-39.

Roberts, G.T., 1948. 'Peter Bailey Williams' *Transactions of the Caernarvonshire Historical Society* 9: 66-81.

Roberts, Janet D., 1985. *O Ben Llyn i lle bu Lleu*. Caernarfon: Cyngor Gwlad Gwynedd.

Roberts, R.H., 1979. 'The Killarney Fern, Trichomanes speciosum, in Wales' *Fern Gazette* 12 (1): 1-4.

Roberts, R.H., 1982. *The Flowering Plants and Ferns of Anglesey*. Cardiff: National Museum of Wales.

Roberts, R.H., 1984. 'Annotations in J.E. Griffith's own copy of the Flora of Anglesey and Carnarvonshire' *BSBI Welsh Bulletin* 39, February: 12-15.

Roscoe, Thomas, 1836. *Wanderings and Excursions in North Wales*. London: C. Tilt, and Simpkin and Co. Birmingham: Wrightson and Webb.

Shankland, T., 1916. 'John Williams, Awdur y *Faunula Grustensis*' *Ceninen Gwyl Dewi*. (Argraffiad arbenig [sic] o'r "Geninen", y cyntaf o Fawrth, 1916): 37-43.

Sidebotham, Joseph, 1844. 'Sketch of a Botanical Ramble to Twll dû, June 19, 1844'. *The Phytologist* 1: 1036-1038.

Smith, W.P. Haskett, 2 volumes 1894 and 1895. *Climbing in the British Isles*. London: Longmans. (Facsimile edition, 1986. Glasgow: The Ernest Press).

Sotheby, William, 1794. *A Tour Thro' Parts of North and South Wales, Sonnets, Odes and other Poems*. London: printed by J. Smeeton, for R. Blamire.

Starr, E., 1847 and 1848. *The Remains of Henry Wellington Starr*. London: F. & J. Rivington. Northampton: G. N. Wetton.

Symonds, Rev. W.S., 1872. *Records of the rocks; notes on the geology, natural history, and antiquities of north and south Wales, Devon and Cornwall*. London: John Murray.

Thomas, W. Jenkyn, 1908. *The Itinerary of a Botanist*. (Translated portion of Thomas Johnson's (1641) *Mercurii Botanici Pars Altera*). Bangor: Evan Thomas, Printers.

Thorne, R.G., 1986. *The History of Parliament: The House of Commons 1790-1820* vi Members G-P. London: Secker & Warburg.

Trimmer, Joshua, 1831. *Proceedings of the Geological Society* 1: 331-332.

Turner, D., (ed.) 1835. *Extracts from the Literary and Scientific Correspondence of Richard Richardson, M.D., F.R.S., of Bierley, Yorkshire.* Yarmouth: printed by Charles Sloman.

Turner, D., Dillwyn, L.W., 1805. *The Botanist's Guide through England and Wales* (vol. 1). London: Phillips and Fardon.

Tyndall, John, 1899. *Hours of Exercise in the Alps* New York: D. Appleton and Co.

UWA, RCG – University of Wales, Aberystwyth. Reports submitted to the Court of Governors.

UWB, RHD – University of Wales, Bangor. Reports of the Heads of Departments

Watson, Hewett Cottrell, 1835. *The New Botanist's Guide to the localities of the rarer plants of Britain.* London: printed for Longman, Rees, Orme, Brown, Green, and Longman.

Watson, Hewett Cottrell, 1874. *Topographical Botany.* Thames Ditton: Printed for private distribution only.

Watson, Hewett Cottrell, 1883. *Topographical Botany.* London: Bernard Quaritch.

Wells, H.G., 1966. *Experiment in Autobiography* (1) London: Gollancz.

Whittaker, G. B., 1825. *The Cambrian Tourist, or, Post-Chaise Companion through Wales.* London: printed by Thomas Davison.

Wiliam, Parch. Dafydd Wyn, 1985. *Cofiant Wiliam Morris* (1705-63). Argraffwyd gan O. Jones, Llangefni.

Williams, Elizabeth, 1951. *Brethyn Cartref.* Gwasg Aberystwyth.

Williams, John, 1830. *Faunula Grustensis: being an outline of the Natural Contents of the Parish of Llanrwst.* Llanrwst: printed by John Jones.

Williams, J., 1893. 'John Williams of Llanrwst' *Bye-gones relating to Wales and the Border Counties.* 1893-94; volume 3, second series, November 22: 225.

Williams, J. Lloyd, 1887. 'Trichomanes radicans in Caernarvonshire' *Journal of botany* 25: 215.

Williams, J.Lloyd, 1897. 'The antherozoids of Dictyota and Taonia' *Annals of Botany* 11: 545-553.

Williams, J. Lloyd, 1899. 'New Fucus Hybrids' *Annals of Botany* 13:187-188.

Williams, J. Lloyd, 1904-1905. 'Studies in the Dictyotaceae'. *Annals of Botany* 18: 141-160, 185-204; 19: 531-560.

Williams, J. Lloyd, 1921. 'The Gametophytes and Fertilization in Laminaria and Chorda. (Preliminary Account)'. *Annals of Botany* 35: 603-607.

Williams, J. Lloyd, 1924. *Byd y Blodau*. Caerdydd: William Lewis (Argraffwyr) Cyf. [Liverpool: Morris & Jones Ltd.]

Williams, J. Lloyd, 1927. *Flowers of the Wayside and Meadow*. Cardiff: William Lewis (Printers) Ltd. [Liverpool: Morris & Jones Ltd.]

Williams, J. Lloyd, 1933. 'Cripian ar ôl Lili Eryri' *Y Ford Gron*. Cyfrol 3, Rhif 10, Awst: 221-222.

Williams, J. Lloyd, 1936. 'Dringo'r Wyddfa i held dail / Atgofion am y Llysieuydd, Dan Jones'. *The Western Mail and South Wales News*. 30 October: 11.

Williams, J. Lloyd, 1937. 'Yr ymchwil am lysiau prin: rhamant y rhedynen fach a'r enw mawr'. *The Western Mail and South Wales News*. 29 November: 9.

Williams, J. Lloyd 1941-45 (4 cyfrol). *Atgofion Tri Chwarter Canrif* Aberystwyth: Y Clwb Llyfrau Cymreig cyf.1-3. Llundain: Foyle, cyf. 4.

Williams, Rev. P.B., 1821. *The Tourist's Guide through the County of Caernarvon, containing a short sketch of its History, Antiquities, &c.* Caernarvon: J. Hulme.

Williams, William, 1891. 'Llythyr at y Golygydd – Y dyn a gollwyd ar y Wyddfa' *Yr Herald Cymraeg*, 2 Mehefin: 5.

Williams, William, 1892. *Hynafiaethau a Thraddodiadau Plwyf Llanberis a'r Amgylchoedd*. Llanberis: argraffwyd gan Richard Owen.

Williams, William, 1907. '. . . I adgofio am farwolaeth arweinydd ieuanc, Griffith Pritchard . . .' *Awel Eryri*, 17 Hydref : 5.

Williams, William, 1917. 'Richard Roberts, Melin y Coed, Llanrwst' *Y Geninen*1: xxxv.

Williams, W. Gilbert [d.d.]. *Arfon y Dyddiau Gynt*. Caernarfon: Cwmni y Cyhoeddwyr Cymreig Cyf.

Wilson, William, 1855. *Bryologia Britannica*. London: Longman, Brown, Green, and Longmans.

Withering, William, 1796 (4 volumes). *An Arrangement of British Plants*. Birmingham: printed for the author by M. Swinney.

Wyndham, Henry Penruddocke, 1781. *A Tour through Monmouthshire and Wales, made in the Months of June, July, and August, 1777*. Salisbury: printed and sold by E. Easton.

Wynter, Andrew, 1861. *Our Social Bees &c. London*: Robert Hardwicke.

Wynne, John, 1861. *Hanes Sir a Thre Caernarfon*. Caernarfon: argraffwyd gan H. Humphreys.

Wynne, Sir John, 1927. *The History of the Gwydir Family*. Cardiff: University of Wales Press Board.

Abbreviations

ANYBG – Archives of the New York Botanical Garden.

BL – British Library, London.

CUL – Cambridge University Library

GAS – Gwynedd Archives Service, Caernarfon.

LMA – Liverpool Museum Archives.

NHM – Natural History Museum, London.

NLW – National Library of Wales, Aberystwyth.

NLWA JLW – National Library of Wales, Aberystwyth. Dr J. Lloyd Williams Music MSS and Papers.

NLWA SHRWDD – National Library of Wales, Aberystwyth. Schedule of the Henry Rumsey Williams Deeds and Documents, vol. 1: 99/292.

NMGW – National Museums and Galleries of Wales, Cardiff.

RBGK – Royal Botanic Garden, Kew.

UWA – University of Wales, Aberystwyth.

UWB – University of Wales, Bangor.

WWCWL – William Wilson Correspondence, Warrington Library.

WWC BLNHM – William Wilson Correspondence, Botany Library, The Natural History Museum.

General Index

Index to Plant Names

258

261